Survey of Cybernetics

A TRIBUTE TO DR. NORBERT WIENER

DR. NORBERT WIENER

Survey of Cybernetics

A TRIBUTE TO DR. NORBERT WIENER

Edited by J. Rose, M.Sc., Ph.D., F.R.I.C., F.I.L.,
M.B.I.M., M. Inst. C.Sc.
Principal, College of Technology and Design,
Blackburn (U.K.)

A VOLUME DEDICATED TO THE MEMORY
OF THE 'FATHER' OF CYBERNETICS
DR. NORBERT WIENER
(1894–1964)

'I am convinced that the world is not a mere bog in which men and women trample themselves in the mire and die. Something magnificent is taking place here amid the cruelties and tragedies, and the supreme challenge to intelligence is that of making the noblest and best in our curious heritage prevail'

C. A. BEARD (Durant, *Meaning of Life*)

LONDON   ILIFFE   BOOKS   LTD

ILIFFE BOOKS LTD
42, RUSSELL SQUARE
LONDON, WC 1

First published in 1969

© Iliffe Books Ltd, 1969

592 03941 2

Printed in Hungary

Contents

Contents

Preface

This volume is dedicated to the memory of Dr. Norbert Wiener, the 'father' of cybernetics, whose untimely death at the age of 70 years occurred in 1964. Dr. Wiener was the author of over 200 papers in mathematical and scientific journals and of 11 books; his last book, *God and Golem, Inc.* (Chapman and Hall, London, 1965) was a penetrating study in the most human terms of the philosophical and religious implications of cybernetics, and won the 1965 American National Book Award in the category of Science, Philosophy and Religion. His services in many fields were recognised by the award of five Prizes and Medals and of three honorary doctorates; it is worth noting that this mathematical prodigy obtained his doctorate in science at Harvard University at the age of 19. Dr. Wiener studied and taught at several universities in the U.S.A., Europe and China, but spent most of his academic life at the Massachusetts Institute of Technology as Professor of Mathematics. He died four years after his retirement as Professor Emeritus of that world famous institution.

In his classical book *Cybernetics or Control and Communication in the Animal and the Machine* (John Wiley, New York, 1948) Dr. Wiener laid the foundations of cybernetics, the youngest scientific discipline of the 20th century. He also coined the word *cybernetics* derived from the Greek *kubernetes* meaning steersmanship. It is interesting to note that Plato used this term in ancient Greece to describe the science of the steering of ships, while in the 19th century the French scientist Ampère designated the science of the control of society by the term cybernetics.

Wiener's definition of cybernetics is still generally accepted despite the appearance of other statements of various lengths and complexity, (Klír, J. and Valach, M., *Cybernetic Modelling*, Iliffe Books, London, 1967). The present tendency is to regard cybernetics either as a scientific umbrella of synnoetics (i.e. computer sciences and technologies, ranging from automation to the theory of programming), or as a philosophical approach aiming at synthesising an enormous variety of sciences, both pure and applied—a veritable 20th century Queen of the Sciences that asserts the essential unity of the animate and inanimate. Whatever the point of view adopted, Wiener's contribution stands supreme and inviolate.

In order to consider the various aspects of cybernetics, this volume is divided into five parts. The first part, entitled 'The Nature of Cybernetics' contains four chapters devoted to a description of the discipline and the tools and possibilities of the cybernetic revolution.

The second part, 'Cybernetics and Living Systems' is concerned with behavioural, medical and physiological cybernetics. Broad principles involved in intelligent behaviour are analysed, the properties of the living brain are described, and medicine itself is studied in terms of a teaching system.

'Cybernetics and Artifacts' forms the backbone of the third part. This section deals with information, learning machines, behavioural models and artificial intelligence control. Learning control systems are studied and cybernetic modelling described with respect to the growth and development of systems.

The fourth part 'Cybernetics and Industry' is concerned with various aspects of industrial applications involving control and man-machine systems, automation and organisation of relevant information.

'Cybernetics and Society' is the title of the fifth and final part of the volume. The topics covered include management, education, social prospects and pathology of automation. The last subject is discussed in the chapter entitled 'The Structure of Disorder'—an apparently self-contradictory title; this is a paradox deliberately created by the author in order to establish adequate 'frames of reference for thinking aloud which may be wrong'—as the author himself put it.

Few editorial changes have been made in the contributions from the authors of six different countries. The editor believes, rightly or wrongly, that freedom of dissent is at the basis of originality, while a freshness of approach and creativity cannot thrive in a climate of officious censorship. Though the editor does not agree with many views propounded by the authors and considers some of these to be over-enthusiastic, the very diversity of attitudes and comments generated by the freedom of opinion form the strength of this memorial volume; it even contains some vigorous criticism of Dr. Wiener himself!

It is a pleasant duty to record my gratitude to the contributors to this volume for their helpful attitude. I am also grateful to Dr. Wiener's widow, Mrs. Margaret Wiener of the M.I.T., for her encouragement and useful information about her late husband. Thanks are also due to Mr.

Stafford Beer for his helpful advice, and to my sons Paul and John, for literature searches and proof reading. Last but not least, I would like to record my gratitude to Professor Georges R. Boulanger, the President of the International Association of Cybernetics, for his kindness in suggesting that this Wiener volume appear in connection with the tenth anniversary of the foundation of the Association. The publication of this book coincides with the twenty-first anniversary of the formal birth of cybernetics and also with the International Congress of Cybernetics in London.

1969   J. R.

PART 1

THE NATURE OF CYBERNETICS

'The coming decade will see an enormous increase in the use of feedback controls in industry, in the military services, in business operations and in situations which may involve all of these elements in our society'.

J. A. Hrones, *The James Clayton Lecture*,
The Institution of Mechanical Engineers,
London (1960)

Chapter 1

Prologue:
What is Cybernetics?

G. R. BOULANGER Ph.D.
President of the International Association of Cybernetics

SUMMARY

The origins of cybernetics lie in the borderlands between the disciplines of engineering and human physiology, hence its concern with the creation of intelligent machines and with the interpretation of the nature of life itself. Cybernetics deals with a wide range of human activities, including such diverse examples as technology, economics, education, politics, the arts and even ethics; to all these branches of human endeavour, cybernetics brings a new approach.

The range of human thought is limited by the very structure of the brain. One can, however, visualise the creation of artificial brains, which would invade realms of human thought now unknown to man, and which would supply solutions to important problems that have puzzled humanity from times immemorial.

DEFINITION

There appears to exist a prevalent idea that cybernetics is a new science, although, in fact, it formally began nearly 20 years ago. It is a discipline that seems to be surrounded by a forbidding aura of mystery, arousing curiosity, interest and even some hostility.

But after all, what is cybernetics? Or rather what is it not, for paradoxically the more people talk about cybernetics the less they seem to agree on a definition. For some, the word means either a complicated mathematical theory or simply the technique of automation. For others, it evokes giant computers or the theory of communication processes. Yet another school of thought regards cybernetics as the means of studying the analogies that may exist between machines and living creatures, while still another regards it as a metaphysical or philo-

3

sophical doctrine that seeks to probe the ultimate mystery of life. For the general public it is simple—it conjures up visions of some fantastic world of the future peopled by robots and electronic brains!

In effect 'the science of robots' is perhaps the most striking and concise definition of cybernetics, for this is the branch of knowledge that allows us to build machines with conditioned reflexes, machines that can learn, machines that can imitate life. Admittedly this definition may seem surprising. After all, are not these machines pure automata? Are they not essentially passive, in contrast to the 'voluntary' nature of the activity of living creatures? And is not life, by its very nature, unamenable to mechanisation?

From the dawn of time the human mind has clung to the tenet that there is a fundamental difference between the qualities of living and inert matter, and it is precisely this belief that has been attacked head-on by cybernetics with an audacity fostered and encouraged by its first triumphs.

Let me give a concrete example.

We all feel that there is an essential difference between the behaviour of a wild animal, hunting in the jungle at nightfall, and the behaviour of a boulder, rolling down a mountainside. The movement of the boulder is governed by physical laws known to us all, whereas the movements of the animal seem not to be bound by these laws. The animal sets out with an aim: to catch its prey. It achieves its purpose despite the obstacles in its way, thanks—we believe—to a certain degree of independence from its environment and a degree of liberty of action which is denied to the falling boulder. The behaviour of the animal is goal-seeking, the behaviour of the boulder is not. For centuries man saw in this factor the essential difference between the animate and the inanimate, between the animal and the machine.

It is hardly necessary to say that this theory is outdated. Our engineers build —and have been building for some time now—machines whose behaviour is purposeful, machines that can pursue and attain aims fixed in advance. A simple example of this is the electric cooker with a thermostatic temperature control. Yet another example is the automatic pilot, while a third is the teleguided projectile, which need only be aimed in the approximate direction of the aeroplane that is to be shot down.

It is to the everlasting credit of the American mathematician Norbert Wiener that he saw the connection between the goal-seeking behaviour of the machine and that of the animal, and that he was the first to state clearly that if we observe examples of purposeful behaviour in nature (that is to say, behaviour directed towards an aim fixed *a priori*), and if we are able to build machines that can behave in the same way, then the basic principles of both are identical. What we are dealing with in both cases is an effect that reacts on the cause that produced it, that is, feedback.

Once the analogy was accepted it was tempting to propose—as Wiener did— that all purposeful behaviour, whether of living or of inert matter, should be studied within the same framework. On that day, cybernetics was born.

'We have been forced to coin a new word', wrote Norbert Wiener in 1948. He then went on to explain how he had created the word 'cybernetics' from the Greek *kubernetes* (the steersman of a ship), forgetting that the term had been used by Ampère in 1834, in his classification of the sciences, to define the science of government, and that the use of the word in this sense goes back to Plato!

Etymologically, then, cybernetics is the science of steersmanship, of government, of control. From the very start, however, Wiener gave a more precise definition in the sub-title of the book he published in 1948 under the title *Cybernetics or the Science of Control and Communication processes in both Animals and Machines.*[1]

The field of cybernetics deals with such systems—both living and inert—which may be termed self-controlled, as opposed to mechanised systems in the commonly accepted sense of the word, and the definition given by Wiener in 1948 still seems to me the best and the most complete.

SCOPE

There is probably no realm of human thought or activity in which cybernetics will have no role to play in the future, for it bears all the hallmarks of an explosive science.

From the technical point of view it is the cornerstone of the second industrial revolution, which is characterised by the introduction of the so called 'intellectual' machines, just as the first industrial revolution was characterised by the introduction of the man-operated machine. What we are witnessing today is the rapid development of cybernation ranging from simple regulators to fully automatic factories and including, on the way, such spectacular achievements as 'automatic' steering for cars on the motorways, or 'automatic' landing of aircraft.

Of course, the idea of an automated factory is not new. It was even put into practice many years ago, as we can see from the famous 'automatic' flour mill built near Philadelphia by Oliver Evans in 1784. What is new is the strength of the movement today that is sweeping the whole of our industry towards cybernation—the modern term for automation (Sir Leon Bagrit's BBC Reith Lectures).

What is more, the machines of the second industrial revolution are not the blind, stupid automata of the past. The machines of the second industrial revolution think for themselves. They do the job they have to do by working towards a given aim but without having to obey detailed orders. They can do without their human slaves while at the same time escaping from complete subjection —cybernation has taken its place. The first industrial revolution produced mechanisation but its development was purely 'material'. Man built more and more machines, more and more powerful machines, but he remained the slave of his machines because he had to control them. They had iron muscles but no nerves (Grey Walter). The task of co-ordination was left to man. In the future it will be left to the machine itself. This is the true significance of the second industrial revolution, and its essential difference from the mechanisation of the 19th century.

But already a third industrial revolution looms on the horizon. It will be brought about by the development of machines that can adapt themselves, that can modify their own structure to suit the task they have to perform, and that can even make others, perfected machines that will, in their turn, engender new models free from human control and its limitations, and capable of organising themselves into autonomous breeding units.

Such predictions may seem to belong to the realm of science fiction, yet they are backed by data of a strictly scientific nature derived from the study of cybernetics in its early days, for the phenomenal thing about cybernetics is that from the very start it pointed in hitherto unsuspected directions.

5

The medical profession was one of the first to appreciate the possibilities of cybernetics. Wiener himself blazed the trail when he demonstrated the connection between certain human reflexes and the reactions of the servosystems, and it was soon seen that the entire field of study of the regulating functions and reflexes fitted into the framework of cybernetics. The cyberneticians, however, went further than this and turned their attention to the study of the higher cerebral functions and the intricacies of intelligence. The application of cybernetics to medicine does not, however, stop there and it seems probable that cybernetics will play a still more vital part in many branches of medicine.

Another sector that is likely to derive great benefit from cybernetics is psychology. Psychology has got partly into a rut, largely because up to the present it has been built on an experimental basis. Cybernetics can help transform it into an exact science, because for the cybernetician unlike the psychologist — the theory of behaviour is a physical theory. It is so complex that he has not yet unravelled it, but he knows that it is just a question of time before the electronic computer enables him to understand it; and at the speed with which his knowledge is being expanded, he can hope for results in the near future.

The field in which society in general will first reap the benefits of cybernetics will probably be that of economics. The establishment and maintenance of the lines of exchange of products imply the existence of systems of regulation and these imply the notion of feedback. With the aid of cybernetics these phenomena can be studied scientifically and we can confidently expect to find the explanation of processes that escape our understanding at the moment.

The social sciences, for their part, will have much to gain from cybernetics in the future, for the science that has set out to study the behaviour of the individual must inevitably have the capacity to study the relationship between individuals in society.

The same reasoning applies to political science. The relationship between governments and the people governed can be analysed by feedback circuits, as can the relationships between governments themselves.

With 'electronic' painting and machines that can write poetry and compose music, cybernetics has gained a foothold in the arts, too, and even the moral sciences have been invaded by this new discipline. Ethics cannot exist without feedback, said Grey Walter, who then went on to add that a whole moral code could be built on that alone!

INTELLIGENT MACHINES

It is clear that cybernetics has its part to play in every branch of human knowledge, but the fields in which we can expect the most startling results are those of engineering and biology.

The imitation and the explanation of the functions of the brain raise very difficult problems for the cybernetician, but it was precisely these problems that were investigated in the very early days of cybernetics by two Englishmen, the neurologist Grey Walter and the psychiatrist Ross Ashby.

We have heard a great deal in recent years about Grey Walter's experiments at the Burden Neurological Institute at Bristol, where he constructed the artificial animals known as 'electronic tortoises.' They provided a good story for the popular press. We might ask here, however, just what are these 'electronic tortoises'? They are models, built to demonstrate that by putting together a few quite simple mechanisms one can, with a correctly planned system of feedbacks, produce extremely complex behaviour patterns of exactly the same type as those seen in living creatures. It had always been believed that such behaviour was quite beyond the scope of machines, so it was partly to underline the significance of this breakthrough, and partly as a joke, that Grey Walter gave his machines the familiar form of a household pet—the tortoise.

It is instructive to see these 'tortoises' in action, to observe the way they explore every inch of the space allotted to them, how they struggle to overcome the obstacles put in their way, and how they search greedily for the 'feeding places' that give them the electric current they need to keep going. In fact, it is necessary to have seen the lifelike behaviour of these man-made creatures before criticising the conclusions that Grey Walter drew from his experiments—namely, that as one can imitate the behaviour of living creatures with mechanisms based solely on the known laws of physics, it is unreasonable to postulate the existence of laws and principles unknown to scientific research at this date to explain the same behaviour in living organisms. In other words, Grey Walter says that one cannot state *a priori* that life does not function like 'mechanics' since it has been shown that 'mechanics' can imitate life.

These experiments in 'electronic zoology' soon found many imitators, all anxious to endow their creatures with greater possibilities. They have developed locomotor apparatus and even sense organs. At the present time there seems to be no reason why one should not be able to create artificial beings capable of communicating with each other, either by language or by other means, and one can already look forward to the possibility of making them sensitive to the harmony of sounds, shapes and colours, and even of producing the mechanical equivalent of the natural processes of growth and reproduction. It has become a matter of technique and not one of principle. For the time being, however, one is not able to go beyond the reproduction of reflex actions; given identical conditions the machines always react in exactly the same way. They are incapable of learning from experience—incapable, indeed, of learning.

But learning is one of the distinctive features of all living matter, and without the ability to learn and adapt, neither vegetable nor animal life could have survived on our planet. It looked for a while as though cybernation could go no further, that the synthesis of life and the machine, which is the very cornerstone of cybernetics, was only a dream and that it was impossible to build a machine capable of learning. Was the ability to adapt to become the criterion of the definition of life after all, just when it was becoming more and more difficult to define life? Had we finally come up against the ultimate barrier separating life from inert matter, the animal from the machine? For a while it did indeed seem so. And then suddenly a new factor emerged: Grey Walter succeeded in mechanising the process of conditioned reflexes.

Just what did this mean? We are all familiar with the experiments conducted by Pavlov. A dog that salivates at the approach of a meal heralded by a bell will soon salivate at the sound of the bell alone, because it has learnt to associate the sound of the bell with the approach of food. It seemed unlikely that any machine could be made to behave in this way, yet Grey Walter's electronic animals, which were attracted by lights, learnt to answer a whistle if the whistle previously had preceded the appearance of the lights.

Some people wrote this off as a silly game; others hailed Grey Walter as a pioneer. For my part I feel I cannot stress too much the importance of Grey Walter's work, and I should like to draw attention to what went before it and to what must logically follow. For the first time in the history of mankind, man had succeeded in building a machine that was capable of learning—and this is the real point of departure of the whole science of cybernetics. The mechanisation of the process of learning is of immeasurable significance for the future development of man. It is an event which can only be compared with the discovery of the machine, when our ancestors in prehistoric times first discovered the principle of the lever or the sling. When we see how far we have progressed in mechanisation and cybernation since then, we realise that it would be futile to try to predict the future for the machines we now term 'intellectual'.

This, indeed, is the crux of the matter, the whole point of the cybernetic revolution. Up to now the machines built and used by man have worked almost exclusively on the material plane. We have built machines that could do things far beyond the physical force of man. We have built machines that allowed us to conquer space and time and to make matter and energy work for us. We have invented machines that calculate faster than man and that have a more retentive memory. What we have not done is to create machines more 'intelligent' than man, for the electronic brains we create are our servants not our masters. With the machines that can learn we enter the era of mechanisms that may be more intelligent—in the true sense of the word—than the men who build them. It is of little significance that Grey Walter's experiments reveal only a rudimentary ability to learn. What matters is the fact that they can learn. We know already that in the future, the intellectual output of man inevitably will be augmented by factors that we cannot foresee. By that time the 'industrialisation of science' will have followed the industrialisation of techniques. By that time, too, the work of the greatest scientists of today will seem, in an age of mass production, to be the work of the isolated craftsmen of a bygone age.

And when we turn to the experiments of Ross Ashby, with his homeostat that foreshadows the automatic pilot of the future, able to modify its manner of handling a plane, if something goes wrong, able to fight against adversity just as a human pilot would do in the same circumstances, and able to use its own initiative to correct a faulty mechanism, then we realise that the age of the robot superior to man in every way is not far off. This, of course, leads us to ask whether man is not preparing his own defeat by producing machines that could eventually dominate him. Theoretically this is a possibility, but at the same time we must admit that if the conception of the 'revolt of the robots' is highly interesting from a philosophical point of view, it has no connection with cybernetic developments in the foreseeable future. In any case we must not be deflected from our work by the horrors of science fiction. We are proud of our cars and our planes, of our computers and our translating machines. Why should we stop there?

POSSIBILITIES

We can now appreciate the vast potential of cybernetics. The Wienerian conception of cybernetics—the cybernetics of reflex mechanisms (mechanical reflexes)—soon gave way to a much broader conception that I propose to call general or generalised cybernetics—the cybernetics that is concerned with 'intelligent' machines and with the interpretation of the phenomenon of life.

In the early stages of artificial thought, the intellectual activity of the machines will probably be no more than an extrapolation, an extension of our own cerebral activites. We cannot rule out the possibility, however, that in modifying the mechanisms used in the initial stages, we shall arrive at the point where we provoke the appearance of modes of thought unknown to the human race.

After all, the human brain, from the physiological standpoint, is an organ geared to ensure the survival of the species. In the course of evolution it has developed solely in the function of its own preservation and the preservation of the organs with which it is associated. It is conditioned to allow us to benefit from the observations on which our existence depends directly, but it is not conditioned to help us to understand the mysteries of Nature. They escape us completely, and it may well be that we shall be eternally unable to penetrate them, thanks to the limitations of our brain.

But while we are limited by the very nature of our cerebral structure, the machines we create are not limited and may be developed and conditioned in various directions. Thus, electronic brains may eventually be able to break away from the patterns imposed on them at the start by their human creators and venture into realms unknown to us, into spheres of thought that are hermetically closed to the human mind and that, like the spacecraft which venture now into realms we cannot reach, bring back to us the data of their intellectual exploration. We may not be able to comprehend or interpret their findings, but if we can, they may bring us the answers to the great problems that have puzzled man since the dawn of time.

ACKNOWLEDGEMENTS

The auther would like to acknowledge the help of Mrs Dorothy Flacon-Galilee, who translated this article from the original Freuch.

REFERENCE

1. WIENER, N., *Cybernetics or the Science of Control and Communication Processes in Animals and Machines*, M.I.T. Press, Cambridge, Mass. (1948).

BIBLIOGRAPHY

ARBIB, M. A., *Brains, Machines and Mathematics*, McGraw-Hill, London (1964).
DEMCZYNSKI, S., *Automation and Future of Man*, Allen and Unwin, London (1964).
FORMBY, J., *An Introduction to the Mathematical Formulation of Self-Organising Systems*, E. & F. N. Spon, London (1965).
GABOR, D., *Inventing the Future*, Secker and Warburg, London (1963).
HUXLEY, J., *The Humanist Frame*, Allen and Unwin, London (1961).
PALOCZI-HOWARTH, G., *The Facts Rebel*, Secker and Warburg, London (1964).
PASK, G., *An Approach to Cybernetics*, Hutchinson, London (1961).
WIENER, N., *God and Golem Inc.*, Chapman and Hall, London (1965).

Chapter 2

The Tools of the Cybernetic Revolution

S. DEMCZYNSKI, Dipl. Ing., C. Eng., M.I.E.E.
Manager, Cord Consultancy Limited, Comino-Dexion Group (U.K.)

SUMMARY

The first industrial revolution brought very considerable increases of man's physical powers by utilising the vast quantities of energy latent in coal, oil and running water, as the sources of driving force for his machines. The cybernetic revolution opens up vistas of a similar increase of our capabilities in a new and even more important dimension. It gives us the means of augmenting some of our mental powers. Its tools are electronic, digital and analogue computers, and complex, feedback-controlled, automatic machines.

Still in its infancy, the cybernetic revolution is already exerting marked and varied influences on the development of industrial countries. Its possible consequences are virtually unlimited. On the one hand, it offers the promise of a millennium of effortless abundance. On the other, it threatens to bring in its train a multitude of economic, social and political problems with which —on present day evidence—the human race is totally unequipped to cope. Hence, in spite of all the dazzling prospects it is an open question, whether the cybernetic revolution is a 'great leap forward' in the development of our civilisation, or whether it marks the last stage of the turbulent history of *Homo sapiens*.

INTRODUCTION

Without tools of any kind man is a rather helpless creature when compared with almost any other animal of similar size. His sensorial equipment may be considered adequate for detecting those features of his environment, the perception of which is essential for his existence, but he is very poorly equipped for securing his survival by flight or fight or for obtaining a sufficient supply of food, and he has little protection against adverse climatic conditions. His teeth and claws are hardly a match for even small carnivorous animals, his running speed is rather unimpressive as is his general muscular strength in relation to his weight. His

10

sweating mechanism offers a reasonable protection against overheating, given an ample water supply, but he is ill prepared to face cold since the vaso-constriction mechanism in the outer layers of his body and his ability to shiver are hardly substitutes for a good coat of fur. One concludes that a tool-less man would only be able to live in a tropical or sub-tropical climate and then only in those places largely inaccessible to even medium sized predators (in trees, among rocks, in swamps, etc.). He could be neither hunter nor farmer (herdsman or grower) but only a food gatherer, picking up small, slow moving and ill armed animals, or fruit, berries, edible roots, etc. In other words, the ecological niche in which he could survive would be severely limited.

Yet, man equipped with tools which he has himself created, is the undisputed master of this planet. By now he has defeated successfully all his animal enemies and he has to fear no other species, except perhaps certain types of micro-organisms. His large scale activities have changed very considerably, for better or worse, the landscape of a major part of the earth's continents and his powers to change his environment are growing at a rapidly increasing rate. Hence we come to the inescapable conclusion that it is the ability to make and use tools which gives man his mastery over this globe.

Some would argue that man's capacity for abstract and rational thought, his ability to speak and to learn by imitation and experience and to pass knowledge thus acquired to the next generation, his apparent gregariousness and organisational abilities are just as important. But it is clear that, in so far as his mastery over nature is concerned, these qualities are quite inadequate in the absence of tool making ability, although it is arguable which of these inter-related prerequisites depends most on the others. Another prerequisite for tool making is man's erect posture, which leaves his forelimbs free for activities other than supporting his body. These extremities have, in addition to the important property of being able to grip firmly by virtue of having a thumb opposing other fingers, enough parts and joints to form a system possessing about seventy degrees of freedom.

TOOLS AND MACHINES

When a tool becomes sufficiently complex, it is usually referred to as a machine. The distinction between tools and machines is not defined at all clearly and remains rather a matter of semantics. For instance, a long bow would normally be referred to as a tool, whereas a very large cross bow, mounted on a carriage, could well be called a war-machine.

To perform the function for which it is designed a tool or a machine needs basically two things: driving energy and guiding intelligence. For the first million years of man's existence the guiding intelligence was supplied, in general, entirely by man himself, although animals can be taught to use tools in an elementary fashion with some supervision—for example, a horse pulling a cart usually requires human intervention only occasionally. The driving energy was supplied by man and animals, with the exception of water and windmills, sailing ships, etc. which utilise other forms of energy and which, in any case, account for only a small part of the total energy required to drive man's tools and machines. It is, therefore, of the utmost importance to realise that this limitation in tool driving power in pre-industrial societies put a very real, and by our standards extremely low, ceiling on what could be achieved per head of population, no matter how cleverly designed and complicated were the tools. Hence, apart from the few rare

11

places where nature provided man with an abundance of resources satisfying all his basic needs, as a race he had to work hard simply to live at a relatively low level of material prosperity. As far as the average man was concerned, there were no marked improvements in his standards of living from the prehistoric time of the introduction of reasonably advanced agriculture (the development of abundantly cropping plant strains, irrigation, the use of manure) and the husbandry of animals, until the industrial revolution; all the civilisations which had developed up until that time were, broadly speaking, comparable in output per head. The power limitation to which they were all subject, makes this hardly surprising.

With the advent of the industrial revolution, beginning about 200 years ago —a period representing about two hundredths of one per cent of man's assumed existence—other sources of energy were employed. These were primarily the energy contained in fossil fuels like coal, oil and gas, which are all stored forms of solar energy, and the energy of rivers, converted into electrical energy by hydroelectric plants. In the last two decades means have been found of employing the powerful source of energy contained in the nuclei of atoms and this new power source has been and is being exploited.

MECHANISATION

Essentially, mechanisation can be described as the utilisation of energy derived from sources other than human or animal muscle as the driving force for machines. The guiding intelligence still has to be supplied almost entirely by human operators. The resulting flood of energy thus released, together with the rapidly increasing versatility and complexity of the machines, altered the nature of our civilisation radically. An output per head many times higher than ever before became a real possibility and was soon achieved. This in turn led to the availability of much greater resources for research, and consequently to the development of still more versatile, complex and powerful machines which again increased the output, making the whole process self-growing. In spite of monumental administrative, political and sociological blunders, resulting in tremendous under-utilisation of machinery, together with monstrous and wholly unnecessary human suffering, so great was the amount of energy available to the countries which were first in introducing mechanisation, that they rapidly grew richer and more powerful than their pre-industrial neighbours. Soon, the first countries to mechanise secured virtual control of the planet and would probably have retained this privileged, if ethically unjustified, position for the foreseeable future but for the destructive wars which broke out between them. In comparison with pre-mechanised or pre-industrial modes of production, mechanisation opens the doors to an accelerating improvement in standard of living and brings in its train overpowering economic, military and political might. It also requires fundamental social changes as the whole structure of society adjusts itself to a virtually entirely new way of working and living and to the new environment created by large scale industrialisation.

As stated above, mechanisation relieves man of the function of acting as a source of energy to drive his tools and machines. Thus he ceases to be a beast of burden, a role which was the fate of the majority of human beings living in pre-industrial societies with a developed agriculture and practicing animal husbandry. There is, however, still plenty of work left for humans, although of an essentially different character. At the mechanisation stage, a large labour force is still needed

12

on the factory floor to control the machines, and a growing number of people are needed in the offices to process the inevitable volume of data which this type of operation creates. Some types of machines require very accurate guidance, in the sense that the initial setup of the machine for a given job and the control during the execution stage have to be very precise and demand skills of an order comparable with that of the pre-industrial master craftsman. However, with the increasing spread of mass production, which has proved to be economically the most efficient means of manufacturing standardised goods, the total task of making a given product has been split into many separate, simple jobs, each being performed by one or more workers. Due to their simplicity and repetitiveness, jobs of this type usually only require intelligence of a very low order and tend to turn men into more cogs in the vast industrial complex. This state of affairs obviously has many highly undesirable effects.

The situation in offices, was, and still is, hardly any better. The increasing complexity of production and organisation in industrial societies created a rapidly growing demand for the data processing essential for control. Masses of clerks processing this data were organised according to the same principles as the workers for mass production on the shop floor. Each of them was employed to perform an essentially simple, repetitive task, engaging only a small part of the intelligence which is the endowment of an average human being. Matters were further complicated by the fact that any large body of clerks engaged to perform certain tasks as a group, generates a lot of internal communication; this, though essential for the functioning of the group, is unnecessary from the point of the main task and consumes a lot of time and effort. Moreover, the rate of increase of the volume of this internal communication is, in general, greater than the rate of increase of the group itself. Other things being equal, the larger the group of data processing clerks, the greater is the part of their time which will be spent on receiving and dispersing internal communication, so that, for example, the useful output of 200 clerks is generally less than twice the output of 100 clerks. The decreasing efficiency of large bodies of clerks, employing conventional methods, leaves management with ill prepared data usually delivered too late and therefore quite inadequate for the purpose of decision making.

Thus, although mechanisation has relieved man of the burden of acting as a power source for his tools and machines and has enabled him to increase his material prosperity very significantly, it has nevertheless imposed on him the tedious and monotonous tasks of controlling the machines and of processing whole mountains of data.

AUTOMATION

The logical development for man, having found ample sources of energy to drive the machine, was to eliminate the need for supplying the guiding intelligence demanded by his machines. Automation and automatic data processing, extended subsequently to electronic data processing, provided the required answer and the large scale introduction of these constitutes the so called second industrial revolution.

As when discussing mechanisation, we will not now concern ourselves with detailed descriptions of all the particular types of gadgets employed, but we will concentrate on obtaining a clear understanding of the basic underlying principles. The operation of automatic machines is based on the principle of feedback, and the hub of electronic data processing is the electronic digital computer. We shall discuss these in turn, although we must not forget that automation and electronic data processing are not two separate concepts but, on the contrary, overlapping ones, so that we have chosen to distinguish between them mainly for convenience in the presentation of the ideas involved.

When employing a machine driven by a source of energy other than human or animal muscle, the operator manipulates parts controlling the performance of the machine in a certain manner. This operation we shall call the input to the machine. The energy input required from the operator is usually negligible compared with that supplied by the machine's main driving source. In response to the input the machine performs the task in a certain way. This we call the output of the machine. The operator watches the output and if it is unsatisfactory either because of inaccuracies in the input itself or in the internal construction of the machine or because of external disturbing factors, he alters the input accordingly, until the desired output is achieved. The application of input, the observation of output and, when necessary, the consequent alteration of the input so that the required output is obtained, constitutes the essence of the controlling process, that is of supplying the intelligence necessary to guide the machine. Thus, as a result of the operator's ability to observe the output through his sensory organs and his capacity to compare the actual output with that desired by means of his mental processes, the input to the machine is modified according to the difference between the actual and desired output, with the object of obtaining the latter.

THE PRINCIPLE OF FEEDBACK

If a machine's output is not sensed or no correction is applied to its input then we have what is known as an 'open looped' machine. With such a machine we have to rely on the precision of its construction and on the absence of non-negligible external disturbances to give us the desired output.

In open-loop machines the input affects the output, but the output cannot affect the input. If the output is observed and the necessary correction is applied to the input, then the loop becomes closed in the sense that not only can the input affect the output, but the latter can also affect the input. In consequence, the machine becomes error actuated. The backward or feedback transmission, consisting of the observation of the actual output, and the determination and execution of the necessary corrections is performed in non-automatic machines by the operator himself. However, it is not too difficult to imagine these functions being performed by the machine itself. Hence, we can define as automatic a machine which employs fully the principle of feedback and by so doing tries to ensure that its actual output approximates closely to the one desired, even in the presence of inaccuracies in the values of the machine's internal parameters and in spite of the existence of external disturbing factors. Such a machine largely dispenses with a guiding human intelligence. The operator now becomes a supervisor, checking from time to time whether the machine is functioning correctly and repairing faults that may occur. But he is relieved of the tedium of the constant, and usually monotonous, guidance of the machine. An automatic machine can guide itself within limits predetermined by its constructor and operator.

Thus, the gist of the principle of feedback is very simple, but like many other simple but fundamental concepts, it took a long time to be grasped and understood fully. Once comprehended, it was soon realised that this principle had been applied extensively by living organisms since the beginning of life on earth. The human body employs literally thousands of feedback loops in its metabolic processes and in the performance of its other functions. Lest anyone doubt this, let him try to run over a very familiar but rough field with his eyes closed. He will soon find that the open-loop transmission, consisting of his memory, those of his nerves which convey the input sent by the brain to activate his muscles and the muscles themselves, is quite inadequate even for such a seemingly elementary task. In constrast, as soon as the loop is closed by the opening of his eyes, he is capable of observing the output of his actions, which in this case in his position with respect to the field, thus enabling his brain to estimate the necessary corrections and rendering the task trivial.

The theory and practical application of feedback systems have both been developed to a high degree of sophistication in the last three decades. Such systems can follow rapidly changing continuous inputs, or those consisting of series of intermittent signals; they can extract the correct message from inputs heavily contaminated with meaningless noise and can thus, even in adverse conditions, perform the desired actions. In the last few years research has been concentrated on the various classes of goal-seeking, self-optimising and learning feedback systems, that is those machines which are able to reach a given goal by various trial and error techniques or can adjust the values of their internal parameters, to achieve the optimum performance of a given task in response to changes in the environment, or can be constructed to learn from past experiences.

The line dividing mechanical and non-mechanical machines and tools is a blurred one, as is the line separating mechanisation from automation. That is to say, the inclusion of a given machine into the non-mechanical, mechanised or automatic class, on the basis of the definitions stated, previously, is somewhat arbitrary. For instance, nobody would disagree that the ordinary car derives its main energy from the combustion of petrol, nevertheless, the driver supplies not only the guiding intelligence but also a non- negligible amount of physical energy to make the machine perform the desired actions. In fact, with some types of tyres and steering mechanisms this physical effort can be quite considerable when manoeuvring the car at a slow speed in a confined space. Hence, instead of thinking of sharply separated classes of mechanical and non-mechanical tools, it is preferable to visualise a gradual transition from machines driven entirely by human energy, through machines where this energy is derived partially from some other source, to those types of machines where the human contribution in terms of pure physical effort is so negligible that they can be considered to be fully mechanised. Similarly, when considering automation, one can start by imagining machines whose guiding intelligence is supplied partly by the human operator and partly by the feedback loops of the machine itself. Then, considering machines requiring progressively less and less human control one arrives finally at a machine which is capable of performing very complicated actions with practically no human intervention at all.

Some machines have been designed to perform tasks so simple that they can operate successfully without feedback and with only a negligible amount of human guidance. Hence, the definitions of mechanisation and automation given previously are only intended to convey the basic ideas involved, not to enable the reader to arrive at a precise classification of all the different types of tools and machines in existence.

15

ELECTRONIC DATA PROCESSING

So far we have covered the basic idea of feedback and the salient features of machines employing it. Now we shall outline briefly the main concepts underlying the construction of digital computers, and describe summarily the powers and weaknesses of electronic data processing as applied at present, and some probable future developments.

For thousands of years before the first industrial revolution man endeavoured—with some measure of success—to invent some mechanical means of aiding his mental powers. The invention of writing, and tools by means of which it could be implemented was an immense step forward because this constituted a decisive help for human memory enabling the experience and knowledge gained by one generation to be transmitted accurately to the next. This process was in turn improved by the invention of printing, which today is performed by many types of machines and ranks among the most important means of communicating and storing information. Writing offers help not only to the human memory but also to those mental processes which are concerned with processing data. Perhaps the most obvious examples in this respect are mathematical symbols.

In addition to writing implements, another outstanding example of the tools which help the human brain to process data is the abacus, which is still used widely in the East. Broadly speaking, these and various other simple tools gave to the human brain sufficient aid to enable it to cope with the data storage and processing required by pre-industrial civilisations. With the advent of mechanisation, however, the complexity of man-machine systems increased enormously, so, that the amount of data which had to be processed and stored grew by several orders. Unfortunately, while right from the very beginning of the first industrial revolution productivity on the shop floor had been increasing by leaps and bounds, due to the rapid introduction of mechanisation, the means of storing and processing the flood of data necessary to control the whole operation remained virtually the same as those used by ancient civilisation. Electronic data processing potentially capable of matching these needs has been developed only in the last two or three decades.

Long before the advent of electronic digital computers it was known that any number which could be expressed in decimal notation could be stated equally well in the binary notation. It follows that the latter notation is capable of representing any letter of any alphabet by means of suitable coding. Hence any data which consists of numbers and letters, i.e. is alphanumeric, can be expressed in the binary notation. It is worth noting that this class of data is much wider than one might at first think, for many forms of data which are not basically alphanumeric can be re-expressed in this form, and hence in binary notation also. For example, most geometrical figures can be described by mathematical equations, and similarly we can approximate to pictures by splitting them into a multitude of points the position of each of which may be uniquely defined by appropriate co-ordinates, to which may be added a code to describe its colour (television). Musical tones can be interpreted in a similar manner. In fact, almost any data required for strictly logical or rational reasoning can be expressed in the binary notation.

Next, consider a physical system consisting of large numbers of components, each of which can assume two distinct states. It is obvious that one could establish the correspondence between any data expressed in binary notation and a

16

given, unique state of this system or, in other words, represent the data by a certain definite state of the system. This is usually referred to as storing the data in the system. Further, large classes of logical reasoning can be broken down into elementary steps, each equivalent to a choice between a 'yes' or 'no' answer. Any such step can clearly be represented by certain uniquely determined physical changes in the state of the system, consisting of alterations of the states of some of its elements.

Having performed all the elementary steps involved, the final state of the system would be the physical equivalent of the final stage of a given piece of a logical argument performed on given initial data. Hence, given a sufficient number of bistable elements and the coding rules for storing and processing the data, the system described above could, at least in principle, store information required for logical reasoning and perform the physical equivalent of rational mental processes. In other words, it could perform the physical equivalent of memorising and processing rationally, according to given instructions, the data desired. It could not, of course, produce the physical equivalents of states of mind which cannot be described precisely in words or symbols, nor could it perform physical operations corresponding to those metal processes which fall outside the class of strict logical thinking.

Although the basic concept of such a system, which one would describe as an automatic data processing machine, is rather simple, the engineering difficulties in its construction should not be under-estimated. In a normal practical application the data, described in binary notation, may require thousands or even millions of bistable elements just to store it. The processing of it may well require thousands of millions of the elementary steps referred to before. A malfunctioning of one single element in any step introduces an error which may easily upset the outcome of the whole process. Hence, from the engineering point of view, the essential prerequisite for building a practically useful automatic data processing machine is the availability of a bistable component which operates extremely quickly and reliably, uses little power, is cheap and dimensionally small. If these requirements are quantified and a numerical specification arrived at, it becomes apparent that virtually all conceivable mechanical and electromechanical two state devices are not feasible from the engineering point of view.

With the advent of modern electronics, however, the construction of automatic data processing machines capable of storing data consisting of hundreds or even thousands of millions of binary units and processing it at speeds millions of times faster than that of the human brain becomes a practical proposition. At first a thermionic valve provided the basic bistable component. Later, semiconducting crystals supplied the means for processing the data, while other types of bistable components, mainly of a magnetic character, were employed for data storage. This latter function can also be performed by components of a mechanical type, e.g. punched cards or punched tape, which constitute for some applications a cheap and convenient medium; but because data can be put into and extracted from them at relatively low speeds it has to be transferred into a fast, magnetic type of memory for the actual processing.

THE DIGITAL COMPUTER

A very brief description of the principal units of a typical digital computer, their salient features, and the interaction between them would seem to be useful at this stage. The machine consists of five basic parts: input, output, data storage, processing unit and control unit.

The input is a communication channel between the machine and the human operator or another machine. Through this channel the data and the instructions as to how it is to be processed are fed into the machine. If a human operator wants to feed in the data and instructions himself, then he usually has to punch them into cards or tape. The machines at present available for commercial purposes are not able to interpret human speech, normal hand-writing or normal type faces. Consequently the feeding of data into the machine by a human operator is a very slow process in comparison with the speed with which this data is processed within the machine. If the data is fed by another machine, then other media, mainly of a magnetic type, can be employed enabling the information to be transferred at a much faster rate.

The output can be punched cards, punched tape or magnetic tape if it is intended to be used as the input to another machine. If the output is intended to communicate to human beings, a variety of printing devices are available, the average of which can print in excess of 1,000 lines per minute. Thus, the machine can produce output information at a rate much faster than any human being can absorb it.

The memory units consist normally of several sub-units which differ from each other in the amount of data which they can store and in access time, that is, the average time interval necessary to locate and transfer one element of data from the given store to some other part of the machine. They also differ in price for a unit of data stored. For instance, punched cards are a cheap medium and of virtually unlimited capacity but have a relatively long access time. Data stored on magnetic tape can be read by the machine much faster than data from punched cards. Therefore, if a given application permits the sequential use of data, then magnetic tape provides an efficient medium. However, in applications where the data required at any instant may be stored on any part of the tape, the rewinding of the tape makes the access time excessively long. In this respect magnetic drums or discs are superior. The so called core store has the shortest access time and usually consists of an array of small magnetic rings interlaced by a network of wires. Each ring can be magnetised in either of two directions by passing a current through the appropriate wires. The access time for this and some other types of core stores can be so short that it has to be measured in thousandths of millionths of a second, or nanoseconds. Their present disadvantage is their relatively high cost per unit of data stored, but great research effort concentrated in this field is gradually bringing the cost down.

In the latest commercially available digital computer, the processing units employ 'circuits' consisting of tiny, suitably shaped crystals of semi-conducting material and metal plated dielectric wafers. Thus, a part of the processing circuitry which, in early computers employing ordinary thermionic valves would be the size of a tea-chest, would use kilowatts of power and would perform the simple processing operations in time intervals measured in milliseconds, can now be reduced to approximately the size of a matchbox, work millions of times faster and consume negligible power in addition to being cheaper and much more reliable. This gives one some idea of the progress achieved in this field over the last 20 years.

The control unit employs components similar to those used in the processing units and the fast access stores. It controls the operation of the whole machine and for this purpose it uses a list of instructions or 'program' stored in the memory unit. It reads these instructions sequentially and causes all the other units of the machine to perform the necessary actions. Thus the machine possesses tremendous versatility because, merely by feeding in different programs or data or both, it can be made to perform a number of totally different data processing tasks.

To avoid the widespread misconceptions concerning the powers and limitations of digital computers, it is essential to keep firmly in mind the distinctions between: (1) the machines and types of programs normally available and used at present in industry; (2) the machines and programs which are now in a state of intensive research and development; (3) the expected progress in this field in the foreseeable future; and (4) the ultimate, theoretically possible powers of these machines. If this distinction is not made, a hopeless confusion of thought may easily arise. A typical example of this is the fact that the first digital computers were named 'electronic brains', implying the possession of powers comparable to those of the human brain. This was manifestly untrue. At the present time, when the machines and programming methods have become immensely more powerful, computers are often considered as being nothing but 'obedient morons' and destined for ever to remain in this category. This down-grading of the status of the machines during the period when big strides forward have been taking place in their construction and methods of usage is probably a reaction to the overstatement of their case at the very beginning. A modern computer employs a fast magnetic core store which can consist of anything between a few thousands and up to perhaps ten million bistable elements and is thus capable of storing this number of elementary units of information, or 'bits' as they are usually referred to in computer terminology. The amount of information which can be stored on punched card, magnetic tape or disc is virtually unlimited if we think of them as a kind of library from which the human operator can choose an appropriate reel of tape or a disc and feed it into the computer. But the number of discs, drums and tapes which can be connected directly to the computer, and from which the machine can draw the information stored on them as required by the program and without human intervention, is limited. At the present time the amount of information which can be stored on magnetic tapes and discs and be under the direct control of the computer can be up to several hundreds of millions of bits. This, together with the salient features of input and output described previously, gives an idea of the data processing powers of modern computers used for commercial and scientific purposes, but it has to be borne in mind that the above figures indicate only the orders of magnitude, as continuous research in this field increases them at such a rate that any definite upper limits would be valid for no more than a few months.

At present, the modern digital computer available for industrial and scientific purposes using the normal methods of programming is certainly nothing more than an 'obedient moron' in the following sense: that while it can perform any, even extremely complicated, processing operation on any data expressible in letters or numbers with the utmost accuracy and at speeds thousands of millions of times faster than a human being, it can only do this if it is given, at every step, precise and unambigous instructions as how to proceed. It is entirely devoid of any feelings, intuition or common sense. It does not learn from experience, nor can it seek for or reach any goal unless it has been instructed how to in precise, minute detail. In other words, its 'creative intelligence', using this phrase in its accepted meaning, is not only impossible of any comparison with human intelligence, it is also lower than that of practically any living creature; in fact, virtually nil.

PROGRAMS

To say, however, that computers are nothing more than obedient morons when considering machines and programs which are currently the subject of research is not true. (In this context programs are the more important aspect, since even an ordinary commercial digital computer can, when suitably programmed, perform tasks for which it is not normally used in industry.) Programs exist which can seek for, and reach, goals by trial and error techniques and which can thus be said to 'learn from experience'. By the latter is meant the following: a goal, for example, to prove a certain logical or mathematical theorem or to win a certain type of game, is given. The appropriate logical rules or the rules of the game are stated. A list of instructions to be followed during the first trial or the initial procedure is also given, together with the rules for the evaluation of the merit of the result obtained and the rules for changing the initial procedure accordingly. The program applies the initial procedure during the first trial, obtains a certain result, evaluates it, modifies the initial procedure accordingly and stores it in the computer's memory. Subsequently, it uses the modified initial procedure during the second trial and goes through the following stages as before.

Programs exist which employ many variants of this basic learning process and some of them achieve remarkable performances. One of them, playing a game of draughts, reached a level approaching the standard of a master player and often won when playing against its own creator, although at present it cannot beat consistently the best player against whom it is pitched. One could argue that if the task is to prove some logical or geometrical proposition, then given the rules of the logic, the initial procedure, the rules for evaluating the merit of the results and those for changing the program, which are, of course, a part of the program itself, then the whole process is predictable and therefore does not deserve to be called learning. But if the same task was performed by a man in a series of trials under the same logical rules, starting with the same initial procedure and applying the same rules for changing this procedure after each trial according to the result obtained, we would surely be tempted to say that this man had learned to perform the task. Further, if the goal is to win a game against a human player, the consequences of any move made by the machine do not depend only on the machine itself but also on the performance of its opponent. Hence, even if the rules for the evaluation of the consequences of any move or series of moves and those for the subsequent modification of the program governing the play of the machine were given, the final program arrived at after many games could not be predicted in advance unless it were possible to predetermine every move of the human player in any situation arising during these games, which is a clear impossibility.

In addition, it would be possible to insert into the machine parts which would change their states randomly. Thus the machine could alter some instructions in a random fashion, evaluate their efficiency, store in its memory the most efficient combinations and thus learn to reach the goal by trial and error, arriving finally at a problem solving program unpredictable in advance.

Programs and machines already exist which are capable of performing the above feats, although only in a limited sense, as nobody has managed so far to write a learning program capable of changing by itself its own basic structure. But there is, at the moment, no theoretical reason why this should be impossible. Concerning the future, it seems that magnetic tape and disc stores directly under the computer's control will soon be able to store an amount of information comparable to that memorisable by a human brain. In the foreseeable future, fast random access stores should achieve similar capacities. The statements above have to be treated cautiously, however, because very little is known about how the human brain works. It is known that it consists of about ten thousand million cells, each one of which may be interconnected to, perhaps, a hundred others. The junctions between these cells, or synapses, seem to perform in a manner which makes them comparable in some aspects to bistable elements. This would imply that the brain has the equivalent of ten thousand million of such elements at its disposal. However, because the actual operation of the nerve cell is very complex or because the seat of memory may not be the nerve cells at all but the glial cells, which form a substantial part of total volume of the brain, the total memory storage of the human brain when translated into the equivalent number of bits may be one or two orders greater than indicated previously. However, it may be expected that fast random access stores will in time match and exceed even this figure.

In the field of processing we seem to be approaching the limits of speed already. It should be remembered that light travels only about one foot in a nanosecond and this is, therefore, the maximum speed of propagation of any impulse within the machine. A computer consisting of bistable elements capable of altering their states within one or two nanoseconds must of necessity be rather small if the operation of all the parts is to be kept in synchronism. In so far as size is concerned, further miniaturisation of the parts from which the processing and memory units are built can be expected, culminating perhaps, in parts of molecular size.

THE FUTURE

The computers of the foreseeable future will probably be able to accept input in the form of print of almost any type, long hand writing and human speech. Speech should also become a common form of output. The energy consumption and especially the cost for given data processing power will probably be reduced dramatically. In programming also, great steps forward can be expected. The first computers had to be instructed in meticulous detail how to perform every elementary operation. Later it became possible to express several elementary operations by one, more comprehensive, instruction. As every one of the latter corresponds to a strictly defined sequence of elementary instructions, the translation or compilation from macro- to micro-instructions is a logically completely determined procedure and can therefore be performed by the machine itself. Hence although the machine itself still works according to elementary instructions, the programmer writes a program in terms of macro-instructions which greatly speeds up and simplifies his job. The sets of macro-instructions known as programming languages, together with their corresponding compilers, are in a state of active development, aiming to reduce still further the human effort necessary to program a computer. The final stage of this process would presumably be a programming language, resembling ordinary human language even closer than do the present codes.

Thus, it is reasonable to expect that in the future we shall have machines performing data processing tasks with the utmost speed, and possessing fast random access memories capable of storing an amount of data comparable to that memorisable by the human brain or even greater. They will be very reliable in operation and capable of diagnosing their own faults, which will be easy to repair by simple substitution of inexpensive circuits; this substitution may even be done by the machine itself. We shall be communicating with these machines by means of print, writing and speech for at least some classes of tasks, in a manner not very different from communicating with other human beings. The enormous quantities of data stored in their memories will consist partly of very large numbers of routine programs for solving certain types of problems. In addition, the machines should be capable of learning by experience or trial and error techniques, the sophistication of which should exceed that of present experimental research models by several orders. Whether these computers of the future will be small portable machines or whether everybody will have access through some communication link designed to carry information at extremely high rates (artificial satellite laser beams?) to one enormously powerful computer, executing millions of programs simultaneously, is a matter of conjecture. Perhaps both alternatives will be exploited.

The question of whether computers will ever achieve the all round intellectual performance of a human being is, at the present, more a theological than a scientific problem. If we believe that human beings are endowed with souls, which are in an entirely different category to any arrangement of matter, then clearly no machine can ever equal man by definition. On the other hand, if we believe that man is nothing more than an extremely complicated physico-chemical system, then there is no compelling reason why some machine, built or grown artificially, (here 'machine' means any system other than one developed directly from living matter) should not be able to match, or even surpass, man's intellectual ability. Although we are so far from the state when such a machine would be a technical feasibility that it is not worth while pursuing the subject much further in this place, one is tempted to say that in developing more sophisticated computers the logical design and programming will present difficulties much more formidable than the purely engineering ones. Very little is known of the logic followed by the human brain at the neuro-physiological level, and what is known indicates that this logic may be very different from that of any of our digital computers. In addition, the feeling of consciousness, the emotions and the various states of mind, some of which cannot even be described adequately in words, are entirely outside the powers of any machine existing at present or likely to exist in the foreseeable future. Whether this state of affairs will persist indefinitely is an open question, the answer to which depends on one's fundamental beliefs.

The principles of feedback and that underlying digital computation, although seemingly different, both form the basis of a similar function, which is to operate on or process data. The final aim is to control certain physical activities or to solve some logical or mathematical problems. Digital computers often form part of complex feedback systems, in particular of those operating on intermittent signals or pulses. Conversely, instead of representing a given physical system by a set of mathematical equations, and thus being able to solve the problems involved by means of digital computation, one can build, by using complex feedback circuits, a replica of this system, or an analogue computer, and solve the same problems by suitable manipulation of the latter. Both methods have certain advantages and disadvantages and which is preferable depends on the case in hand. Detailed discussion would be out of place at this point.

CYBERNETIC MACHINES

We can attach the adjective 'cybernetic' to those machines which employ the principles of feedback or of digital computation or both extensively. These machines are the tools of the cybernetic revolution, which has already begun in industrially advanced countries. We shall now examine briefly the possible consequences of employment of these machines.

The central fact of the cybernetic revolution is that it is introducing machines which augment our human capacity for rational data processing on a scale analogous to that on which steam, electrical and internal combustion engines augmented our physical powers in the first Industrial Revolution. The effects of mechanisation proved to be tremendous and few would argue that it has left the course of human civilisation unchanged. Yet mechanisation multiplied those powers which are certainly not the most important assets of man—his physical strength and energy. But man owers his mastery over this planet mainly to his mental capabilities. Cybernetic machines, since they augment the latter, have, therefore, much greater potential for increasing man's total control over his environment. The potential of cybernetic machines should not be under-estimated on the grounds that, at present, they are only capable of performing operations which are the equivalents of the lower mental functions of the human brain. Machines introduced during the early stages of the first industrial revolution were similarly inherently incapable of manufacturing goods identical to those produced by master craftsmen, even when under the control of the best machine operators. Yet, by radically changing the design and methods of manufacture, these machines were soon producing a flood of goods of acceptable quality, and doing so incomparably faster and cheaper than craftsmen could. The majority of the mental tasks performed at present by human beings can also be modified so that they can be executed by existing cybernetic machines millions of times faster and much cheaper. One must not forget that at the moment the cybernetic revolution is still in its very early stages and employs data processing machines, which are rather primitive in comparison with those which can be expected in the future, yet they are already capable of performing practically all desired functions, suitably modified where necessary, and of controlling almost any manufacturing process, at least in principle. They can perform a multitude of managerial and executive functions and have proved themselves invaluable tools in research and development. In fact, certain kinds of current scientific research would be practically impossible without digital or analogue computers. Computers are making inroads into the field of design and the latest computer models were actually designed with the aid of machines built previously.

Today, even the largest scale industrial and commercial applications of automation and electronic data processing are lagging far behind what is technically possible with currently available machines. There are three principle reasons for this—lack of funds required to finance them, lack of adequately trained people and lack of skill in developing the potential application of cybernetic machines. But the trend is unmistakable.

Advanced cybernetic machines give us the technical means of producing an abundance of goods and services while requiring only a minimum of physical and mental effort on the part of their human operators. Hence, barring atomic wars and an uncontrolled growth of population, and given a satisfactory solution to the problem of the under-developed countries, the cybernetic revolution is potentially capable of bringing us to the threshold of an age of plenty and of leisure. It will also increase tremendously, our control over our environment. This will create a situation unprecedented in human history and coping with it will pose possibly the greatest problem the human race has ever faced, mainly because the change is likely to be, on the historical scale, so rapid.

Since the beginning of mankind, man has had to use practically all his physical and mental powers to fulfill his role as provider for himself and his family and to ensure their survival. Only a tiny surplus was available to the very small, privileg - ed ruling minority. Our whole system of ethical, social and political values grew in accordance with this basic fact of life. These values were adjusted to the envi- ronment and hence to the mode of production and the state of technology at a given time. Because the rate of technological change was slow until the first industrial revolution, our organisational and ethical systems also changed slowly, indeed in some basic aspects they have remained unaltered (nearly static) since Neolithic times.

The first industrial revolution caught man entirely unprepared organisationally and ethically. Very few people realised that the technological changes wrought by it would necessitate corresponding organisational and ethical changes on a scale amounting to the alteration of the very foundations and structure of man's social and moral systems. Those people who could see this problem were neither able to agree on a solution, nor had the power necessary for implement- ing one. Hence the cataclysmic sociological and political upheavals accompanying the technological innovations in the last two centuries happened in an unplanned or haphazard manner, causing a tremendous amount of strife and human suffer- ing over the whole world. One does not have to look far for examples to support the above statements.

Wars over limited human and animal energy resources and scarce material goods made some sense in the unavoidably poor world of the pre-industrial era. They were already obsolescent in the age of advanced mechanisation, when it should have been obvious that given suitable social and political organisations a good standard of living could have been enjoyed by all members of the human race with only a moderate amount of work. In the presence of automatic machi- nes, leading us as they do into an age of effortless abundance, and helping us to build weapons of mass destruction which threaten us with total annihilation, wars became sheer lunacy. But our tribal mentality, encouraging us to indulge in armed competition, although completely out of date, does not seem to show much change. Similarly with the great problem of over-population. In times when mortality from disease and continuous tribal warfare was high it was neces- sary for a given tribe to produce as many offspring as possible just to keep the numbers static, and ethical values were developed accordingly. But when the great advances in medical science were employed by a society still governed largely by the old ethical values, the present rapid growth of population was in- evitable. This has to be controlled somehow because, even assuming the develop- ment of some as yet undreamt of methods of food production, the number of inhabitants which the earth can support is obviously finite. However, the magni- tude of the change required in basic ethical values, given the poor organisation and low educational level of the majority of people in over-populated countries, makes the introduction of large scale contraceptive methods an extremely difficult task and little progress has so far been achieved, in spite of the fact that over-population constitutes one of the major threats to the future of the human race.

The introduction of mechanisation led to the creation of vast industrial systems interacting in a complicated manner, which in turn led to the unavoidable necessity of abandoning true economic liberalism and of substituting in its place a planned economy. But it took two centuries of social and political strife, ruthless exploitation of the working masses, an endless succession of booms and depressions, two World Wars and competition from cruel totalitarian regimes before we arrived at the state when even those countries still professing economic liberalism are in fact resorting to the increasing use of national planning. At the same time the totalitarian regimes are learning to appreciate the value of individual initiative and realise that human hecatombs are not a necessary prerequisite for industrialisation. But although the real difference in social structure between West and East, excluding present day China, is now far smaller than might appear from the pronouncements of their appointed spokesmen and is growing progressively less, and although it is obvious that, given time, either of the two competing systems can produce an abundance of material goods, struggles over largely outdated issues continue, sometimes at a pitch which threatens mankind with extinction.

The inability of the human race to cope with the problems posed by large scale mechanisation makes it very doubtful whether it will be able to cope with the even more fundamental problems arising from the cybernetic revolution. Cybernetic machines can ultimately make a poorly educated man redundant as a producer of goods and services, just as mechanically powered machines made redundant men who had little but physical energy to offer. It can be foreseen that in the not too distant future a man of only average intellect will be virtually unemployable on purely economic grounds. It will be cheaper to build or to program a machine to perform the great majority of jobs which it will then do speedily and at low cost, than to teach him to do it and pay his wage. With the progressive perfection of cybernetic machines we may finally reach the stage when only a man with, by present standard, exceptionally well developed mental powers will have omething to offer in economic terms. This would mean, given our present soscial systems, massive unemployment in the presence of an abudance of goods. It is difficult to imagine how a competitive, free enterprise system could cope with this situation without undergoing such radical changes that in effect it would become something quite different, whatever the label attached. The co-operative, socialist society would probably find it easier to adjust itself to such conditions in so far as the purely economic side is concerned. However, the sets of basic values on which both systems, capitalist and socialist, are built, although not identical, have at least one thing in common: the routine type of work ranks very high in either. The virtual abolition of such work would clearly create, for the majority of people, a situation with which no social system existing today is capable of dealing. The devaluation of work, as this word is understood today, would alter radically the outlook prevailing within our industrial civilisation and with it the social structure. The educational system, instead of concentrating on preparing men and women to do certain specific types of work, would have to be re-directed in the cybernetic era to the general development, to the utmost limits of those human mental powers which are most difficult for the machine to imitate. Among these are creative thinking, artistic abilities, curiosity, and the development of new abstract ideas and their associations, particularly those outside the strictly logical field.

The possible age of plenty which will require only a minimum of physical and mental work on the part of the majority of the population and the increased control of our destiny which will result from scientific and technological progress will soon, on an historical scale, force upon us a weighty choice. This choice will be between, on the one hand, almost unlimited leisure, idleness in luxury and consequent degeneration and, on the other, the full use of creative human powers released from physical and mental drudgery for the further cultural, scientific and perhaps even genetic advancement of our race, together with the chance of experiencing to the full a joy of living, uninhibited by the straight jacket of outdated pre-scientific and pre-industrial ideologies.

Unfortunately, as a race, we seem to have an almost complete lack of comprehension of our true present position. Our greatest and most immediate needs are the remodelling of our basic system of values and our social and political institutions, to find out what we really are and what way of living suits us best and to establish just how we want to live and develop as individuals and as a race. We should be attempting to answer these problems in the most objective and scientific manner possible, by concentrating the best brains available and large material resources on research in the fields of psychology, physiology, sociology, ecology and other related domains.

Instead, we are trying to deal with the immensely complex questions facing us by leaning dogmatically on outdated ideologies and concentrating enormous material and human resources in the fields of technical research, although it is obvious that with techniques already in existence we could create a material paradise on earth, given the right social and political structure.

As a result, our priorities have got hopelessly confused. We are engaged in a race to the moon, mainly for complex reasons of national prestige, politics, militarism and muddled economics. The resources spent on this race would comfortably suffice to bring the under-developed countries to their economic 'take-off' point. Even greater sums are spent on the arms race, when no side can hope for victory but only fear universal destruction. So, while our cybernetic machines land on the moon, two-thirds of our race live at or near starvation level, and the rest live under the threat of total thermo-nuclear destruction, often in conditions of intolerable stress rising from general insecurity, overcrowding, noise and in an environment unsuitable for human beings. There is overwhelming evidence that we are quite unable to derive full benefit from our scientific and technological advances, as embodied in the form of our powerful and complicated machines.

The creation and introduction of any tool or machine, apart from the direct aim for which it was constructed, has also many side effects. We ought to have been taking these side effects into account at least since the beginning of the first industrial revolution—but we have not been, and as a consequence we have brought upon ourselves a heap of disasters. Now the powers and even more far reaching effects of cybernetic machines force us to take these considerations most seriously into account—otherwise catastrophies of incalculable magnitude are bound to occur. The history of the last 200 years provides ample evidence to show that such prophecies of doom are not the fanciful concoctions of a paranoic mind but very reasonable predictions.

SLAVES OR MASTERS?

We shall end this chapter on the tools of the cybernetic revolution by considering briefly a question which has fascinated people over the centuries—'Can machines (and in this context we mean cybernetic machines) ever change from mechanical slaves into the masters of mankind?'. If this means 'are we ever likely to see the arrival of a machine more intelligent than human beings and capable of achieving purposefully and consciously its mastery over them?', then the answer is certainly negative for as far as we can see into the future. But if it means certain types of hidden, unintentional control, then the answer is far from simple.

It is a well known fact that modern weapon systems require very quick decisions based on the correct evaluation of many factors which interact in a complicated manner. Because of the necessity to perform beforehand a massive amount of data processing in a very short time, such decisions have to be made by a computer. True, the human commander still has over-riding control, but this may be something of an illusion because, as he may be unable to evaluate the situation himself within the time available, he might have no option but to follow the recommendations given by the machine. Thus a nuclear strike, aiming at the prevention of an apparently imminent threat of nuclear attack by the enemy could be made on the basis of an erroneous evaluation of the enemy's intentions by a digital computer. Of course, the machine would perform this evaluation according to a program written by human beings.

But as pointed out before, with the growing sophistication of learning and goal-seeking machines, the interaction between the user and the computer becomes so complex that it may be difficult to differentiate clearly between the contributions of the human and that of the machine to the final rules of optimum strategy. Thus it might legitimately be forecast that at some time cybernetic machines may unconsciously and therefore unintentionally, plunge us into the final thermo-nuclear catastrophe. They could in a similar manner influence the decisions of managers, executives or governments is many other fields.

There is another, conceptually much simpler, way in which machines can influence the course of our civilisation. Machines constructed during the first industrial revolution augmented only our physical powers. But, once their use became widespread, could we have dispensed with them even had we wished? In theory, yes, in practice, no, not without creating untold misery. No sane person would suggest that an ordinary car can think or that it wishes to influence our way of living. Yet its widespread use has done precisely this. If now, by employing cybernetic machines, we become increasingly dependent on mechanical aids not only for the execution of physical but also of mental tasks, the influence of machines on our lives will grow immensely. And with the arrival of the self-optimising, goal-seeking and learning machines of the foreseeable future which will be more sophisticated and powerful in data processing abilities by several orders than any machine existing at present, and with their insertion into the complex network of a cybernetic civilisation, it might become increasingly difficult to answer the question, 'who is really giving the orders: man or machine?'.

In conclusion, the tools of the cybernetic revolution give us power in a new dimension: the power to increase our mental capabilities. This power, as any other, can be used for good or evil. But its arrival coincides with the development of weapons of mass destruction, and is taking place at a time of over-population and enormous technological and economic disparity between the rich and the under-developed countries. It is happening in a period when man's scientific and technological achievements are probably thousands of years ahead of his social organisation and real ethical level and when the world is torn apart by dogmatic and mutually hostile ideologies.

Taking into account all the above and the well known history of mechanisation it is difficult to decide whether the cybernetic revolution is leading to a long dreamed of paradise on earth or whether it is the end of an evolutionary blind alley, which man entered with his discovery of fire and the chipping of the stone hand axe.

ACKNOWLEDGEMENTS

I am very much indebted to my colleagues Messrs. J. R. Deavin, R. L. Dunnett and A. E. Murton for constructive criticism and linguistic corrections. However, none of them should be in any way associated with or held responsible for the views expressed in this chapter.

I am also very grateful to Miss M. A. Sharpe for her gallant efforts in typing my almost illegible handwriting, and to the Comino-Dexion Group for providing facilities for typing and duplicating the manuscript and for a generally helpful and encouraging attitude towards this work.

Chapter 3

What a Robot Can and Cannot Do

J. F. SCHUH Ph. D.
Philips, Eindhoven (Holland)

SUMMARY

The author tries to explain, in simple words, what makes it possible to construct machines that can imitate many actions that until now were thought to be the exclusive attributes of man. It is contended that the essential elements of intellectual activities are the presence of a memory and the possibility of making choices of decisions. This is demonstrated by means of some simple examples. The problem of pattern recognition, particularly the recognition of printed and handwritten letters, is considered in more detail and compared with the corresponding biological action.

INTRODUCTION

Man's dislike for work is apparently such that ever since his appearance on earth, he has been trying to make others work for him: first the beast and the slave, then the steam engine and the electric motor, now the automaton or robot; the latter is capable of doing calculations, playing chess, solving puzzles, keeping books, guiding rockets, etc.; and even if it doesn't always do this better than man, at any rate it does it at an immensely higher speed. The question which we shall consider here is: how does the robot, for example, play chess, and how does man? Are their ways of doing it at all analogous, or are they fundamentally different?

All mechanical calculating machines reckon according to a principle which, in fact, is that of the abacus. But this is not the case with the modern electronic computing automaton. In my view, the characteristic feature of the modern automaton is that after each step in a process, the automaton decides for itself what the next step will be, making a choice from several possibilities each time. *It is the recognition that it is possible to design an apparatus which makes its own decisions that ushers in the new era, which at present is generally referred to as the second industrial revolution.*

29

The decision made by an automaton depends on three factors:

1. The results of preceding actions performed by the automaton.
2. Data the automaton receives from its surroundings.
3. Chance.

In purely calculating automata, only the first case is preponderant. In automata having to perform some controlling function, a combination of factors (1) and (2) generally is found. It may, however, be desirable or practical to make the operation of the automaton more or less dependent on chance (this may make sense even with purely calculating automata). If this is done by incorporating a chance-introducing device (usually called a noise generator) in the automaton, the case then comes under (2) since this device may be considered to form part of the automaton's surroundings. An example of an automaton, in which a certain amount of chance is of great advantage, is the automatic pilot of a military air craft. The less predictable its manoeuvres, the more difficult it will be to hit. Animals act similarly; a wolf chased by hunters will begin to zigzag. The French word *louvoyer* (to tack) is derived from *loup* (wolf).

Summarising the above we arrive at the following definition:

An automaton or robot is a mechanism capable of performing a sequence of actions, after each of which the decision as to what will be the next action is determined unambiguously either by the results of the preceding actions or by data received from the surroundings, including any noise generators, or by a combination of both.

PRINCIPAL PROBLEMS OF DESIGNING AN AUTOMATON

To achieve an understanding of the possibilities and (perhaps temporary) limitations of automation, let us consider the following aspects:

1. How can a machine be made to remember?
2. How can a machine be made to decide?
3. What results can be achieved by performing a sharply defined sequence of sharply defined actions?

REMEMBERING

The problem at issue is remembering things or facts (from now on, referrred to as messages) of the greatest diversity. This is made possible by coding the messages to be remembered, that is, identifying each message with a certain signal. The word 'signal' is used here in its widest sense. For example, a signal may be a group of spots on a tape or drum coated with a magnetic material, the spots being magnetised in one or the other of two different magnetic states, a combination of the presence and absence of currents in a group of wires. A signal can also be a printed, written or spoken sentence or a grouping of symbols of some sort. *An essential feature of a code is that the signals used have a meaning which is known to the receiver*. Which signal is identified with a certain message is a question of 'agreement'.

Generally, a signal is composed of a number of elementary signals. By way of illustration, each letter of the English alphabet may be identified with a combination of the presence and absence of current in five wires. The presence or absence of current in a wire is, then, an elementary signal.

It is usual to represent the presence of current by the symbol 0 and its absence by the symbol 1. Thus the letters a, b, c, ... correspond to the signals 00111, 01100, 10001,.... These representations of the signals are usually called code groups, the symbols (0 and 1) of which the code groups consist being called code elements. The terms 'signal' and 'code group' on the one hand, and 'elementary signal' and 'code element' on the other are thus in effect synonyms; the terminology used is merely a matter of language.

In the examples given so far, the elementary signals can assume only two different values. Therefore, these signalling systems are referred to as bivalent. Generally, a system of signalling in which the elementary signals can assume only a finite number of different values is called *digital*. The signalling systems used in automata are almost always bivalent.

A signalling system of a completely different nature is the *analogue signalling system;* in this, every elementary signal may assume an infinite number of values, for example all the values between 0 A and 1 A. Since, however, every continuously variable quantity can only be measured with a finite accuracy, each apparatus using analogue signalling has a certain margin of uncertainty. As far as I know, it is still an open question whether this is the only difference between digital and analogue signalling.

A signalling system may be used not only for the storage of messages, but also for the transport of information. This may take place either simultaneously (several elementary signals at the same time) or sequentially (the elementary signals one after the other). Instead of 'simultaneous' and 'sequential', the terms 'parallel' and 'serial' are sometimes used.

TAKING DECISIONS

Expressed in the terminology introduced above, the taking of a decision means to replace a signal (or combination of signals) by another signal (or combination of signals), i.e. a signal transformation. In addition to a memory (or store), the signal transformer is to be considered as a characteristic component part of the automaton.

Consider, for example, an automatic pilot for an aircraft. This receives continously a number of signals which have been produced partly in the aircraft itself and are identifiable with data such as the positions of the control surfaces (rudders, elevator and ailerons), the speed relative to the ambient air, the height, etc., and signals which have come partly from outside the aircraft, for example, radio signals which indicate the position of the aircraft or contain flight instructions. The automaton must respond by transmitting certain signals to the controls of the aircraft to give them the desired positions. Hence, at each instant, the automaton must decide which output signals it must produce, and viewed as a whole, the automaton performs a signal transformation.

In many cases the decision consists of giving an answer to a question. In this case both question and answer must be identified with a signal (or code group). Obviously, a real problem arises only when the relationship between incoming and outgoing signals (for example, question and answer) is too complicated to be set down in a simple table. In this event one must try to solve the problem by constructing the automaton from a number of comparatively simple signal transformers. The principles of this operation cannot be considered here, but the principle on which a simple signal transformer for bivalent signals may be constructed will be outlined. Such a signal transformer may be represented as shown in Fig. 3.1.

In this figure, *a*, *b* and *c* are three bivalent elementary input signals and *x* is the bivalent output signal. Then suppose the transformer has to perform the transformation shown in Table 3.1.

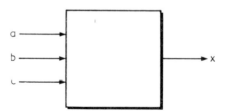

Fig. 3.1. A signal transformer

Table 3.1.

TRANSFORMATION TO BE PERFORMED BY THE SIGNAL TRANSFORMER IN FIG. 3.1

No.	a	b	c	x
1	0	0	0	1
2	0	0	1	1
3	0	1	0	0
4	0	1	1	1
5	1	0	0	0
6	1	0	1	0
7	1	1	0	1
8	1	1	1	1

The table gives the value of the output signal for every combination of values of the input signals. The transformation can be represented by the formula:

$$x = \bar{a}\bar{b}\bar{c} + \bar{a}\bar{b}c + \bar{a}bc + ab\bar{c} + abc \tag{3.1}$$

which is to be interpreted as follows. Each term on the right hand side corresponds to a case in which the output signal has the value 1. For example, the term $\bar{a}\bar{b}\bar{c}$ refers to the case in which the input signals *a*, *b* and *c* all have the value 0; the term $\bar{a}\bar{b}c$ to the case in which the input signals *a* and *b* have the value 0 but the input signal *c* has the value 1, and so on. The five terms on the right hand side indicate the five cases in which the output signal *x* has the value 1. The formula as a whole indicates that the output signal *x* has the value 1 when one of these cases occurs and only when this happens.

This immediately leads to the construction shown in Fig. 3.2, in which the three members designated by the letter I are so called negators (or inverters). From the signals *a*, *b* and *c*, they form the signals *ā*, *b̄* and *c̄* (for example, by converting the absence of a current into the presence of a current and vice versa, or generally by changing the value of a bivalent signal).

32

The five members designated by the letter A are *and-gates;* each of these produces an output signal of value 1 when, and only when, all the input signals have the value 1.

Consequently, the five and-gates produce exactly five signals which are identified with the five terms $\bar{a}\bar{b}\bar{c}$, $\bar{a}\bar{b}c$, $\bar{a}bc$, $ab\bar{c}$ and abc on the right hand side of formula 3.1. Finally, the member designated by the letter 0 is an *or-gate*, which produces an output signal with the value 1 when at least one of its input signals has the value 1, and an output signal with the value 0 when, and only when, all its input signals have the value 0. In the circuit arrangement of most interest, one of the input signals can assume the value 1, but this is not essential for the concept or-gate. The or-gate produces the desired output signal *x*, which may be called the answer to the incoming code group.

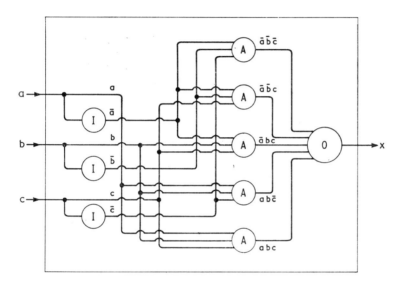

Fig. 3.2. A digital signal transformer

One could term the circuit arrangement of Fig. 3.2 'the translation of formula (3.1) into circuitry'. It will be clear that, on this principle, a signal transformer may be constructed for any known signal transformation.

The negators, and-gates and or-gates from which any desired signal transformer can be built, may themselves be considered as the simplest types of signal transformers possible. Several types of these building stones, which consist of diodes or transistors, are known, and some of them are capable of forming their output signal from their input signals in less than one nanosecond (10^{-9} second).

In this connection another interesting circuit arrangement may be mentioned, the *adaptive signal transformer*. In the literature, circuits of this type are often called *learning circuits*, but in my view this name is rather pretentious, hence I prefer a more neutral appellation.

The circuit arrangement of such a signal transformer is shown in Fig. 3.3. The circuit as a whole has three input terminals, 1, 2 and 3, which receive the three elementary signals *a*, *b* and *c* (which together form an incoming code group); an output terminal 4, which delivers the answer, *x*, to the incoming code group; and

33

two additional input terminals 5 and 6. The circuit of Fig. 3.3 is intended, not to perform an *a priori* signal transformation fixed once and for all (as does the signal transformer in Fig. 3.2) but to be able to adapt itself to any desired signal transformation. This is effected in the following manner.

When the signal transformer has received a certain code group at its input terminals 1, 2 and 3, it must subsequently, but at any rate before receiving the next code group, receive at its additional input terminal, 5, a signal y that indicates which answer the transformer must give to the code group received. Therefore, the signal y applied to the additional input terminal 5 is called the desired answer.

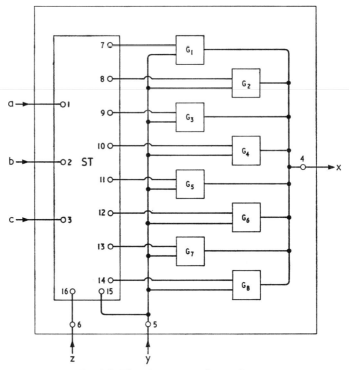

Fig. 3.3. The adaptive signal transformer

Once the signal transformer has received the desired answer y to every possible incoming code group (in the example under consideration there are $2^3 = 8$ code groups) a sufficient number of times, it can give this answer without first having received the signal y. The signal transformer is then set to the desired signal transformation.

Subsequently, however, the signal transformer may be made to adjust itself to any other signal transformation by merely communicating to it a sufficient number of times the desired answer, y, to each incoming code group. When the signal transformer has adjusted itself to the new signal transformation, it can again give the answer x to an incoming code group without having previously received the desired answer y.

The circuit arrangement itself consists of a normal (i.e. non-adaptive) signal transformer ST and eight gate circuits, $G_1, G_2, \ldots, G_8$.

34

The signal transformer ST is so designed that, on reception of a code group at its three inputs 1, 2 and 3, it delivers a signal at its eight outputs 7, 8, ..., 14, which is such that there is produced at one output an elementary signal having the value 1 and at the seven other outputs an elementary signal having the value 0. This type of signal is frequently referred to as 1-out-of-n code group (in the present case, 1-out-of-8 code group). Thus each of the eight outputs corresponds to just one of the eight possible incoming code groups.

The signal transformer ST delivers an output signal only when it receives a pulse either at its terminal 15 connected to the additional terminal 5 or at its terminal 16 connected to the additional terminal 6 or at its terminal 16 connected to the additional terminal 6. It is assumed that the elementary signals delivered by the terminals 7, 8, ..., 14 and the signal y applied to the terminal 5 are positive (signal value 1) or negative (signal value 0) pulses, and that the signal z applied to the terminal 6 always consists of a single pulse.

The gate circuits G_i ($i = 1, 2, ..., 8$) are of a special type. Each includes a counter having, for example, ten positions 0, 1, ..., 9. The position of such a counter changes only when the respective gate circuit receives the signal y and, simultaneously from the signal transformer ST an elementary signal having the value 1. The counter then jumps either to the next lower or next higher position according to wheither the signal y has the value 0 or the value 1. However, from the 0 position, the counter can only jump to the 1 position when $y = 1$, but it remains in the position 0 when $y = 0$. A similar condition applies to the 9 position. When there is no signal y, the counters of all the gate circuits always remain in the positions they are occupying. Furthermore, each gate circuit is designed so that it never passes negative pulses supled by the signal transformer ST and only passes a positive pulse supplied by the signal transformer ST when its counter is in one of the 5, 6, 7, 8 or 9 positions; it does not, however, pass a positive pulse, when its counter is in one of the 0, 1, 2, 3 or 4 positions.

It may be ascertained readily that the adaptive signal transformer will start to give the answer $x = 0$ or $x = 1$ to a certain incoming code group depending on whether it has received predominantly the signal $y = 0$ or the signal $y = 1$ as the desired answer to that code group. Suppose, for example, that the desired answer y to the ith code group has successively been:

$$00110111010011110111010111101101110$$

If the counter initially occupied the 3 position it successively assumes the positions:

$$3212323454543456767898989999989989998$$

If the adaptation process is now terminated, the counter remains in the 8 position and the signal transformer replies to the ith code group by giving the answer $x = 1$, but only after having received a pulse z, which must therefere be supplied before the next code group is received.

Renewed application of the signal y after each incoming code group enables the counter to leave the 8 position. It may then assume, for instance, one of the 0, 1, 2, 3 or 4 positions. In that case the signal transformer will reply to the ith code group by giving the answer $x = 0$.

Thus, for its adaptation, the adaptive signal transformer needs an adapting time. The duration of this adapting time increases with increased spread in the answers to be given to the respective code groups. The behaviour of this signal transformer shows a striking resemblance to some human and animal learning processes.

GENERAL STRUCTURE OF THE AUTOMATON

Now that we have become acquainted with the essential component parts of the automaton using digital signalling, something should be said about the construction of such an automaton as a whole. Reduced to its simplest form, it is shown by the block diagram of Fig. 3.4. Basically, it comprises an input device, an output device, a store, a signal transformer and control circuits which ensure a meaningful co-operation between the first four units.

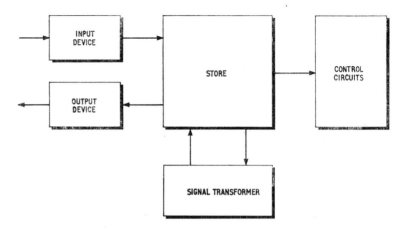

Fig. 3.4. Block diagram of an automaton using digital signalling

The automaton receives signals from the outer world through its input device and delivers signals to the outer world through its output device. The input device may be a punched tape reader, the output device an electrically controlled typewriter. The signal transformer is usually called the arithmetic unit, especially if it can perform the elementary arithmetic operations. If, however, the automaton is an automatic pilot, the input unit is a set of measuring instruments and receivers indicating the positions of, for example, rudder, elevator, ailerons, or air pressures; the output device comprises a set of servomotors which control the rudder, etc.

In outline, the following sequence of events takes place in the automaton: The signals supplied by the outer world which reach the input device are passed to the store and stored in it. One of the signals stored is requested by the control unit; the control circuits ensure that the signal, which is stored in a location that is determined by the first signal, is transferred from the store to the signal transformer; here, it is subjected to a signal transformation, the nature of which is also determined by the first signal. The transformed signal is returned to the store, where it is stored; the control circuits again request a signal from the store, and so on, until the process to be carried out is terminated; a number of the signals thus collected is delivered to the outer world through the output device.

A signal requested by the control unit and which causes a signal transformation to be carried out on another signal or, more generally, which causes the automaton to perform some operation, is called an instruction. An instruction may contain the following data:

1. The location in the store from which a signal is to be transferred to the signal transformer.
2. The nature of the signal transformation to be executed by the signal transformer on the signal received from the store (e.g. addition, multiplication, etc.).
3. The location in the store where the result of the signal transformation is to be stored.
4. The location in the store where the next instruction to be carried out is stored.

A signal, or part of a signal, from which a particular location in the store can be deduced, is called the address of this storage location. The preparation of a sequence of instructions which enable the automaton to perform a particular function is called *programming the automaton for this function.*

An essential feature is that some instructions contain two or more addresses of instructions to be subsequently demanded and carried out; the result of the latest signal transformation determines from which of the addresses the next instruction is to be taken. Such instructions are called branch instructions (or conditional instructions); they enable the automaton to influence the course of a process. An automaton whose instruction set does not contain branch instructions is no more than a banal mechanism. Admittedly, it might be programmed for calculating a fixed number (e.g. 25) or terms of the expansion of, for example, $\log(1+x)$ in a series, and for calculating the sum of these terms, but not for calculating $\log(1+x)$ for an arbitrary value of x with an accuracy specified *a priori*. The latter calculation requires the automaton to determine each time whether the required accuracy has or has not been reached and to decide, on the basis of this determination, whether the arithmetic process is to be continued or stopped. This, however, involves the execution of a conditional instruction. Even the solution of a simple problem such as determining the maximum of, say, 25 numbers requires the provision of a conditional instruction, for this requires two numbers to be tested each time for equality or inequality; and this process has to be continued, in the case of equality, with either of the two numbers, but in the case of inequality, with the greater one. This again means taking a decision by way of a conditional instruction. *Consequently, the invention of the conditional instruction is the step which has led to the modern all purpose automaton.*

Another possibility of the automaton outlined above is that an instruction may involve a signal transformation that is carried out on a signal, which will itself act as an instruction shortly afterwards. This enables the automaton to alter the program stored in it and to adapt this program to the instantaneous stage of the process to be executed. It permits the automaton to continue a never ending process for an indefinite period of time (provided it is not lacking in storage space for a certain instant).

The above shows that in principle there is no difference between instructions and other signals stored in the storage unit. Each stored signal becomes an instruction by its being demanded by the control circuits. *A signal has no meaning sui generis, but has the meaning ascribed to it by the receiver.*

Usually, the signal transformer is not of the adaptive type but is designed so that it is able to make a choice between several different signal transformations. From this, it would appear that the functions which the automaton is capable of performing are more varied and complicated in direct proportion to the ability of its signal transformer to perform more varied and complicated signal transformations. This conclusion, however, is wrong. It can be shown that every signal transformation, however complicated, can be reduced to the repeated performance of a single simple, signal transformation on pairs of elementary signals. It would carry us too far afield to prove this statement, but an example may serve to make it creditable. The addition $285+367$ may be performed in any of the following manners:

$$285+ \quad 1+1+\ldots(367 \text{ terms})\ldots+1+1,$$
$$285+300+60+7,$$
$$285+367$$

the second manner requiring a more complicated signal transformer than the first, and the third manner requiring an even more complicated one. This example also demonstrates that an automaton can carry out a particular function at a higher speed if its signal transformer is more specialised in performing this function. It explains why all modern automata have signal transformers capable of performing various signal transformations from which the control circuits can choose.

Broadly speaking, the above may be summed up by saying that *an automaton is capable of carrying out functions which are more complicated if its storage capacity is larger; and it works at a higher speed if its signal transformer is more complicated and its store is more rapidly accessible.* Stated succinctly, *a worm would be a genius if only its memory were better.*

WHAT CAN A ROBOT DO?

HISTORICAL

One of the first to have visions of an automaton of the above kind was Charles Babbage (1791-1871), inventor, designer and builder of a (never completed) purely mechanical calculating automaton, which was to have been capable of doing anything which today only our large electronic computers can do. Augusta Ada, Countess of Lovelace (1815-1852), daughter of Lord Byron and biographer of Babbage, wrote as early as 1842 about this 'Analytical Engine', 'It can do whatever we know how to order it to perform'.

No more terse definition can be given of what an automaton is capable of, although it is a fact that what Lady Lovelace and Babbage had in mind must have differed greatly from what we now think of when we ask ourselves for what an automaton can be programmed. That it is possible, for example, to program an automaton for processes which can be reduced to purely arithmetic operations, such as solving n linear equations in n unknowns, the approximation of a root of a non-linear equation, the computation of functions such as, for example, $\tan x$, $\log x$, etc., will not surprise the reader after the foregoing. It is, however, more surprising that an automaton can be programmed for problems such as carrying out integrations by non-numerical methods, proving geometrical theorems, reading or recognising printed or written letters, recognising figures, etc.

EXAMPLE—RECOGNITION OF LETTERS

As an anything but obvious example of a job which a normal so called general purpose computer can do, let us take the recognition of patterns. To prevent the problem from becoming too abstract, we will restrict ourselves to the recognition of letters. Now, it is self-evident that, the smaller the differences between the letters to be recognised, the simpler is the process taking place in the automaton. Hence, the first reading automata were able to read highly standardised letters only.

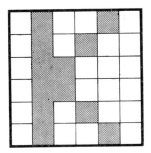

Fig. 3.5. Recognition of letters

The principle of such an automaton is illustrated in Fig. 3.5. Each letter is written in a prescribed manner in a square comprising $6 \times 6 = 36$ square cells. Each letter then corresponds to a particular configuration of white and black cells. If a white cell is identified with a code element 0 and a black cell with a code element 1 and each cell is assigned a particular position in a code group having 36 code elements, each configuration of white and black cells, i.e., each letter, corresponds to a code group of 36 code elements; for example, the letter K corresponds to:

$$010010,010100,011000,011000,010100,010010$$

Thus the problem is reduced to that of the recognition and transformation of code groups, and this, though but very briefly, has already been discussed above. Obviously, however, an automaton based on this principle is capable of very indifferent achievements, and this in itself was a sufficient reason for many experts to look for more universal methods.

A far better and also more general method is for the automaton to test each letter to be read for a number of predetermined characteristics or features. Since the possession or lack of a particular feature can be identified with a code element 1 or 0 respectively at a particular position in a code group, in this method also each letter corresponds to a code group. Nevertheless, this method is considerably less type-dependent than the preceding one, especially as each letter may correspond to various combinations of present or absent features. Naturally, the production of an automaton based on this principle depends in the first place on the nature and the number of the features for which the letters are tested.

In many cases it is practical to precede the recognition process proper by a few auxiliary processes, the principles of which will now be stated.

Removal of noise

The term 'noise' in this context means small black spots or very thin lines not belonging to the letter; small white spots in the middle of a line belonging to the letter; irregularities in the boundaries of the lines belonging to the letter; small gaps in a line belonging to the letter; and so on. Some of these noise phenomena are readily recognisable as such and consequently are readily removable.

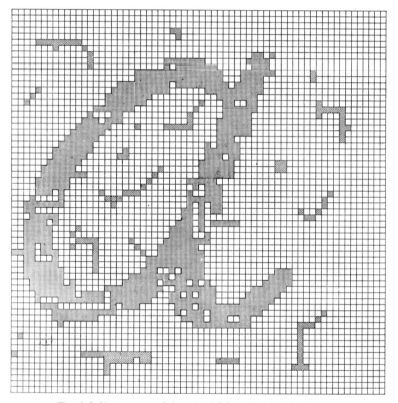

Fig. 3.6. Noise removal (cursive 'a' heavily loaded with noise)

A fairly satisfactory noise removal process is the following. The letter to be read is depicted on a square subdivided into, for example, 64×64 square cells (see Fig. 3.6). Except for the cells situated along the edges of the square, each element is regarded as the centre of 9 cells arranged in a square (see Fig. 3.7). Irrespective of this central cell being initially white or black, it is replaced by a white or black cell according to whether at least 5 of the 9 elements concerned are white or black.

This noise removal process may be carried out in various ways.

1. All the cells not situated along the edges are (simultaneously or sequentially) corrected in the manner described, neglecting any previous corrections.
2. All the cells of one row, which is not situated along the periphery, are

40

corrected (simultaneously or sequentially) in the manner described, neglecting any previous corrections of the cells of the relevant row but using the corrected cells of the previously corrected row.

3. All cells not situated along the periphery are sequentially corrected, using the previously corrected cells each time.

In each of these forms the removal process may be repeated several times. In this event, the three methods mentioned produce substantially equivalent results and therefore, the entirely simultaneous execution of method (1) is to be preferred as being the quickest.

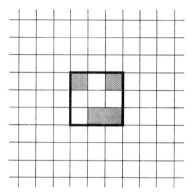

Fig. 3.7. Principle of noise removal

Thinning down the letter

The detection of features is slightly simplified by the 'cleaned' letter being previously 'thinned down' so that every line of the letter is just one cell thick and possible points are reduced to just one black cell. This may be achieved, for example, by first determining the central cell in any group of adjacent black cells of one row; by then determining the central cell in any group of adjacent black cells of the column passing through this first central cell; and, finally, by determining the central one of the said two central cells. Subsequently, a corresponding process must be carried out starting from a group of adjacent black cells of one column. Obviously, there must be a rule by which the central cell of a row or column of adjacent cells is always determined unambiguously.

When the letter has been treated in this manner, the resulting thinned down letter may still be too thick or still show one or several gaps. These imperfections may, however, be eliminated by means of a process analogous to the noise removal process described above.

The features of the letters

Naturally, the most important step in the recognition process is the detection of the features of the letter. The features, for which a letter may be tested include:

1. The number of vertical or nearly vertical straight lines and their positions and lengths (entirely on the left, entirely on the right, approximately at the centre, short, long).

41

2. The number of horizontal or nearly horizontal straight lines and their positions and lengths.

3. The number of intersections and their position and order (corners are to be considered as intersections of the second order).

4. The number of closed loops and their position relative to the detected straight lines.

5. The number of ends of lines.

Detection of features by the mask method

There are two methods of detecting a given characteristic, the mask method and the analytical method. The principle of the mask method will be explained with reference to a very simple example, the detection of a vertical line of a given length at a particular position in the picture. Suppose the line segment, the pres-

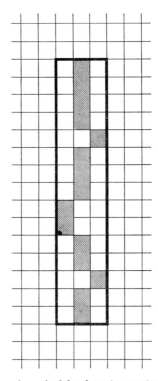

Fig. 3.8. The mask method for detecting vertical line segments

ence or absence of which we want to ascertain is exactly 15 cells long. A rectangle of $3 \times 15 = 45$ cells is drawn around the centre cell of this line segment (see Fig. 3.8). It can now be assumed that the line segment is present if at least 13 of these 45 cells are black and is absent if this is not the case. This procedure also allows for the line segment including small 'twists' or intersections and/or some imperfections (such as gaps and locally thickened parts) missed in the removal of noise.

Detection of characteristics by analysis of the picture

This method enables, for example, curves and closed loops to be detected. For this purpose every element is designated by two co-ordinates, x and y. Each of these co-ordinates may have any of the values 1, 2, ..., 64. Suppose (a_0, b_0) to be a cell of a line segment which furthermore contains the cells (a_1, b_1), (a_2, b_2), ..., (a_n, b_n). The line is straight (or nearly straight) when $a_0, a_1, a_2, \ldots \ldots, a_n$ and $b_0, b_1, b_2, \ldots \ldots, b_n$ both form (at least approximately) an arithmetical progression, and is curved when this is not the case. The line forms a closed loop when $a_n = a_0$ and $b_n = b_0$. Thus, the detection of straight or curved line segments and of closed loops is reduced to a simple arithmetic operation, the computation of so called first and second differences. (It is assumed here that the reader is willing to accept that every 'general purpose' computer can be programmed for computations of this type.)

The technical realisation

So far, the principles of automating a letter reading process have been explained, if only very briefly, but little has been said about how an automaton working on these principles can be realised technically. This will now be described.

The first requirement is that a member is available on which a picture, as shown in Fig. 3.6, can be recorded. Such a member may be simply a mosaic of photo sensitive elements (for example, photo-resistors, photo-diodes and photo-transistors). Then every white cell corresponds to a small current and every black cell to the absence of a current. If desired, the resulting pattern of present or absent currents may be converted into an equivalent pattern of storage cores magnetised counter-clockwise or clockwise, or of states of other bistable elements, for example, flip-flops.

Another workable method consists of projecting the letter to be read onto the screen of a camera tube; the image projected on to this screen is then converted by some kind of television technique either into a pattern of storage cores, magnetised counter-clockwise or clockwise, or into states of a mosaic of flip-flops, or other bistable circuit elements.

A mosaic of bistable elements, on which an image of the letter to be read can be produced, is particularly suitable for noise removal by the method described earlier and for detecting features by the mask method.

The removal of noise, for example, only requires that each group of nine bistable elements is connected to a 'threshold member', which delivers a bivalent signal showing whether five or more, or four or less of the respective bistable elements are in the state which corresponds to black. This bivalent signal is then used to bring the centre cell to the state corresponding to the majority, irrespective of its initial state. Correspondingly, all the relevant features may be detected by means of the threshold device.

Using circuits of the above type, both noise removal and feature detection can be carried out simultaneously for all the elements from which the noise is to be removed and for all the features to be detected, enabling a reading automaton working at a tremendously high speed to be designed on this principle.

VISION IN ANIMALS

In this section a comparison will be made between the automatic recognition of patterns, and animal vision. To begin with, it is highly probable that in each animal species, the interpretation of perceived light sensations is in the first place differentiated into what is indispensable, or at least highly important, for its struggle for life and what is not so essential. In the lower animals, the faculty of interpretations will presumably hardly, if at all, exceed this level, for the animal would not be able to cope with additional information anyway. Therefore, an

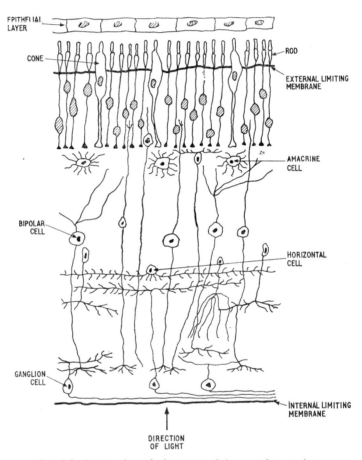

Fig. 3.9. Section through the retina of the eye of a vertebrate

explanation of vision in a given species requires knowledge, not only of the anatomy and physiology of its seeing apparatus, but also of its ethology and psychology. The structure of the retina of the eye of a vertebrate is given in Fig. 3.9.

The frog is one of the few species for which this combined knowledge, or at least its rudiments, is available. Summarising the relevant facts:

1. The frog is an animal which depends on its sight; it hunts for its prey (flies, etc.) and escapes its enemies on the strength of visual perception.
2. The eyes are secured rigidly to the head and the retina has no point of clearest vision (cf the *fovea centralis* in man).
3. The retina comprises about 10^6 receptors (rods and cones); every optic nerve *(nervus opticus)* has about half this number of nerve fibres (axons).
4. A nerve fibre, or axon, of the optic nerve does not originate in a receptor or photo sensitive cell of the retina, but in a ganglion cell lying in the retina; the ganglion cells are not connected to the receptors directly, but through a complicated network of processes of other nerve cells, the horizontal cells, (having axons which extend parallel to the retina), bipolar cells (having two axons) and amacrine cells (having only comparatively short processes or dendrites). Thus, each ganglion cell is connected with a large number (1,000 or more) receptors and vice versa.
5. Each receptor responds only to variations in luminous intensity and there are three kinds of receptors:

   (a) Receptors which respond to the transition dark→light
   (b) Receptors which respond to the transition light→dark
   (c) Receptors which respond to both kinds of transition.

6. Each ganglion cell and consequently each axon of the optic nerve is connected (indirectly) to receptors of one kind only.
7. All the axons of the optic nerve, which are connected to receptors of one kind terminate in one layer *(stratum)* of the brain.

The first conclusion we may draw from the above is that the faculty of sight in the frog differs fundamentally from that of man. *The frog perceives only changes in its surroundings; as long as there is no change in its surroundings, it probably does not see anything, but the slightest change rouses it from its apparent lethargy.* A curious feature, however, is that it does not respond to rotary or translational displacement of its surroundings as a whole and hence it probably does not perceive them. Irrespective of whether on not all these conclusions have sufficient foundation, it is certain that in interpreting animal behaviour one must proceed with extreme caution.

A second important conclusion which can be drawn from the foregoing is that the optic nerves do not, as was thought until recently, transmit to the brain a kind of copy of the image formed on the retina, but *that an important amount of signal processing is already performed in the retina so that the information available in the retina is transmitted to the brain in a highly coded form.* To all appearances the signal processing effected in the retina is similar in character to the detection of features by the mask method described earlier. Experimental investigation into the features which are detected, however, is still in its infancy. On the other hand, it is clear that what an animal (or human being) can recognise and distinguish as significant differences depends greatly on which features are detected in its (or his) retina. It has been shown experimentally that the frog is capable of detecting features such as a small moving spot, which becomes stationary at some point in the field of vision (prey), and 'light-dark' transitions, which move across the field of vision (enemy). We are still completely in the dark as to the manner in which the data that are of importance to the animal are deduced from the coded information received by the brain.

CONCLUDING REMARKS

What I have tried to make clear in the foregoing is that all actions, functions, processes, for which it is possible to give unambiguous instructions can be automated. But conversely, these are the only actions, functions, processes, which can be automated, that is, for which an automaton can be programmed.

Good progress is being made in the art of programming. For instance, it took on automaton only a few minutes to prove over 200 theorems from Whitehead and Russell's *Principia Mathematica*, some of these proofs being even more elegant than the known ones.

But the robots ability has peculiar limits. For example, no automaton has so far been built which in the matter of reading handwritten addresses can match even a mediocre post office sorter; neither has an automaton been constructed which is capable of converting idiomatically correct French into idiomatically correct English.

Let us return for a moment to the automaton which can prove theorems. The question which immediately arises is whether it is also possible to build an automaton capable of finding theorems, which is quite another thing. To illustrate this, consider Euclidean geometry. In theory, starting from the axioms of this geometry, one should inevitably find all its theorems by connecting these axioms in all possible combinations by means of all known rules of logic. But at once the question crops up as to how the automaton, by itself, could ever manage to find the axioms. Passing over this ticklish question, and assuming that we have informed the automaton of these axioms, the automaton would, before arriving at, for example Pascal's theorem on conics, have to search a 'tree' of possibilities having so many branches that the Universe does not contain enough matter to build a memory of sufficient capacity to store them. In addition, a systematic search of this 'tree' would take a time exceeding the age of the Universe. This is because the 'tree' comprises an overwhelming number of dead-end branches and, at least at present, the automaton cannot be given means of recognising these branches at their beginnings. How the *coryphaei* of science have ever been capable of this feat, still remains one of the mysteries of life, and everybody is free to think, as did England's great economist (and theologian, philosopher, biologist and philologist), Adam Smith (1723–1790) of guidance by an 'invisible hand'.

What has emerged in a striking manner from the foregoing is that some functions which we are apt to consider as having a primitive and far from intellectual nature, are much more difficult to automate than certain other functions which we regard as typically intellectual. It is certainly surprising that we can design a chess playing automaton, which plays a better game than many good human players, but are unable to design a reading automaton which gets anywhere near the performance of a mediocre mail sorter.

It seems to me that the cause of this apparent paradox is that we, at least at present, know more about the principles on which we play chess or prove theorems, than we do about the principles on which we recognise patterns, put our thoughts into words, etc. This comparative ignorance again is due to the fact that the latter functions take place entirely or largely at a subconscious level and are inaccessible to introspection. Scientific thought, especially creative thought, occurs for an important part, probably even for its major part, in our subconscious. *And it is for those functions which take place subconsciously that no satisfactory automata have been built.* (Cf. Lady Lovelace's statement, p. 38.)

Chapter 4

Contemporary Cybernetics

V. M. GLUSHKOV, ACADEMICIAN (A.S., U.S.S.R.)
Director of the Institute of Cybernetics, Kiev (Ukr. S.S.R.)

SUMMARY

This chapter reviews the theoretical fundamentals of cybernetics as a science concerned with the general laws of data transformation in complex control and information processing systems.

The basic forms of mathematical data transformation are described by means of alphabetic operators. Algorithms are constructive methods for defining the alphabetic operators. An automaton concept is the main tool for studying discrete transformers.

The algebra of regular languages is discussed as a means of defining the operation of finite automata. Kleeny's theorem is considered, characterising the behaviour of finite automata in terms of regular languages.

A new technique is needed for describing the operation of the automaton with an infinite number of states. A concept of context-free languages is of great importance, and these languages are represented in automata by an infinite number of states of a special type called push-down automata. Representations of Boolean functions are considered as tools for describing the structure of discrete automata.

The most widely used algorithmic systems are characterised, and a normal algorithmic concept is described in detail. General features of algorithmic systems are investigated in terms of the interaction of two automata—control and operational.

Finally, the principal results are given of the theory of self-organising systems and problems concerning the automation of creative work are discussed.

INTRODUCTION

It is usual nowadays to define cybernetics as the science of general laws of data transformation in complex control systems and systems of information processing.

When defining the subject of cybernetics it is important to avoid two extremes. These are, first, including in cybernetics everything which concerns control; and secondly, attempting to reduce cybernetics to a comparative study of the relation between control systems in engineering and those in living beings.

To make this clearer, let us consider an example. Take, for instance, such an established branch of mathematics as the theory of ordinary differential equations. It is well known that any problem involving differential equations is nowadays considered to be mathematical. To be considered as such, the problem or the methods by which it is obtained must possess a sufficient degree of generality. Otherwise a similar approach will apply to mechanics, the theory of automatic control or to any other field of science employing the theory of differential equations as a technique for investigating objects specific to each science. It is clearly unreasonable to regard the main object of the theory of differential equations as only a simple transfer of regularities obtained, say, in celestial mechanics, to the theory of automatic control or vice versa.

According to our assumed definition, cybernetics has an object of investigation of its own, namely, abstract concepts of any forms of transformers of a sufficiently general kind. Particular cases of such transformers include: automatic controller, computer, brain, economic control system, etc.

Dealing with abstract and basically mathematical concepts, cybernetics is essentially a mathematical branch of science. It is no wonder therefore, that some of constituent parts of contemporary cybernetics, for example the general theory of algorithms, have been developed until recently within the limits of such a traditional field of mathematics as mathematical logic.

At the same time, cybernetics cannot be reduced completely to mathematics since, in contrast to the latter, it employs not only deductive analytic methods but also experimental methods. Moreover, being concerned with extremely complex objects, the behaviour of which is beyond description by analytic methods within any visible compass, cybernetics frequently resorts to simulating an object on a computer (mathematical analogue) or in reality (physical analogue). Properties of an object, of interest to investigators, are studied during a properly conducted mathematical or physical experiment.

Undoubtedly, among the most interesting objects involved in cybernetics, are abstract analogues of the brain, that is, models of various thinking processes. The main technique of simulation in cybernetics, however, in an all purpose computer giving a good basis for the construction of the most complex artificial data transformers. Modern computers use a discrete form of data presentation, and to a great extent this relates also to the brain. It is not surprising, therefore, that at present the problems connected with discretely stated data and their transformations in cybernetics are receiving considerable attention.

It is these problems only which will be dealt with in the present chapter. This does not signify however, that analogue forms of data presentation have already lost their significance.

ALPHABETIC OPERATORS

One of the fundamental notions in studying discrete data transformations is of an alphabetic mapping or *alphabetic operator*. An alphabetic operator denotes a correspondence between words in abstract alphabets.

It must be noted that an abstract alphabet is an arbitrary finite totality of objects named as letters of the given alphabet. We do not care anything about the nature of these objects. If desired, one may regard letters of an abstract alphabet to be complete words or phrases of any language, pictures, any typographical symbols, etc. It is important only that the alphabet be finite, that is, consists of a finite number of letters.

Any finite ordered sequences of abstract alphabet letters are named *words* in this alphabet. A number of letters in a word is usually the *length* of this word. Words of length 1 consisting of a single letter, and a zero-length word, the so called empty word, are not excluded from consideration.

An alphabetic operator is any correspondence (function) relating words of some alphabet X to words of another alphabet Y. Alphabet X is called an input and alphabet Y an output alphabet of a given operator. Alphabets X and Y may differ and may coincide.

The alphabetic operator φ is determined, generally speaking, not by all words of an input alphabet but by a part of words, constituting a region of definition M for this operator only. Further, an operator may prove single-valued or multi-valued, depending on whether or not it relates to each word of M_φ, a single word in an output alphabet. All alphabetic operators under consideration will be referred to hereafter as single-valued unless otherwise specified. Multi-valued operators, will be subdivided into non-deterministic and random (probabilistic) types. In the first case, an operator relates to one input word p the whole set $N_p = \varphi(p)$ of output words. In the second case, a probability distribution function is additionally assigned to set N_p, and in each application of operators φ to word p, an access to one word of set N_p is obtained according to the stated distribution law.

The concept of an alphabetic operator is extremely general. Any processes of data transformations can be reduced to this concept in a sense. In a number of cases, for instance, such a reduction is done simply when a vocabulary of numerical data is transformed. A decimal number, say, written in a usual manner, can be considered as a word in an alphabet comprising, in addition to 10 digits, the decimal point. When data are expressed by several numbers, a separating character, for example, a semicolon, should also be added to these symbols between the individual numbers.

In the event of transformation of analogue data, for example, arbitrary visual or auditory signals, the problem is more complicated. Taking into account, however, the fact that continuous data transformations are effected by non-ideal devices, the transformations may be reduced to an alphabetic operator in this case also.

Let us take visual data as an example. A limited *resolving power* of devices perceiving these data prevents discrimination of nearly dots. This brings about the result that the data can be regarded as specified not over an infinite, but over a finite set of points. Further, a limited *sensitivity* of the device leads to the fact that a quantity of levels of the parameter carrying the data (e.g. brightness of indidual dots) can be made finite. Upon confronting each of the above levels with a special symbol-letter we shall have a finite alphabet X. A single letter word is required in the alphabet for representation of dot data at each moment. Remembering that the total number of dots in an image is finite, then by ordering these dots in a certain way (e.g. by scanning) we represent each momentary picture perceived by the device with a word of l length (l—number of dots in an image) of X.

When the representation of data changing in time is required, the third limitation of each actual device has to be considered, a pass-band limitation of each actual device, which is equivalent in the last resort to the introduction of conditional *discrete time*. In other words, it is necessary to perceive an image being transformed, not at all moments, but merely at moments differing from one another by τ, 2τ, 3τ, etc. Here τ is a constant inversely proportional to a device pass-band.

As a result, transfer of changing images per any finite moment (t_0, t) can be replaced by transfer of a *finite* number of momentary images at moments t_0, $t_0+\tau$, $t_0+2\tau$, $t_0+3\tau$, ..., $t_0+n\tau$, where $t_0+n\tau \leqslant t$, but $t_0+(n+1)\tau > 1$.

According to the above, each of these images can be represented by a word of X. But any finite sequence of words can be represented in the form of one word by the addition of a separating character in X between words, or by simply writing these words in succession.

Since what has been said above is applicable to input or to visual information, the following conclusion is arrived at. *With regard to limitations inherent in all existing data transformers, the action of each of these transformers can be reduced to an alphabetic operator.*

It is also possible to include the transformation of analogue data in our discussion without utilising limited properties of actual transformers. For this purpose it is sufficient to assume the possibility of handling words with both finite and infinite lengths. However, such a procedure would call for the introduction of a number of additional concepts and would distract us from the next immediate task—a description of the methods of specifying alphabetic operators.

SPECIFICATION OF ALPHABETIC OPERATORS

If a region of definition of an alphabetic operator is finite, the task is solved easily (at any rate in theory). In this case, an operator can be expressed by a simple *table of correspondence;* all words involved in a region of definition of an operator are put down on the left side of the table, and all output words corresponding to them, on the right side. In practice, of course, this method may prove excessively cumbersome if a region of definition of an operator is very large.

When regions of definition are infinite, the method based on writing out complete tables of correspondence turns out to be impossible in principle, since we cannot write an infinite table of correspondence. In practice, this difficulty is overcome by specifying certain rules assisting in the construction of any line of the table of correspondence, e.g. replacing each letter x in an input word by word *xyx*, and each letter y by an 'empty' word. *Alphabetic operators stated by finite sets of rules are usually called algorithms.* Since lines of the table of correspondence may also be considered as rules, in accordance with the above assumptions, alphabetic operators expressed by finite tables of correspondence may be regarded as algorithms.

The distinction between an alphabetic operator concept and that of an algorithm is that for the former, the correspondence proper, established by an operator and not by the way of stating this correspondence, is essential, while for the latter the manner of stating the correspondence is emphasised.

The distinction between the definitions of *equality* for alphabetic operators and algorithms follows from the foregoing. The two alphabetic operators φ and ψ are considered to be equal if, firstly, their regions of definition coincide: $M_\varphi = M_\psi = M$, and secondly, if for any word p of M, $\varphi(p) = \psi(p)$. The concept of algorithms comprises that of equality for alphabetic operators corresponding to them, but it also calls, in addition, for coincidence of set of the rules stating these algorithms.

Algorithms in which only alphabetic operators defined by them coincide, and generally speaking, not methods for expressing them, are usually termed *equivalents*.

In equivalent transformations of algorithms, their input and output alphabets remain unchanged. It is possible, however, to change these alphabets in a relatively easy way without changing, to a certain degree, an algorithm itself; this special operation is called the *coding* of one alphabet in the other.

Let X be an arbitrary alphabet and Y be any alphabet of n letters, where $n \geqslant 2$. If N is a number of letters in X, then there exists a natural number k such that $n^k \geqslant N$. This means that we can so adjust each letter x of X to a word of length k in alphabet Z, so that different words will correspond to different letters. The word $\alpha(x)$ is named a code of letter x in Y. If p is an arbitrary word in X, then writing a respective code for each letter of this word we shall have a word in Z which we shall call a code of p and denote by $\alpha(p)$.

Operator α, constructed in this way, will be called a *code mapping*. It is easily seeen that if one knows a code mapping and uses code $\alpha(p)$ of p, one can determine this word in an unambigous way. Essentially, this is the only feature possessed by a code mapping. A letter-after-letter coding by codes of equal length (assumed by us) represents one of the simplest methods of coding. But an arbitrary coding of words of one alphabet (say X) in the other alphabet (Z) simply implies a reversible mapping of set $F(X)$ of all words in the first alphabet into a set $F(Z)$ of all words in the other alphabet.

Let P be the alphabetic operator with input alphabet X and output alphabet Y, α and β—codings of words of these alphabets in a certain alphabet Z. Since mapping α is reversible, there exists the inverse mapping α^{-1}. The input and object alphabets of operator $P' = \alpha^{-1}/P\beta$ and coincide with Z. Also, knowing the transformed operator P', one can easily recover the initial operator using the formula $P = \alpha \cdot P' \cdot \beta^{-1}$.

This result makes it possible to confine ourselves, if required, to discussing alphabetic operators and algorithms of some fixed alphabet Z, serving both as an input and output alphabet. The only requirement to be met by this universal algorithm Z is the availability in it of not less than two different letters. According to the above, this assures the possibility of a simple letter-after-letter coding. As a universal alphabet, a two letter alphabet consisting of two symbols 0 and 1 may be taken.

The possibility of reducing an arbitrary transformation of data to alphabetic operators in the universal alphabet (e.g. the two letter one) represents one of the fundamental principles of cybernetics. This principle permits one to simulate data transformers by others. Although modern computers employ the simplest two letter alphabet for internal presentation of data, they can accomplish complex transformations of numerical and letter information in order to simulate many forms of human mental activity.

AUTOMATA AND FORMAL LANGUAGES

Automata (also called abstract automata) represent a further illustration of the alphabetic operator concept. Apart from input X and object Y alphabets, an automaton also has a set of (internal) states S. This set can be any non-empty set.

The automaton works in discrete time, the sequential moments of which can be identified (by proper choice of a measuring unit) with a sequence of numbers $t = 0, 1, 2, \ldots$.

Automaton A is in a certain state $a = a(t)$ of set S at each given moment of *automaton* discrete time $t = 0,1,2,\ldots$ State $a_0 = a(0)$ is called an *initial state* of the automaton. This state can be any state of S. If we fix a choice of this state, automaton will be called *initial*. A single letter $x = x(t)$ from input alphabet letters is fed to the automaton input as an *input signal* at each moment, t, of the automaton time, starting with $t = 1$. State $a(t)$ of the automaton at the moment t is determined by the function $a(t) = \delta[a(t-1), x(t)]$ of the automaton of previous state $a(t-1)$ and input signal $x(t)$ at a given moment. Function $\delta(a, x)$ is called a transition function of a given automaton. At the same moment t, automaton A gives one of the letters $y = y(t)$ of Y, as its output signal. The output signal is determined by an automaton *output function* which can exist in two forms: $y(t) = \lambda[a(t-1), x(t)]$ or $y(t) = \mu[a(t)]$. In the first case we have Mealy's automaton, and in the second Moore's automaton.

The automaton is considered to be completely determined if its transfer and output functions are stated over all pairs (a, x).

Assume, first, that we deal with a completely determined automaton A. In this case, having fixed once and for all its initial state, we can deliver to the automaton input one letter after another making up any word p in X in succession. In accordance with the automaton behaviour described above, some object word q will appear at the output of A made up of one letter after another. With the stated automaton A and fixed initial state a_0, a word q will have one-to-one correspondence with the input word p. This results in a relationship between each initial automaton A and the related alphabetic mapping φ (representation of words in the input alphabet into object alphabet words). We say that φ is *induced* by A, or that it is represented by A.

For the completely determined automaton the relevant mapping is determined over all input words. In the case of a partially determined automaton φ will be determined only over a set consisting of *acceptable* (for a given automaton) words, owing to the presence of indeterminate transitions and outputs φ.

It is obvious that any φ, determined by the automaton, satisfies the following two conditions.

1. *Any acceptable input word p has the same length as its image $\varphi(p)$ at mapping φ.*
2. *If p is any acceptable input word then any initial segment p of this word $(p = p_1 p_2)$ is acceptable and $\varphi(p_1) = q_1$, where q_1 is the initial segment of input word $q = \varphi(p)$ having the same length as segment p_1.*

Any alphabetic mapping satisfying the two given conditions is called an *automaton mapping*. It may be shown that *any automaton mapping can be represented by the automaton* (by both to Mealy's and Moore's automata).

The conditions for being an automaton mapping very much restrict a class of mappings, which may be represented by automata. It is, however, not difficult to get rid of these restrictions using a fairly simple method. This consists of adding a special *empty letter* to the input and output automaton alphabets. This letter enjoys equal rights with those of other letters when the automata operate. However, the empty letters should be struck out both from input and object words when interpreting mapping φ induced by an automaton. For example, if the empty letter is denoted by the symbol Λ, and an input word $xyz\Lambda$ is related to an object word $\Lambda\Lambda zz\Lambda$ by the automaton, then we can say that $\varphi(xyz) = zz$. This is a new mapping, but we shall preserve the symbol φ for its designation as before. It will be shown that with such interpretations of induced mappings *any alphabetic mappings can be represented by automata.*

Let us assume that these representations are made with precision up to the *empty letter.* An arbitrary automaton is not an effective object since a proper representation of arbitrary functions $\delta(a, x)$ and $\lambda(a, x)$ with an infinite set of S states (with the purpose of their actual computation) is, generally speaking, impossible. This necessitates a narrowing of the class of automata under consideration.

The first and simplest type of effective automata represents *finite automata,* i.e. automata having finite sets of internal states. Functions of transitions and outputs for the finite automata can be represented simply by tables called transition and output tables respectively.

The second type of effective automata represents *push-down automata.* A set S of states of such push-down automata consists of various pairs of the form (a, p), where a runs over a certain finite set S, and p is a set of words in some alphabet Z called the internal alphabet. Transition and output functions of the push-down automaton satisfy conditions

$$\delta[(a, p_1z), x] = \delta[(a, p_2z), x]; \quad \lambda[(a, p_1z), x] = \lambda[(a, p_2z)x]$$

i.e. they actually depend not on word p but on the last letter of this word only. In addition, the automaton can jump from state (a_1, p_1x_1) to states having the forms (a_2, p_1) or $(a_2, p_1x_1x_2)$. In other words, either the striking out of the last letter of state word p is made at each successive time step of the automaton operation, or an addition of one letter is made to the word on the right.

Due to these restrictions, the functions of transitions and outputs of the push-down automaton can be stated by finite tables comprising $m \cdot n$ inputs, where m is the number of elements in S, and n is the number of letters in Z. Therefore, in spite of infinity of the number of states, the push-down automata are quite effective.

Automata having any finite number of push-down storages can be determined in a similar way. States of the 3-storage automaton, for instance, will be represented by quadruples (a, p_1, p_2, p_3), where $a \in S$ and p_1, p_2, p_3 are words in Z. As before, the automaton functions of transitions and outputs will depend on the last letters of words p_1, p_2, p_3 only, and transitions in each time-step can only effect any combination by striking out the last letters of words p_1, p_2, p_3, or by the addition of new words to them.

All algorithms known at present can be represented with a precision of up to one empty letter in push-down, two-storage automata. In addition, it can be proved that all methods of constructing algorithms now accessible to us, lead to mappings again representable in the push-down, two-storage automata. Numerous attempts to construct examples of algorithms which are not representable in such automata, have been unsuccessful. All this enables us to state the following general scientific principle:

All the constructively determinable alphabetic operators (algorithms) are representable in push-down two-storage automata.

Not all algorithms are represented in push-down one-storage automata. This relates to a greater extent to finite automata, which can be regarded as a particular case of the push-down one-storage automata with an empty internal alphabet Z. The present classification of the various alphabetic mappings is relatively little developed, therefore, another method is utilised for characterising the feasibility of representing the mappings by different types of automata. This involves a language representation in automata, instead of a mapping representation.

LANGUAGE REPRESENTATION

A formal language over any (finite) alphabet is any set of words in a respective alphabet. True, only such languages for which an effective procedure is available are ordinarily discussed which permits the writing (possibly with repetitions) of all words of the given language. Such languages are called *recursively enumerable*.

Let L be the recursively enumerable language of an alphabet X. If the complement L of this language (the totality of all words in X not included in L) is also recursively enumerable, then it is possible to construct an effective procedure enabling us to determine each word in X, whether this word belongs to L or not. The language satisfying this latter feature is called *recursive*.

Assume A to be the initial automaton with an input alphabet X, L any language over this alphabet, and y a letter of the object alphabet of the given automaton. L is said to be represented in A by the output signal y if L coincides with the set of those, and only those, input words which produce signal y on the automaton output at the moment when the last letter is applied to the input. This condition implies that all words of L are acceptable to A.

If we know languages $L_1, L_2, \ldots, L_n$, which can be represented in any *initial* automaton A by all its output signals $(y_1, y_2, \ldots, y_n)$, and all these languages are recursive, then we can recover a mapping induced by this automaton. Let $p = x_{i_1}$, $x_{i_2}, \ldots, x_{i_k}$ be an arbitrary input word. We find a language which contains the word $p_1 = x_{i_1}$. If such a language exists it will evidently be determined in one particular way. The corresponding output signal y_{j_1}, will obviously be the first letter of the object word q corresponding to p. But if p_1 does not belong to any of languages $L_1, L_2, \ldots, L_n$, then, apparently, p_1 and hence, p, are words unacceptable to A.

Then, considering the word $p_2 = x_{i_1} x_{i_2}$ we recover the second letter of q; if $p_2 L_{j_2}$, this letter will be y_{j_2}. However, if p_2 does not belong to any languages L_1, $L_2, \ldots, L_n$, then p_2 and p are unacceptable to A. In a similar manner we shall either recover all letters of q, or establish the unacceptability of p to A.

Owing to the above considerations one can, to some extent, replace representability of mapping in automata by that of languages. However, it is first of all necessary to describe the methods for stating languages of any class. Finite languages (finite sets of words) can be, in principle, expressed in the simplest way —by writing out all their elements. For representing infinite languages, other methods are required.

The first method is based on the use of operations on languages, permitting the construction of new languages using the known ones. Natural theoretically-multiple operations are those of *unification* $L_1 U L_2$ and intersection $L_1 \Lambda L_2$ of two (similarly of any finite set) languages. The complementary operation L of language L over the alphabet X represents the formation of a set L of alphabet X words not included in L. The multiplication operation L_1L_2 constitutes a new language, of which many words are of the type p_1p_2, where $p_1 \varepsilon L_1$, $p_2 \varepsilon L_2$. Finally, the *iteration* operation L^* of L results in language L^*, consisting of various words of the form $p_1, p_2, \ldots, p_n$, where $p_2 \varepsilon L$ ($i = 1, 2, \ldots, n$), and n runs over all values from zero to infinity (with $n = 0$ we obtain an empty word, and with $n = 1$ a word of source language L).

Languages obtained from finite languages by the application of any finite number of unification, multiplication and iteration operations, are called regular languages.

Any finite language represents a unification of a finite set of words. But a word regarded as a single element language is represented as a finite multiplication of letters, each of which is identified with the simplest language consisting of the only single letter word. Therefore, any regular language can be built up with the help of a finite number of unification, multiplication and iteration operations of the empty word l and the simplest 'single word, single letter' languages, which we shall identify by letters of a selected basic alphabet.

Consequently, any regular language can be presented by a formula constituted of an empty word symbol, basic alphabet letters and symbols of unification, multiplication and iteration operations (a part of these symbols only, of course, can be involved in the formula). Such formulae are called *regular expressions*. As in elementary algebraic representations, the multiplication symbol is omitted.

It should be emphasised that one and the same language can be represented by various regular expressions. For example, regular expressions $R_1 = xuxx \, (x)*$ and $R_2 = (x)*x$ represent the same language consisting of all words in the single letter alphabet $\{x\}$, except for the empty word. In other words for regular expressions, as in elementary algebra, identical (equivalent) transformations are possible which do not alter objects (languages in the given case) represented by them.

In accordance with the strict definition of regular languages, unification, multiplication and iteration operations again give regular languages if they are applied to regular languages. It can be shown, however, that the same remains true for intersection and complementary operations of regular languages.

The fundamental result determining the place of regular languages in automata theory is the following theorem, from S. K. Kleeny:[1]

Only regular languages can be represented in finite automata.

This result applies to both Mealy's and Moore's automata, the latter being a particular case of the former. Convenient methods have been developed for constructing the transition and output tables of finite automata, representing arbitrary regular languages that are given by corresponding regular expressions.[2] The same also relates to a reverse problem—construction of regular expressions for languages represented in a finite automaton that is defined by its transition and output tables. The first problem is called abstract automata synthesis, and the second automata analysis. Methods for solving these problems have been developed for both Mealy's and Moore's automata.

The methods so far introduced for describing languages that are not representable in finite automata have been found to be unsatisfactory. It is necessary either to introduce new operations on languages, or to use fundamentally different methods for representing the languages.

In recent years the method for representing the recursively enumerable languages by means of the so called *formal grammars* has become of great importance. To construct a formal grammar determining any language for a given alphabet, some complementary (finite) alphabet Y is introduced which will be referred to as the meta-alphabet. The meta-alphabet should be non-empty and should have empty intersection with the basic alphabet. We fix in it some letter, y_0, which will be termed initial.

Each letter of the meta-alphabet can be regarded as a 'grammatical concept'. In this case the initial letter is nothing more than the most general grammatical concept—that of a correctly constructed word of the given language from the standpoint of grammar. We shall emphasise that, according to the definitions assumed by us, a word in an abstract language is thought of as a whole phrase or even a set of phrases in natural human languages (it is enough, for this purpose, to complement the language alphabet with punctuation marks and with a separating character).

Formal grammar Γ is stated by a finite set of *substitution rules*. The substitution rule of a general form comprises two words in a unified alphabet $Z = XUY$, connected with an arrow $w_1 \rightarrow w_2$. A single application of the substitution $w_1 \rightarrow w_2$ to any word p in Z amounts to a replacement of one of the occurences of a word w_1 into a word p by a word w_2. Naturally, the replacement of a given word may prove impossible or ambiguous. For instance, the replacement of $x \rightarrow xy$ by word yy is inapplicable, and when applied to word xx it leads to different results, xyx and xxy.

The use of a substitution having an empty left hand portion is subject to some restrictions. This can be exemplified by substitution $\rightarrow Z$ which, when applicable to word xy, will lead to three different results: ZXY, XZY, XYZ.

A sequence of words $p_0, p_1, \ldots, p_n$ in the alphabet $Z = xuy$ is called an inference of word p_n from word p_0 with the help of grammar Γ, if for all $i = 1, 2, \ldots, n$, a word p_i is obtained from a word p_{i-1} as a result of the application of some substitution from grammar Γ.

A language over alphabet X determined by grammar Γ is said to be a totality of all alphabet X words for which there exist (finite) inferences with the aid of grammar Γ from word p consisting of one initial letter y_0 of grammar Γ meta-alphabet.

If all grammar rules have the form $\alpha \rightarrow \varphi$, where α is a single-letter word, and φ is a non-empty word, then a language determined by such a grammar is called *context-free*.

It is worth mentioning that the construction of formal grammars for natural languages is a rather difficult task (due to the enormous quantity of substitutions constituting such grammars), and at present there is no language for which it has been accomplished completely. At the same time, for many artificial languages used in mathematics, the construction of formal grammars requires little effort. For example, signs of the four arithmetical operations and signs of the opening and closing parentheses may be expressed by Roman letters of the alphabet. We shall assume that the meta-alphabet consists of one initial letter α. We shall write the 31 rules of formal grammar Γ: $\alpha \rightarrow (\alpha)$, $\alpha \rightarrow \alpha + \alpha$, $\alpha \rightarrow \alpha - \alpha$, $\alpha \rightarrow \alpha \cdot \alpha$, $\alpha \rightarrow \alpha : \alpha$, $\alpha \rightarrow a$, $\alpha \rightarrow b$, $\alpha \rightarrow c$, $\ldots$, $\alpha \rightarrow z$.

It is clear that the language determined by grammar Γ consists of all algebraic expressions having no numerical coefficients, constructed from 26 variables a, b, c, $\ldots$, z (not necessarily all in each given expression) by means of four arithmetical operations.

In a more complex grammar it is possible to describe algebraic expressions containing coefficients, indices of power and root, etc., but we shall not do that here.

The above example represents a context-free but non-regular language. Context-free languages constitute a very wide and practically important class of languages. The connection between context-free languages and automata theory is established by the following theorem.[3]

Any language representable in single-storage push-down automata is a context-free language.

It is possible to give examples of recursively enumerable and even recursive languages which are not context-free.

Apart from the problem of synthesis and analysis of abstract automata, the problem of *minimisation of automata* is of great importance (in the first place in the case of finite automata). The relevance of this problem is that one and the same alphabetic mapping can be represented by various automata. At the same time, in the actual designing of automata, those which have as a rule a smaller number of states are preferable. It is, therefore, necessary to be able to find an automaton having the minimum number of states possible, which represents the same alphabetic automaton as the given automaton *A*. This problem is termed a *problem of minimisation of the given automaton A.*

If *A* is fully determinate (not partial), the problem of its minimisation has a single solution. For solving this problem in the case of finite automata, convenient practical methods have been constructed based on the so called *equivalent* states and on the unification of each set of equivalent states into one state.[4]

In the case of partial automata this problem becomes more complicated. Generally it now has more than one solution. If the partial initial automaton *A* is given with partial mapping φ induced by *A*, a minimal automaton (in the general case one of several) is looked for in a type of all initial automata *B*, which induce mappings coincident with φ in a region of definition of mapping φ, but which belong, in general, to a wider region of definition.

An accurate solution of this problem is extremely cumbersome, since it involves trial and error methods for numerous variables. In practice, simplified methods are used, giving a solution close to the minimal.

BOOLEAN FUNCTIONS

Functions are said to be Boolean if both the functions proper and their arguments can have two values only.

In cybernetics, the role of Boolean functions is conditioned in the first place by the fact that components of most modern discrete data transformers operate in a binary alphabet, and secondly, by Boolean functions being used widely in mathematical logic, representing one of the fundamentals of the automation of thinking processes. Hence these functions have been named after an English mathematician, G. Boole, a founder of mathematical logic.

As regards their application in logic, the two values of variables used to define Boolean functions are assumed to be identified with truth (*T*) and lie (*L*). We shall also denote truth by a unit, and lie by a zero. A region of definition of an *n*-argument Boolean function cannot consist, obviously, of more than 2^n elements. Just such a number of various sets of values can assume *n* binary (Boolean) variables.

One of the principal problems in the theory of Boolean functions is the development of the method of expressing one function by another. Since arbitrary Boolean functions can be substituted for any variable of any Boolean function, each Boolean function may be regarded as an operation over a set of Boolean functions. Boolean functions include trivial single-argument functions recurring for the values of their arguments $f(x_i) \equiv x_i$. Those of a simple nature have also functions-constants $(\varphi(x_i, \ldots, x_n) \equiv 1, \psi(x_1, \ldots, x_n) \equiv 0$. Let us call all such functions the simplest ones.

A system of Boolean functions is said to be complete if any Boolean function can be built from the simplest Boolean functions (variables and constants) by the application to them of a finite number of operations determined by functions of the given system.

Let us introduce six operations over a set of Boolean functions. A single-argument inversion operation $\neg$ is stated by relations $\neg 0 = 1$ and $\neg 1 = 0$. The remaining five operations are two-argument. These are:

disjunction $\vee$, stated by relation $0 \vee 0 = 0, \quad 0 \vee 1 = 1 \vee 0 = 1, \quad 1 \vee 1 = 1$

conjunction $\wedge$, with relations $0 \wedge 0 = 0, \quad 0 \wedge 1 = 1 \wedge 0 = 0, \quad 1 \wedge 1 = 1$

implication $\rightarrow$, with relations $0 \rightarrow 0 = 1, \quad 0 \rightarrow 1 = 1, \quad 1 \rightarrow 0 = 0, \quad 1 \rightarrow 1 = 1$

equivalence $\equiv$, with relations $0 \equiv 0 = 1, \quad 1 \equiv 0 = 0, \quad 0 \equiv 1 = 0, \quad 1 \equiv 0 = 1$

negation of equivalence $\not\equiv$, also named modulo 2 addition, with relations $0 \not\equiv 0 = 0, \quad 0 \not\equiv 1 = 1, \quad 1 \not\equiv 0 = 1, \quad 1 \not\equiv 1 = 0$

Functions expressed by the simplest functions only with the aid of the modulo 2 addition operation are named linear.

An interesting class of Boolean functions represents *monotonous functions,* that is those functions whose values cannot decrease (to pass over from 1 to 0) with an increase (change from 0 to 1) of any of their variables.

Altering one of the results obtained by E. Post,[5] one can now formulate the necessary and sufficient condition of completeness of a system of Boolean functions:

A system of Boolean functions is only complete when it contains at least one non-linear and at least one non-monotonous function.

Of the six functions stating the above operations, the negation function is non-monotonous but linear, both disjunction and conjunction are non-linear but monotonous, implication is non-linear and non-monotonous, equivalence and negation of equivalence are non-monotonous but linear.

Therefore, complete systems involve, for instance, a combination of negation with conjunction or disjunction. One implication also constitutes a complete system. But negation of equivalence (binary addition) should be complemented with disjuntion or conjunction to obtain a complete system.

Owing to the foregoing criterion of completeness, any complete system of Boolean functions can be reduced to not more than two functions. This result is of great importance in constructing discrete data transformers.

Consider, for instance, an automaton A with no memory (i.e. having a single internal state), and with the input and output signals coded in a binary alphabet. It is quite clear that an alphabetic operator, which can be realised by the automaton in question, is described by a system of Boolean functions.

Let us manufacture a set of automata with no memory, each of which realises a function of some complete set of Boolean functions. Application of an output signal of one of these automata to the input of the other results in the substitution of a Boolean function corresponding to the first automaton for one of the arguments of a function determined by the second automaton. In other words, a composition of automata induces a corresponding composition of Boolean functions and vice versa. Due to the completeness theorem we can now construct any automaton having no memory by the use of a selected set of elementary automata with no memory called ordinarily *logic elements*.

In the case of arbitrary finite automata, logic elements only are insufficient. For the construction of such automata it is necessary to have at least one form of elementary automata with a memory (having more than one internal state). Such elementary automata are usually called memory elements. The complete Moore's automata are usually taken as memory elements. Completeness of an automaton means, first, that for any pair (a, b) of its states, there exists an input signal changing over the automaton from one state to the other. Secondly, each state of the complete Moore's automaton corresponds to an output signal of its own (differing from others). This enables one to identify output signals of each automaton with its internal states. A two-state Moore's automaton is usually taken as a memory element.

Let us now have an arbitrary finite automaton A (Mealy's or Moore's). We shall code states of this automaton, as well as its input and output signals, in a binary alphabet. Input signals, then, will be represented by sequences of values of Boolean variables $x_1, x_2, \ldots, x_m$. For output signals we shall denote the respective sequence of Boolean variables by $y_1, y_2, \ldots, y_n$, and for internal states by $z_1, z_2, \ldots, z_k$. In this coding, functions of transitions and outputs of the automaton will be represented by systems of Boolean functions. The next state $(z_1', z_2', \ldots, z_k')$ will be determined by a system of Boolean functions of $m+k$ arguments $x_1, x_2, \ldots, x_m; z_1, z_2, \ldots, z_k$, and the output signal by a system of n Boolean functions of $m+k$ arguments for the case of an arbitrary Mealy's automaton, or of k arguments for a Moore's automaton.

The values of variables $z_1, \ldots, z_k$ are then identified with internal states of k memory elements $A_1, A_2, \ldots, A_k$, which we will consider to be one and the same two-state complete Moore's automata. Then the Boolean variables S_{ij} are placed at each binary input channel of the i memory element ($i = 1, 2, \ldots, k$; $j = 1, 2, \ldots, p$). For each transition $(z_1, z_2, \ldots, z_k) \rightarrow (z_1', z_2', \ldots, z_k')$ of A we select one of sets of values of signals S_{ij}, which causes this transition. Such a choice is always possible, owing to the assumption of completeness of automata $A_1, A_2, \ldots, A_k$. Since each transition of A is determined fully by a set α of values of Boolean variables $x_1, x_2, \ldots, x_m; z_1, z_2, \ldots, z_k$, then with the choice of input signals made, the required set of these signals will also be determined by the same set α. Hence the variables S_{ij} ($i = 1, 2, \ldots, k; j = 1, 2, \ldots, p$) will be determined by Boolean functions of $m+k$ variables $x_1, x_2, \ldots, x_m; z_1, z_2, \ldots, z_k$. These functions will be referred to as *excitation functions* of given A.

The functioning of A is thus determined fully by the statement of $n+mk$ Boolean functions, viz. of n output functions and of mk excitation functions. A synthesis of systems of each function by initial (abstract) automaton A is called a *structural synthesis* of this automaton. Upon completion of this operation, the further procedures on synthesis of the A networks are connected by building a *logical network* only (i.e. a network with no memory) consisting of

logic elements for representing obtained systems of excitation and output functions.

An important task in the automaton structural synthesis stage is a reasonable
choice of coding of states of this automaton. The choice of the reasonable coding,
and the degree of ambiguity in a general case of building excitation functions,
make it possible to lay the foundations for constructing the most economic
logical networks. Such tasks connected with the choice of the optimal coding
are, however, very labour consuming, since they require application of the trial
and error method for numerous variants. These tasks become even more complicated when the used memory elements are not complete or have more than
two internal states.

As to the synthesis of logical networks, in the case of binary logic elements,
this problem is reduced (as has been shown above) to the expression of one
Boolean function by others. For solving such problems, theories of algebras of
Boolean functions have to be developed. Boolean functions serve as elements
of such algebras, and a system of operations of algebra is constituted with
operations determined by functions realised by a chosen system of logic elements.

When writing Boolean algebra expressions, an agreement on order of seniority
is used to save parentheses, as in ordinary elementary algebra. Negation is the
most senior, then conjunction and, finally, disjunction. Thus, for instance, the
formula of Boolean algebra $x \lor \lnot y \land z$ is to be understood as a formula

$$x \lor [(\lnot y) \land z], \quad \text{and not as} \quad [x \lor (\lnot y)] \land z \quad \text{or} \quad x \lor [\lnot (y \land z)].$$

Let either of two expressions, A or $\lnot A$ be denoted by $\tilde{A}$. Expression $x_1 \land x_2 \land$
$\ldots x_n$, $(n \geqslant 1)$, where all x_i are Boolean variables different in pairs $(i = 1, 2,$
$\ldots, n)$, is called an *elementary conjunction*. A disjunction of any finite number
$m \geqslant 0$ of elementary conjunctions different in pairs is called a disjunctive normal
form (abbreviated to dnf). In this case, a disjunction consisting of one member
$(m = 1)$ coincides with this number, and a disjunction of zero members $(m = 0)$
is considered to be zero by definition.

Any dnf of variables $x_1, x_2, \ldots, x_n$ is the Boolean function of these variables,
and we shall say that this function is *represented in* dnf. As it so happens any
Boolean function can be represented in dnf.

Such a representation proves to be not the only one in a general case, and
a minimisation problem arises, i.e., the finding of a dnf which would have
a minimum number of letters. For instance, a function represented by dnf
$x \land \lnot y \lor x \land y \lor \lnot x \land y$ consisting of 6 letters can also be represented by dnf $x \lor y$
comprising 2 letters only. The latter form proves minimal.

The reduction of a dnf to a minimum form is based on the theory of identity
transformations in Boolean algebra. This theory has at its core a relatively
small number of base identities, e.g. $A \land (B \lor C) = A \land B \lor A \lor C$, $A \land \lnot A = 1$,
$1 \land A = A$, $A \lor A = A$, etc. By writing out a system of elementary identities, the
dnf minimisation quoted above is accomplished.

With a large number of variables the dnf minimisation problem becomes very
cumbersome, while the minimisation problem of arbitrary Boolean algebra expressions is even more difficult. Apart from accurate methods for solving these
problems, approximate techniques have been developed which give solutions
sufficiently close to the minimal with far less computation than the required for
accurate methods.

ALGORITHMS AND ALGORITHMIC LANGUAGES

An algorithmic language is a totality of means necessary for describing a certain class of algorithms. We shall first describe a class of the so called normal algorithms.[6] It should be noted that both the input and output alphabets in any algorithm may be combined in one algorithm which will be referred to as a main algorithm. In some cases we shall resort to an extension of the main algorithm while transforming information. In such a case a respective algorithm is said to be constructed not in the main algorithm but over it.

Any normal algorithm is stated by a finite ordered set of substitutions of the form $p \to q$, where p and q are words over the main alphabet. The substitution $p \to q$ for word w refers to the substitution of w for p farthest to the left. Thus, for instance, the substitution $xx \to y$ for word $xxxy$ will result in a word yxy, and not in xyy. Some of the algorithm substitutions are termed concluding. The application of an algorithm to a specified input word occurs all the time, beginning with the first substitution. If this is inapplicable, we shall pass to the second one, and so on. Nevertheless, after each application of any substitution we return to the first one. An algorithm is completed if one of the substitutions is no longer applicable, or if one of the concluding substitutions has been applied. An algorithm is inapplicable to an input word if the algorithm handling takes place infinitely without ending in one of the above ways.

We assume an algorithm language or a class of algorithms, described by the latter, to be endowed with a *completeness feature* if for any algorithm (or an alphabetic operator stated in the design) in a given class, it is possible to find an algorithm equivalent to the said one.

It so happens that the class of normal algorithms possesses the completeness feature. This suggestion, which can be proved, is equivalent to the statement about the representability of any algorithm in two-storage push-down automata. The arguments proving the correctness of the last statement have been given above.

The second important property with which an algorithmic language, or a class of algorithms described by it, is endowed is the *universality feature*, which may be explained as follows.

Each language has the means of describing an algorithm in the form of a certain sequence of symbols, for example, if, a universal alphabet (e.g. binary) is introduced, and a method is fixed for coding in this alphabet the letters of any alphabets in which algorithms of the given class operate, as well as the symbols required for describing these algorithms. Then, for each algorithm Q we can build a universal alphabet word q' describing this algorithm. In exactly the same manner we can imagine any input word p of Q in the form of the word p' in the universal alphabet. Let U be the algorithm over the universal alphabet that turns word $p'q'$ into a word r', which is the output word $r = Q(p)$ of algorithm Q coded in the universal alphabet.

In other words, the algorithm U simulates operation of any algorithm of the discussed class, in the universal alphabet. In this case U is said to be the universal algorithm of the discussed class of algorithms, and this class proper is endowed with the universality feature. It can be shown that the universal algorithm exists in the class of normal algorithms.

Consider another class of algorithms called a Turing machine.[1] Information is recorded in a Turing machine on both sides of an infinite tape divided into

61

individual cells. A single letter of the main or complementary alphabet, including a special empty symbol, is recorded in each cell. Only a finite number of cells contains non-empty words at a given instant. An input word to be handled is recorded on the tape at the initial instant. As well as the tape, a Turing machine has a head which is a finite initial automaton. This automaton can view one cell on the tape at each given instant, a letter recorded on the tape being an input signal for the automaton. An output signal records a letter instead of viewing one, and shifts the tape by one cell to the right or left hand side. On reaching one of the discriminated final states, the automaton stops and an output word of the algorithm remains on the tape.

The completeness and universality features are also true for a machine of the Turing class. It is not difficult to see that a Turing machine is essentially nothing else other than a two-storage push-down automaton with no external input and output signals.

Another class of algorithms is used for constructing electronic computers. Imagine that we again have an infinite tape (memory) divided into cells, each of which is furnished with a number—the so called address. An algorithm is written as an ordered enumerated sequence of instructions. Instructions can be of the following forms: 'Write down letter x in the cell with address i' (i and x are arbitrary); 'Transfer the contents of the cell with address i to the cell with address j' (the content of the cell with address i being left unchanged); 'If the content of the cell with address i is x, start executing the instruction numbered j, otherwise pass on to the instruction numbered k'; 'Pass on to the instruction numbered j'. One more instruction is formed by the instruction 'Stop'. The execution of an algorithm is begun with the first instruction. If the instruction has no indication to the number of the next instruction, as in the instructions of the third and fourth types, the transfer should be made to the instruction next in order, until arriving at the 'Stop' instruction. The information written in the memory at the moment of stopping will be only the result of algorithm work. At the beginning of the work the input word being handled is written in the memory.

The class of algorithms described closely resembles Post's algorithms.[8] The completeness and universality features are also true for this class of algorithms.

In practice, the above class of algorithms is somewhat extended when computers are used. First, some letters of the main alphabet are identified with figures, or even with large numbers, since modern memories have individual cells containing up to 64 binary digits, giving over 10^{19} various combinations. Therefore, instructions for the execution of arithmetical operations are introduced together with the above instructions. In addition, provision is made for cutting down the number of instructions when identical operations over a large array of numbers are carried out.

Thus, the universality and completeness features are preserved. The first feature makes it possible to construct universal computers, simulating all algorithms of the class considered. The completeness feature ensures that this class involves all algorithms with the accuracy of equivalence. However, all alphabetic operators which can actually be built are covered by algorithms. But alphabetic operators, as stated above, cover all conceivable data transformations to a certain extent, which is why universal computers are so powerful for simulating arbitrary data transformers. For such a simulation it is only necessary to describe the network of the transformer being simulated precisely and to code the network in the universal computer alphabet or, as it is usually termed, to program it.

Naturally, this relates in full only to ideal computers which have a memory of infinite capacity. For actual computers this capacity, though large, is still limited. Also, despite the enormous speed of modern computers, their use for simulating very complicated data transformers may require excessive time, so that in practice they become ineffective.

We have considered only a few of the existing new classes of algorithms and the algorithmic languages describing them. Even these examples show a great variety of methods for describing algorithms. However, despite this variety, studies of algorithmic languages and classes of algorithms can be combined in one common scheme.

Consider a set B, each element of which presents information worked out by an algorithm. The set will be referred to as the *information set*. Being based on a purely theoretical standpoint which makes no distinctions among letters of the main alphabet, we can say that each element of B is simply a word in the main

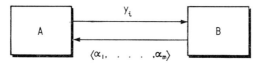

Fig. 4.1. Network of two automata

alphabet. In practice, however, it is convenient to specify some of the letters by, say, separating characters between the letters. Then each element of B can be a totality of words, formulae, and other alphabetic formations.

B is defined by *elementary operators*, which are the mappings (generally speaking, partial) of B into itself. Moreover, elementary conditions are stated, i.e. single-argument logic functions (partial in a general case), by assuming concepts of 'truth', 'lie' that refer to B.

To represent a particular algorithm in a given language we take a finite set of elementary operators $y_1, y_2, \ldots, y_n$ and a finite set of elementary conditions $\alpha_1, \alpha_2, \ldots, \alpha_m$. We shall construct a finite automaton A with a fixed initial state a_0, and with a set of concluding states, the output signals of which will be symbols of the elementary operators $y_i (i = 1, 2, \ldots, n)$, the input signals being various combinations of values of elementary conditions $\langle \alpha_1, \alpha_2, \ldots, \alpha_m \rangle$. Set B can also be regarded as an automaton, the states of which are elements of B, the input signals—operators $y_1, y_2, \ldots, y_n$—and the output signals—combinations of values of logic conditions $\alpha_1, \ldots, \alpha_m$. We shall call it the operational automaton. Being actuated by input signal y_1, automaton B passes from state b_1 to state b_2, to which state b_i is passed on by operator y_i. As a result we obtain a network of two automata working jointly (Fig. 4.1).

Put A in initial state a_0, and B in state b_0 corresponding to the described algorithm input word to be worked out. A and B, while exchanging signals, will pass on from one state to another. Three possible forms of functioning of a pair A and B are relevant to us. First, it may happen that A will reach one of the concluding states after several cycles. In this case we shall consider the work completed, with state of b_1 of B at this instant—the result of the application of a described algorithm P to an information word $b_0 : b_1 = P(b_0)$. Secondly it may happen that A encounters a forbidden transition or an indeterminate signal during the operation. The same might happen with automaton B, since elementary operators and conditions might not be determinate over some of its states. In all these cases we consider P, being simulated, to be indeterminate for a selected information word b_0.

Finally, it may happen that A will work indefinitely without reaching one of the concluding states. In this case P is also regarded as being inapplicable to an input word b_0.

Thus, after selection of a set B with a system of elementary operators and conditions, the statement of an algorithm is reduced to the selection of automaton A, which will be referred to as a *control automaton*. Consequently, an algorithmic language should, include a means for describing this automaton. For this purpose we can simply use tables of transitions and outputs, complemented with enumeration of initial and concluding states. Other forms of writing, however, are usually employed.

The most widespread form of programming consists of writing out a row of elementary operators complemented with jump operators and a stop operator introduced specially for this purpose. Moreover, some of the operators, when written out, are furnished with labels, that is, with special words as distinct from information words. For this purpose one can complement the main alphabet with new letters utilised for denoting the labels only.

A jump operator can have the following form: 'If given conditions are met, pass on to execution of the operator labelled μ_1, otherwise pass on to executing the operator labelled μ_2'. It is easily understood that such *conditional* jump operators enable us to describe any transitions in the control automaton A. It may, of course, require several conditional operators together.

Side by side with conditional operators, *unconditional* jump operators are used, i.e. operators of the form: 'Pass on to execution of the operator labelled'.

A stop operator serves to describe concluding states. Having reached this operator an algorithm stops working. In general, in the description method taken, states of A are identified with operators produced in these states. Therefore, one and the same operator can be written out in an algorithmic form many times. At first glance, this appears to diminish generality, because an automaton described in this manner will only be the Moore's automaton. It can be shown, however, that for any finite Mealy's automaton there exists the equivalent finite Moore's automaton. But from the standpoint of the interaction scheme of A and B, it is not an internal structure of A that is of importance, but only a mapping represented by A, which will be the same in equivalent automata. The type of algorithm writing thus described is called an *algorithm program*.

Finally, certain techniques are usually provided in algorithmic languages for a short designation of complex operators constituted from several elementary operators, including jump operators. Such pieces of program when considered separately are named the sub-routines or composed operators.

The scheme of interaction of two automata described provides a technique for solving many practical problems by the equivalent transformations of algorithms.[9] With the help of this technique it is, for instance, possible to transform the algorithm by purely formal methods to the convenient practical forms used in up-to-date computers, once the multiplication algorithm has been written down in the most primitive form (as a successive adding).

It is worth emphasising that the problem of establishing the equivalence of two algorithms in complete classes of algorithms is an example of an algorithmically insoluble problem. At present, for a large number of mass problems (dealing with an infinite number of objects), including the problem of equivalency of algorithms, the impossibility of constructing algorithms solving such problems is proved. Nevertheless, even for these problems we can build partial algorithms solving most tasks in the area covered by the problem.

SELF-ORGANISING SYSTEMS

In describing the performance of automata, we suggested that an automaton returns to its initial position after each cycle of work (perception of an input word and delivery of an output word corresponding to the input one). Because of this the mapping induced by the automaton was fixed rigidly and subjected to no alterations during its work. However, if the automaton does *not* return to its initial position but begins each successive cycle in the state in which it was found at the completion of the previous cycle, then the automaton answering to the same input words will, generally speaking, change depending on the history of its previous operation.

Experiments with such self-changing automata may be conducted as follows: at first, a sequence of words called a *learning sequence* is applied to the automaton input. Thereby, the automaton can work in two regimes. In the first regime, called a *learning regime*, each automaton answer is accompanied by an additional input signal—*an evaluation of this answer*. In the second regime, called a *self-learning regime*, each cycle consists of a question and an answer not accompanied by an evaluation. In both cases the above period will be called a *learning period*. On its completion, an examination period occurs, consisting also of an application of one or several words—questions to the automaton input, and of a registration of words—answers corresponding to them. From these answers one can judge the character of alterations that have occurred in the automaton during its period of learning.

We shall distinguish between two such alterations: *self-organisation* and *self-improving*. Self-organisation simply means an increase in the definiteness of the answers without an attempt to evaluate their correctness. To estimate quantitatively the ability of automata for self-organisation, one can use the concept of a quantity of information or the concept of entropy which is akin to information.

The law of joint distribution of probabilities of occurence of any learning sequences in the learning period of the automaton, and of any questions in the examination period, is called the *experimentation rule R* for a given automaton A. This distribution, together with the functions of jumps and outputs of A, determines the probability distribution function $\beta(q, r)$ for pairs [question (q)—answer (r)] with a one-to-one correspondence in the examination period. The entropy of this last distribution, i.e. H^R (exam) $= -\sum_q \beta(q, r) \log \beta(q, r)$ is called the *entropy of examination*.

Class K of the experimentation rules R and distribution $\varphi(R)$ of probability density in this class should also be specified. In class K we now select rule R_0 having a maximum entropy, and denote the integral:

$$\int_K [H^{R_0}(\text{exam}) - H^R(\text{exam})]\, \varphi(R)\, dR \quad \text{by} \quad S(A, K)$$

$S(A, K)$ can be K taken as a measure the ability of the automaton A for self-organisation. If the automaton possesses this ability then, with an increase in definiteness in constructing, the learning (in a transition from R_0 to R) the definiteness of answers during examination should increase, i.e. the entropy of examination must decrease on the average.

To introduce a quantitative estimate of the ability of automata for self-improvement, a criterion of the quality of automaton answers is required. The easiest way to do this is to state, on a set of [question (q)—answer (r)] pairs, a real function $f(q, r)$, the value of which at one and the same question q increases with improvement of answer r quality.

Using the above distribution $\beta(q, r)$ we obtain an average value f^R of the examination criterion f by means of the formula $f^R = \sum_{q,r} f(q, r)\beta(q, r)$. One can-

not, however, characterise self-improvement of the automaton as a simple difference between average evaluations of its answers, by an examination before and after learning. Imagine that a designer has built an automaton A which is being investigated in the form of a combination of two automata, A_1 and A_2, the former answering all questions randomly, the latter answering them in the best way. At first, an input and an output of A are connected to A_1 and then after some time, to A_2. At this moment a rapid improvement will occur in the performance quality of A. Yet such an improvement can hardly be called self-improving, as it does not actually depend on learning at all.

This difficulty can be avoided by stating the difference, $f^R - f^{R_0}$, of the average evaluations of the quality of the answers using two laws of probability distribution, R and R_0, of the frequency of learning sequences and questions during the examination; i.e. *a self-improving quantity of automaton A*. Here R_0 is the *a priori* law of distribution known to the designer when creating the automaton, and R is an *a posteriori* distribution law (real during the automaton learning). This very difference implies useful information acquired by the automaton in the learning period.

Self-organising and self-improving automata are used when an information handling algorithm is known in advance, the complexity of the latter being such that its preliminary study (prior to constructing the automaton) would result in an unjustifiable consumption of time. It is not, however, to be thought of as a case where the operation of such automata goes on in a particular non-algorithmic way. Any device having even a trivial effectiveness is a combination of two algorithms—*operative* and *controlling*. The first algorithm is actually not a single algorithm (e.g. due to the changing parameters available in it) but a full class K of algorithms. At first, an arbitrary algorithm of this class is put into operation. The controlling algorithm, evaluates the performance of the operative one at all times, and replaces the latter by another algorithm from a chosen class, K, if required.

In more complicated cases a multi-stage network is possible where controlling algorithms of higher levels are arranged over the first-level, controlling algorithm. The higher-level algorithms not only influence the operative algorithm immediately, but also the lower-level controlling algorithms. This is why we speak not of self-organising algorithms but of self-organising systems of algorithms or, simply, of self-organising systems.

Factors of great importance in designing self-organising systems include the various methods for finding the extrema—linear, convex and dynamic programming methods of successive analysis, and selected retrieval in discrete ordered sets, etc.

Self-organising systems play an important role in solving these problems. As an example, consider the problem of pattern recognition, particularly the recognition of optical images. The sense of pattern recognition consists of the unification of observed objects or phenomena into one or several classes called patterns. For instance, a human being possesses an abstract image of a tree, although particular representations of various trees constituting this pattern, differ greatly from one another.

In the general case, when solving the problem of the recognition of pattern representations in space, some concepts of the proximity of distance between representations are introduced explicitly or inexplicitly. Moreover, the hypothesis is employed that if any representation *r* pertains to pattern *R*, all the representations which are sufficiently close to *r* also belong to the same pattern. If various representations, i.e. sets of dots in space, are located far enough from one another, then such a method enables one to imagine the whole pattern by means of a relatively small number of the pattern representations shown. Representations situated between patterns and beyond them however, usually have zero occurrence during an examination. Therefore, their inclusion or non-inclusion into any pattern will not in practice affect the examination.

The application of various analogues of neurons and nerve circuits to the pattern recognition learning problem, as well as to other problems of automata learning, is of great interest. Take, as an example the simplest continuous neuron. Such a neuron has a certain number of excitatory inputs $x_1, x_2, \ldots, x_m$, and a certain quantity of inhibitory inputs $y_1, y_2, \ldots, y_n$. One of the signals identified with the numbers of segment [0, 1] can be transferred through each of these inputs. In addition, two more numbers, p and D, in this case considered to be integers or rational numbers, are ascribed to the neuron. The first of these is called the threshold and the other the weight of the given neuron. The neuron has one output through which a signal equalling the neuron weight is transferred whenever a condition exciting the neuron is met: $\sum\limits_{i=1}^{n} x_i - \sum\limits_{j=1}^{n} y_j \geqslant p$. Otherwise, the output signal of the neuron equals zero. The triplet (m, n, p) is called a type of the given neuron. A weight of the neuron can vary in the process of its operation.

F. Rosenblatt[10] suggested a device for pattern recognition constructed from such neurons and termed it the perceptron. Let each pattern $R_1, \ldots, R_K$ to be recognised correspond to a large number of neurons called neurons of a given pattern. Outputs of all these neurons are connected to a retina consisting of a finite number of receptors. The image is projected upon the retina and excites signals in the receptors, the signals being proportional to the brightness of the image dot projected on the receptor. Output signals of all neurons of a given pattern are summed and the sums obtained are mutually compensated. It is understood that the perceptron relates the image to the pattern corresponding to the greatest sum.

A reinforcement rule is also introduced. The essence of this rule in the operation learning regime is basically an increase in weight of all excited neurons of that pattern to which the displayed image actually belongs, and a decrease in weight of the excited neurons of the rest of the patterns. In the self-education regime, an increase in weight of excited neurons takes place for that pattern to which the greatest sum of signals corresponds, while the weight of all the rest of the excited neurons decreases.

In a similar way we can also consider *discrete* neurons, the input signals of which can assume only two values, 0 and 1.

The analysis carried out by Glushkov,[11] showed that the learning and self-education processes of these simple perceptrons differ very considerably from those in the human brain. Later, F. Rosenblatt[12] suggested multi-layer perceptrons in which neurons are divided into layers. Neurons of a lower layer are connected to the retina, their outputs serving as the retina for neurons in the next layer, and so on. According to simulation on a computer, this type of perceptron (especially with the introduction of cross-over couplings from the higher layers to the lower) displays a much closer resemblance in its behaviour to those processes which accompany pattern recognition learning in the human being.

At present only the most self-improving and self-learning systems are simulated on computers and many such systems are built specifically for this purpose. It is possible to build systems which can be taught to distinguish between meaningful phrases of a language and those having no sense. Successful experiments have been conducted on the extrapolation of discrete mappings based on partial automata minimisation. For example, the following task was solved. There are a certain number of correct translations from one language (say, Basque) into another (say, Hungarian.) A partially defined automaton A is constructed containing an alphabetic operator, input words of which are phrases of the first language, the output their translations into the second one. After minimisation of A its region of definition is widened, thereby providing the possibility of correct translation of several new phrases from Basque into Hungarian. These phrases, of course, were constructed from the same vocabulary (but from different combinations) in which the initial phrases had been given.

AUTOMATION OF THINKING PROCESSES

The examples given at the end of the previous section show that wide possibilities exist for simulating complicated thinking processes on computers. The limitations of these possibilities present an interesting question; the problem of the automation of scientific investigations, in particular of proving theorems in various fields of mathematics, is especially noteworthy.

It is known that present mathematical theories are constructed formally. First, all sentences of a given theory can be written in the form of formulae, i.e. essentially in words of a formal language. Second, certain sentences of this theory are taken as *theory axioms*, i.e. sentences, the truth of which is postulated *a priori*. Third, a system of alphabetic operators *(rules of inference)* is used which converts the true sentences of the theory into other true sentences. A theory sentence is called *derivable* if it can be obtained from axioms as a result of the application of any finite number of times (and in any order) of rules of inference of this theory.

Rules of inference always represent design operators, that is, algorithms. Hence, at first glance, a problem of inference automation of true sentences of any theory is a purely technical task of coding theory sentences and programming inference rules for a computer. In practice, this task is far from simple.

First, it is an established fact that in most cases a set of all inferred sentences of theory are not recursive but merely recursively enumerable. Programming of rules of inference results only in the process of automatic enumeration of true sentences of theory. Given a particular theory sentence, it is uncertain whether it is false or true—the latter not yet being arrived at in the discussed process—if the sentence has not yet been inferred after a certain number of enumeration process stages. In general, such a process can prove the truth of a sentence, but not its falsity.

68

In the case of the so called solvable theories, where a set of false sentences is also recursively enumerable, it is possible in principle to obtain a complete automation of the proof process of sentence falsity too. However, as has already been noted, most mathematical theories are not solvable. In this case various particular ways are implemented for proving respective sentences, fit not for all false sentences but for a part of them only. At first glance, this proves the impossibility of effective automation of scientific investigations and demonstrates a considerable advantage of man over the computer. Still, this is at first glance. In reality, if one proceeds from the almost indisputable fact that man bases the process of scientific investigations on *finite information*, then all above restrictions relate to the computer to the same degree as they do to man. And what is more, the volume of real knowledge (proved true and false sentences) in any theory at a given instant is always finite. Therefore, that part of theory, which will be really known to mankind in, say, 3,000 years from now, shall be finite and, consequently, solvable. That is why there are no fundamental obstacles to the fact that in, say, 2 years' time we shall have an algorithm solving that part of the theory which would be solved only in the year 3,000 in the usual way, without using this algorithm.

The same is true for Gödel's theorems.[13] The point is that it is impossible to build a complete non-contradictory system of axioms in any theory containing a sufficiently large quantity of concepts (e.g. in arithmetic of natural numbers), i.e. a system of axioms, in which sentence P or $\neg P$ would be provable for each closed P (which can be either true or false).

This case is similar to the previous one. The obstacle revealed by Gödel relates to man and to the computer to the same extent. It should also be emphasised that all above restrictions are established for close systems having no communications with the environment. If such communications are to be assumed to exist, and a 'non-constructive' environment hypothesis taken, then the proofs of insolubility of theories and the Gödel's theorem become invalid.

In other words, if we suppose that the constructive automaton, attempting to solve a theory, has a complementary input channel through which non-constructive sequences of signals are transferred (i.e. such sequences which can be generated by no algorithm), then with a certain form of these sequences the automaton can solve a theory which is insoluble in a usual sense. Actual difficulties to be dealt with in automation of scientific investigation processes are on a quite different plane. Experience shows that frequently a well compiled system of programs covers practically a much greater part of an insoluble theory than programs compiled according to universal decision procedures for soluble theories. Theoretical decision procedures, as a rule, are far from taking into account the quantity of operations needed for proving a theorem. And what is more, the attempt to simplify a formulation of the decision procedure itself leads as a rule, to a decrease in its practical efficacy, since the procedure working time for deciding even the simplest sentences becomes excessively great. The difficulty is that practically effective procedures for solving (though not completely) a certain theory should be based on large preliminary information, exceeding a total volume of a minimal system of axioms and inference rules of this theory by several orders. All this leads to a sharp increase in complexity of programs for computers and hence to growth of difficulties in their compilation.

Here we approach one of the most fundamental shifts in philosophy of scientific investigations, caused by cybernetics and electronic computers. During the pre-cybernetic epoch one of the principal doctrines under which sciences developed was that the world is arranged simply. Therefore, sciences, using mathematics, attempted to simplify initial premises to a maximum in order to construct their theories. In some cases (mechanics, physics) they were successful. In other cases, however, (linguistics, biology, economics, etc.) this doctrine did not play a decisive role. Today, it is understood clearly that a complete, even to a small degree, formalisation of, say, evolutional biology, or any human living language, cannot be effected on the basis of a few initial premises as, for example, can celestial mechanics. A corresponding formal technique will necessarily be cumbersome due to the complexity inherent in the theory itself. Such a technique is practically useless for its direct utilisation by the man. However, up to date computers increase our possibilities of processing data, and enable us to use, practically, much more complicated formalised systems.

The development of such complicated systems and the compilation of respective programs for computers remain extremely laborious processes. Everybody engaged in simulation of thinking processes on computers knows that the first symptoms of 'intelligence' of a simulator are obtained fairly easily, but the finishing of such simulators to a degree enabling us to employ them effectively in practice is a much more difficult task. Therefore, when giving assurance that any forms of mental activity can be made automatic by means of computers, one should, at the same time, be definitely conscious of the enormous volume of work that has to be accomplished before this purpose is achieved. The universe is actually simple in many of its parts, but it is extremely complex in others. This complexity requires for its investigation and practical use, the joint and hard work of many thousands of scientists and engineers of many generations.

REFERENCES

1. KLEENY, S. K., *Representations of Events in Nerve Nets and Finite Automata*, Automata Studies, Princeton Univ. Press (1956).
2. GLUSHKOV, V. M., *Synthesis of Digital Automata*, Moscow (1962).
3. EVEY, R. J., *The Theory and Applications of Push-down Store Machines*, Cambridge, Mass. (1963).
4. AUFENKAMP, D. D. and HORN, F. S., *Trans. Inst. Rad. Engrs.*, **EC–7**, No. 7 (1958).
5. POST, E. L., 'Introduction to the General Theory of Elementary Propositions,' *Amer. J. Math.*, **43** (1921).
6. MARKOV, A. A., *Proc. Steklov Math. Inst.*, **42** (1954).
7. TURING, A. M., *Proc. Lond. math. Soc.*, **42** (2) (1936) and **43** (1937).
8. POST, E. L., *J. Symb. Logic*, **1** (1936).
9. GLUSHKOV, V. M., *Cybernetics*, No. 5 (1965).
10. ROSENBLATT, F., *Mechanisation of the Thought Process*, Symposium, Nat. Phys. Lab. (U.K.) (1958).
11. GLUSHKOV, V. M., *Introduction to Cybernetics*, Kiev (1964).
12. ROSENBLATT, F., *Principles of Neurodynamics*, Spartan Books, Washington (1962).
13. GÖDEL, K., *On Undecidable Propositions of Formal Mathematical Systems*, Princeton Univ. Press (1934).

PART 2

CYBERNETICS AND LIVING SYSTEMS

'But beyond the bright searchlight of science,
    Out of sight of the windows of sense,
Old riddles still bid us defiance,
    Old questions of Why and Whence'

W. C. D. Whetham,
Recent Development of Physical Science, p. 10

Chapter 5

Behavioural Cybernetics
(Models of Cognitive Behaviour)

F. H. GEORGE, M.A. (Cantab.), Ph.D. (Bris.), F.S.S., M. Inst. C. Sc.,
M.B.C.S.

Director, Institute of Cybernetics, Brunel University; Chairman, The Bureau of Information Science; Chairman, Council of the Institution of Computer Sciences (U.K.)

SUMMARY

This chapter is concerned with the broad principles involved in intelligent behaviour. It is concerned with the simulation of human behaviour, although some appeal is made to animal studies and syntheses.

It is clear that, to some extent, the different aspects of cognition form a total integrated pattern and therefore it is impossible to separate these into separate concepts (perception, learning, etc.) without doing some violence to the facts. It is also impossible, however, to treat them all together. Therefore, with the awareness of the dangers inherent in the approach, a brief analysis is made of perception, followed by more detailed analyses of the theories of learning, thinking and problem solving.

That human intelligence is intimately bound up with the use of language implies that concept formation is a vital ingredient of any sufficiently intelligent artificial system.

With these ends in mind, a formalisation of some of the features of cognition is attempted, which at least suggests a mode of approach to the more detailed study of these problems. It is assumed that computer programming is the main method of approach, and this is because digital computers are the only sufficiently large 'universal machines' in which we can manufacture worthwhile models. It is this fact that creates the need for formalised and detailed descriptive languages.

SYNTHESIS AND SIMULATION

There are many different problems of modelling and simulation in the various fields of human and artificial intelligence, and various different methods have been used to achieve these models. This paper will deal specifically with the problem of simulation—the simulation of human problem solving. This is to be considered primarily with the digital computer program as the model in mind.

It is first necessary to distinguish between synthesis and simulation. By the *synthesis* of an artificially intelligent system, is meant the development of a system capable of producing intelligent results or showing intelligent behaviour of one kind or another, without any pretence that the methods used bear any necessary resemblance to those used by human beings. *Simulation*, on the other hand, which is a particular case of synthesis, not only attempts to achieve the same ends, but also claims to produce them in a way similar to the way in which they are produced by human beings. Indeed, simulation is concerned with producing what might well be a somewhat less than perfectly reliable intelligence system, in keeping with the unreliabilities observable in human behaviour. There is of course, no pretence that the simulation models we are going to discuss are constructed of the same fabrics as human beings—this is another problem again—and we are going to talk only of simulation methods.

Let us envisage a large set of automata working on a closed-loop principle with a very large storage capacity. We are concerned with the principles of programming and self-programming that are used to promote the behaviour of an automaton in a social environment. Given that the environment bears some resemblance to the human environment, our task is to show that the behaviour of the computer bears some resemblance to that of human beings. We may, of course, expect to proceed in stages to try to solve this particular problem, starting with a simpler and more general model and moving gradually towards the point where our model bears a close resemblance to a human being, or at least to human behaviour.

Although this paper is built up mainly around programs written for the digital computer, it should be said that the author himself has used many other modelling techniques, particularly those of neural or logical nets as well as purely mathematical or mathematical-logical models. And although the author has had no great experience of actual hardware models, it should be remembered that, particularly during the earlier stages of development of these simulation methods, hardware models of the simpler sorts of adaptive behaviour and intelligence were often constructed.[1,2]

Our input-output automaton must be capable of simulating at least the properties of perception, recognition, recall, conceptualising, inference making, thinking, problem solving, and the use of language. It should be borne in mind throughout this discussion that the names used above do not refer to linearly isolatable properties (or mechanisms) of the human being, but are to be thought of as rough labels for complicated overlapping processes. This means that, whereas we might be able to give a sufficiently precise contextual definition to words like 'conception' or 'learning', we would not necessarily wish to be forced to adhere to such definitions when constructing the system as a whole.

This last point is of special importance, because we are forced to consider whether we are building an automaton, however simple, as a whole, or whether we are constructing models (simulations) of different parts of the human being with the hope of ultimately putting them all together to make a whole. Both the whole and the piecemeal methods have been followed to some extent, but most people have found it necessary to pursue the latter. We hope to be able to utilise some of the general characteristics of different forms of piecemeal model, while bearing in mind the overall framework in which the details are to be placed, thus providing a coherent 'whole' story from the start. In practice, of course, this might turn out to be impossible, and continual adjustments and developments will be made as our empirical knowledge increases and experimental tests are carried out to decide between various alternative possibilities, all of which at any particular time might seem to be equally appropriate.

We can now supply a number of models of different cognitive functions but we are not in a position to say with any great measure of certainty which, if any, is right, or nearest to the real thing. It seems quite likely that in many cases the central nervous system operates in such a way that integration of various models is a practical possibility, whereas in other cases it may be that we have to make a definite decision between one of a number of possible models since one, and only one, of the models can be the right one.

The main problem on which this chapter will concentrate is that of *problem solving* and to some extent *thinking*, which overlaps it, and to this end relatively little will be said about other activities such as perception. But in accordance with the principle stated above, and in the light of a great deal of psychological experimentation, it seems likely that we cannot wholly understand problem solving activity and the allied fields of learning and thinking without having some knowledge of how information is received (as well as recognised and recalled) in the first place. So a relatively short section will be devoted to a general consideration of an attitude to human perception, the section being intended for heuristic purposes only.

PERCEPTUAL MODELS

By 'perception', we mean roughly the process of interpreting stimuli in the environment. This involves *classification* of novel stimuli or novel combinations of stimuli, and the *recognition* of familiar stimuli, or sets of stimuli, where the interpretation of the input is clearly connected with the process of recall.

The clear assumption is that we can only perceive or recognise by means of some form of comparison between the input and what has previously been stored. In other words no perception, in the sense intended here, and as a result no intelligent behaviour, can occur in any automaton which is not able to store information from the past. This is not to say that the innate structures of the organic system do not play a significant part in the actual process of perceiving (Gestalt theory), but whilst this structural consideration is accepted as a relevant factor, the most significant factor is the method of perceiving, which must lie in a comparison between the present and the past.

The basic method suggested by Hayek[3] and Uttley[4] is that of classification. If one could label all the 'primitive stimuli,' or sense data, to which the human being is subject, it could then be argued that every physical object and every sensory occurrence could be built up by classification. Indeed, we could expect to build a system which could recognise anything whatever; the logical argument that a complete classification system is capable of complete recognition seems unanswerable. Unfortunately, as far as simulation is concerned, the difficulties

75

spring from the fact that the number of neurons needed for such a recognition model is astronomical and far in excess of the number available in any human nervous system. The answer to this could lie in a misunderstanding as to the way in which the human classification system is constructed. Perhaps a neuron is not a single element in any one single neural network, but is capable of playing a part in various different networds as a result of different states of the nervous system prevailing at any particular time. But on the whole this seems less probable than the alternative argument, which is that classification in the nervous system cannot be complete, but must be partitioned, partial and adaptive. Partitioned means that the system must be built up in modalities as in a family tree (obviously initially separate for each sensory modality); 'partial', means simply incomplete; and 'adaptive', means subject to change as a function of changing circumstances.

In describing models of perception, it is emphasised that this chapter is in no sense an attempt to survey the field. We should, however, mention the two types of model called 'genotypic' and 'monotypic', a distinction made by Rosenblatt.[5] In a genotypic model it is supposed that the detail of the structure of the recognition model is not to be specified with full anatomical detail. Instead, mathematical and statistical operators are used to specify the function rather than to provide complete detailed structures. The monotypic system, on the other hand, supplies detail with as much structural precision as is needed. The networks of Uttley[6] are an example of a monotypic system. George[7] pointed out another consideration which cuts across the difference between a monotypic and a genotypic system, and that is whether a model is 'special purpose' or 'general purpose.' Sutherland[8] has argued in terms of specific special purpose receptor systems whereas Hebb,[9] for example, has argued in terms of general purpose principles.

At this stage the sort of decision that seems called for is to say that a monotypic system is desirable as long as it is feasible, and a genotypic system is acceptable when a monotypic system has ceased to be feasible. There is, indeed, no exclusive distinction between these two types of modelling procedure. As far as the labels 'special purpose' and 'general purpose' are concerned it seems again that both are possible; and although the human visual system, for example, seems to have specialised receptors with certain inevitably specialised characteristics—and this is the point that the Gestalt theorists made so often—in the form of eyes (ears and the sensory endings of touch and taste, etc., are also relevant to the full sensory range), the principles on which this information is processed more centrally seems capable of being stated in general terms. It seems likely that the distinctions made in the past about such models are not quite as important as they first appeared. We shall at any rate, in this chapter, try to discover general principles since, although we recognise the existence of special purpose sensory equipment, we shall suppose that it supplies information which is capable of being processed in the most general way possible.

This is much like saying that if a system has digitisers, it does not matter by what sort of equipment the sensory information is acquired—radar set or magic eye—but when collected, the information is all digitised into a common language and processed accordingly. This last statement may be taken as supporting the general perceptual model theorist against the special purpose model theorist, and to some extent this is true. But it is still recognised that special purpose sensory equipment does exist.

Our basic problem is that of *pattern recognition* and, although this occurs at all levels, including the conceptual levels, of human behaviour, it is here considered in the narrow context of visual pattern recognition. We are suggesting that the basic method by which this is possible is one of classification of information, where that classification does not necessarily take place at the actual retinal level. It is suggested that the classification is partial and hierarchical and takes place at the first stage, second stage, and perhaps at a third and fourth stage in the visual cortex. It is further postulated that complete classification must be replaced by adaptive classification, although there is a possibility that maximum flexibility occurs in the early years of the life of the organism, but as time goes by, the classifying system loses a great deal of its adaptability. This is plausible on purely logical grounds, of course, since as all the vacant spaces are filled in a filing system or any other sort of classification system, so the number of spaces for new information diminishes. This implies, probably correctly, that the human nervous system finds it more difficult to re-organise combinations of stimuli than it does to organise them in the first instance.

It might be asked at this stage what merit there is in what may be termed partial self-classification. The answer is that whereas a complete classification caters for every conceivable possibility, a partial classification system includes only those events which actually occur 'say' in the visual field. We can think in terms of the visual modality, even though the argument seems to be perfectly general. This means that every possible set of properties, i.e. every event or physical object, is either recognised by comparison with an existing record, or classified as 'new' and put into an existing, but general, classification. Alternatively, a new classification may be set up, as a result of the properties it possesses. No doubt such classifications are complicated and 'cross-associative' but we shall not discuss that here. In any case 'new' must always be related to what is already known.

The term self-classifying is applied to classification having possible re-organisation in the light of further experience, and this is really a form of adaptation. If the picture at this stage seems too symmetrical and too well organised, let us say that we are concerned here with simulating brainlike methods. This means starting with idealised models and concepts. Models with standard sets of artificial neurons working in a highly systematic and symmetrical way can be built. In practice, human beings have sets of neurons which vary enormously in their sensitivity, and in other properties, and operate partly by chemical and partly by physical stimulation and transmission of stimuli, even though they probably do so on rather generalised principles of combination which are subject to a considerable amount of error.

As a result of the above, it seems likely that the actual neural classification system available in a human being is a rougher, cruder approximation to the sort of abstract conceptual model we have in mind at this moment. This is accepted as a necessary part of the evolution of any simulation model.

It is assumed, for the perceptual model we are pre-supposing that the partial self-classifying system takes place in a series of stages, involving special purpose receptors and transmission through partial herarchical classification to the cortical centres. At the same time, information is passed to other control centres in the brain; this is followed by further visual classification, then by sensory classification and finally by other (possibly many) stages of conceptual classification and reclassification.

If perception is thought of as the process of classifying and possibly reclassifying, and recognition is thought of as the comparison between an existing input and a previously stored input (which in practice will certainly involve an 'attempt' in humans to remember the name of the object or objects), then the process of recall is involved in this latter stage. This does not mean that recall is concerned

77

only with remembering names of physical objects; it is not. One can be told a name and asked to recall the face, as distinct from recognising the face when shown a set of photographs and asked to say who the person is. So recall can involve the complex matter of *imagery*.

Although we are concerned primarily with problem solving the importance of imagery must be considered; this presents a very complicated and difficult problem, and we shall here limit ourselves to only a general attitude to imagery. One of the properties of the human nervous system is to be able to recall things from storage; this produces an effect similar to that of the original stimulation which took place at original perception or at stages of recognition, and has some of the 'conscious feelings' associated with the original stimulation. This is because some, usually small, percentage of the original input fibres are reactivated, and one has almost a reconstructed picture of events from the past. It is well known that people cannot actually see the details of a building or a face again, but have the feeling that they 'almost can'. We feel that this is the basic feature underlying the process of imagery, and is essential to the process often called imagination. We will not discuss this matter further, but will turn to the more central matter of cognitive simulation of problem solving.

LEARNING, THINKING AND PROBLEM SOLVING

Having distinguished between synthesis and simulation, and having considered in general terms perception and its relevance to cognition as a whole, we now come to our central test. This is the classification of the central cognitive processes and the setting up of a precise descriptive language to describe (simulate) these processes. The principles of cognition—whether known or guessed—must be stated rigorously to form the basis for clear cut testing. Testing may be done by constructing an automaton, but we shall endeavour to provide a computer program providing sufficient detail to enable programs to be written easily from our descriptions.

Our problem, then, is to deal with the central cognitive processes, and to this end we shall give a preliminary definition of some of the principal terms involved.

Learning is defined as the process of adapting to changing circumstances. This means that we envisage a system which has the necessary flexibility to adapt to a change in environment, although distinction should be made between adaptation which is built-in (instinctive, innate) and that which is acquired as a result of transactions between the organism and environment. 'Learning' is normally applied to the latter category although, there is a practical problem is distinguishing one from the other. It may also be argued that learning must lead to some sort of reduction in need, but this is not vital to our purpose here.

Thinking is the process of symbolising events and then manipulating the symbols by various processes of logical and illogical inference, where the processing —a sort of data processing—may be accompanied by imagery. Imagery may be considered as the resuscitation of an input system in a diminished form at some time after the original input took place. *Imagination* is rather more than this, since it may combine various previous inputs into a pattern which has never actually occurred before.

Problem solving is the process of acquiring an appropriate set of responses to a 'new' situation. The appropriateness of response to a stimulus, or a stimulus complex, must also depend on motivation; we are, as adaptive and problem solving organisms, motivated to respond to our environment and to achieve goals. The major goal for the human species is presumably that of survival, and responses to primary motivators, are processes such as eating when hungry, drinking when thirsty, and the satisfaction of other basic needs such as sex, self-esteem, etc. It has been assumed that goals often imply sub-goals, and furthermore the achievement of goals leads by association to the need to achieve secondary goals or secondary sources of satisfaction. Identification of sub-goals can be carried out deductively.

This complicated situation may be clarified by saying that human beings have purposes, some of which are long term, and some of which are relatively short term. These purposes represent goal-seeking activity, and this implies goals and sub-goals, where sub-goals imply sub-purposes. It is selective reinforcement, where satisfaction stems from the achievement of goals and sub-goals and dissatisfaction springs from the failure to achieve goals and sub-goals; this is basic to intelligent behaviour.

It is against this background that we have to view problem solving as a complex behavioural activity. The organism is already thought to perceive, recognise and recall information. The problem now is the central organisation or central processing of the input data, which makes problem solving occur or demands that it should occur. Following our general policy of proceeding by degrees to the 'hoped for' final solution, we shall attempt to envisage a problem solving activity of a reasonably realistic kind, which nevertheless does not involve any sort of 'emotional contamination'.

There are, broadly speaking, two types of problem that we want to consider, sequential and non-sequential. The sequential kind are those where a series of events occurs in time, and where an appropriate response may occur which achieves the goal of optimising certain features of that sequence; alternatively, the sequence may be in the form of a symbolic description, where a specific solution may be arrived at. Whether the sequence is symbolic or non-symbolic, or whether the solution to the problem is precise and determinate or an optimisational process, is not of fundamental importance. Various problems come under the heading of sequential and the types of problems and types of solution may be distinguished much more finely than we have done. An example of the second type of problem is that of knowing what the problem is. Under these circumstances, it is the search to understand the problem, usually in the light of knowing that goal-seeking activities are not yet being carried out effectively, that is itself the problem.

The second type of problem is not sequential in time, but is nevertheless a definite puzzle involving a collection of items, which may reduce to one which is sequential in time by virtue of the way the human organism scans the puzzle. But the scanning of a puzzle which is fixed is comparable to a chess board at any particular instant of time where the problem is to decide the next move; this is, in a sense, non-sequential. In the same way, a crossword puzzle which demands a synonym, or the solution to a particular verbal question, is not in itself sequential although it may be tackled as a process which is sequential in time. A similar distinction in computer terms, is called 'on line' (sequential) or 'off line' (non-sequential); this resemblance, however is only partial.

Another way of looking at this distinction between sequential and non-sequential problems, is to consider the formation of a hypothesis, where the hypothesis, applies to something operating over a sequence of events in time, as opposed to a hypothesis which applies to something operating over occurrences already documented. Although the processes of acquiring the necessary hypothesis—clearly inductive—may vary from circumstance to circumstance, the methods remain essentially the same. We can now see that this is the basic problem of induction or inductive logic. This means in turn that we must have all the available deterministic, probabalistic or statistical types of model at our disposal for an ideal problem solver. We are arguing, in a sense, that the human being has some of these models available to him in the form of existing, corporately derived techniques; other forms of possible solutions he can acquire from existing documented knowledge such as in books, which allow him to apply standard corporately derived techniques for inductive problems.

Problems which are initially inductive are still problems when they are reduced to the deductive. But now the nature of the problem has changed. The inductive generalisations are now assumed to be available: the problem is really one of *recognition*. The problem is to recognise which inductive generalisations are appropriate to the solution of the problem. Another problem may also arise because, although the appropriate generalisations are given or recognised, it may still not be obvious how they should be *applied*. The next stage in our argument is to show how these various types of problems arise in isolation, and then show how they are likely to be combined together in the more realistic 'emotional circumstances' of actual human behaviour. We shall start with a stimulus-response problem and move to the more general question of concept formation.

A large number of classical conditioning situations exist where a cat, rat or dog responds discriminatingly to environmental stimuli. A Thorndike[10] cat will learn by a series of stimulus-response activities to escape from a cage. It is motivated to do so. Being captive is a state which seems always to motivate an attempt to escape. There is a sense in which the act of pulling a lever releasing the animal is a specific response, even though in physiological terms it may represent a series of responses.

The question now arises as to whether the cat has formed a concept, even when placed repeatedly in the same situation and escape is immediate. The answer would seem to be 'yes', and when we think of this process as applying to human problem solving, the answer is certainly 'yes' since the word 'concept' in this context, means the identification of individuals, classes, and relationships in the environment in terms of names. We can of course talk of connotation and denotation, in this human context, and the approach can then be made more precise, but we now have to be careful to identify concepts as functions of properties and classes. The concept 'cat' is the conjunction of properties such as four-legged, tailed, two-eyed, etc. There is something about a cat which makes it different from a dog and we can, if we are careful, enumerate these differences. We can also run into borderline cases between concepts (or classes), and these can be resolved by finer distinctions, made as and when they are needed. Classes are, in other words, often vaguely defined and shadowy.[11]

We are now approaching the problem—one of the basic problems—of formulating a precise descriptive language. This language, which may take many forms, should map a rigorous symbolic model onto different aspects of human experience. By 'human experience', we include that which is immediately given at a particular instant and also that which has already been acquired and may be in a general form. Specifically, we are seeking a formal model of the central cognitive process, and that model has to be reproducible as a computer program.

For the notation we keep close to that developed by Banerji[12] and George.[13, 14]

We use letters, and subscripts as needed:

$$x, y, \ldots\ldots, w$$

denote individuals

and $a, b, \ldots\ldots, n$

denote classes.
We can write:

$$Aab$$

to denote the conjunction of the classes a and b, where A means 'and'.
In general, we could say:

$$x = AA\ldots.Aab\ldots n$$

where some individual was the conjunction of some n classes.

Similarly we use letters such as $D, N, \ldots\ldots$, etc., for disjunction, negation, etc.

We must also deal with disjunctive classes and associated concepts.[15] Thus, every property is itself a class, and every class of objects (individuals) is a set of properties. We can of course distinguish properties and classes when we need to.

These classes (properties) are related to each other in a variety of ways by operators:

$$AB, \ldots, N$$

where the operators stand for connectives as discussed, and also for verbs such as 'is', 'runs' and for relational phrases such as 'to the left of', 'wide apart from'.

We shall argue that all these apparently different interpretations of the operators are in reality the same, or at least, sufficiently similar to allow a common description. So we now have acceptable canonical forms:

$$Axa$$
$$Byb$$
$$Cab$$
$$Dcd$$

representing, for example, individual-class and class-class relationships, which when attached to an operator, allow a description.

We are now thinking of problem solving within the symbolised world.[16, 17] Symbolised problem solving is more general than, and includes, the non-symbolised form. The obvious case of non-symbolised problem solving is the actual learning stage of a maze-running problem, although even for the subhuman organism, it cannot be certain that symbolisation in some form does not occur.

Problem solving involves more than language alone, the ostensive process being the means of acquiring most basic knowledge in infancy. Subsequently, knowledge is derived from both *acquaintance* and *description* which can be regarded as an informative process acting as a basis for the solution to such problems.

Let us now consider some particular examples. The following **problems** were selected more or less randomly:

1. How do we get from Bristol to Stratford-upon-Avon in the least time, on a Thursday afternoon?
2. How can we explain compiler languages to a senior schoolboy who has never heard of them?
3. How do we get to know the combination lock on the safe and retrieve the contents of the safe by tomorrow?
4. On what principles do we base our tactical play for the game called noughts and crosses (referred to as *OAX* from here on)?
5. How do we solve algebraic equations of the form $ax^2 + bx + c = 0$?

Immediately we see that realistic problems can take various forms; they can have, for example, optimisation 'solutions' with or without incomplete information. They can be problems of definition, extended here under the name 'explanation'. They can involve inductive generalisations, deductions, heuristics or algorithms. They do not, however, necessarily require what Newell, Shaw and Simon[18] called *creative* problem solving.

We must also note that one common feature exists; *a problem is a situation for which a response is required and that response has not already been acquired, or is not known to have been acquired.* Problem solving is therefore, a sort of recognition and discrimination, a perception of similarities among differences and differences among similarities.

We must now recognise that a human problem solver has, through the medium of language, the possibility of using knowledge which has been acquired not by himself, but by the community in which he lives, so that a problem may be recognised as fitting into a standard technique of, say, logic or mathematics.

Broadly speaking, we need to be able to carry out the steps shown in Fig. 5.1. This, although a generalised picture, serves to show the importance of logic, concept formation, trial-and-error processes and hypotheses.

The formulation of hypotheses requires the use of concepts.[13] We may have much data in store which has not been named; take, for example, the circumstance recognised by human beings as 'the situation when your mother-in-law and your mother meet and talk of the grandchildren.' We could name such a situation as 'mothronte' say, but generally we do not wish to name every circumstance individually. We in fact do so only when they occur with a high degree of frequency and similarity. Similarly, not every shape has a name; triangles, circles and regular polygons sometimes have, but there are a whole host of shapes which have not. In other words language is incomplete in vocabulary, and is like a sketchy map of territory, bringing out some features more prominently than others.

The formulation of new hypotheses requires either the sorting of existing concepts, (with their class names) or the creation of new concepts and the manufacture of new class names (see Fig. 5.2.).

The biggest problem is, of course, that of relevancy. What is relevant to a problem? The general answer (to the symbolised problem) is that if the problem (statement or question) contains terms, individual variables or names of individuals such as in the set $x = \{x_1, x_2, x_3, x_4, a_1, a_2, a_3, a_4\}$ then any *directly relevant* possibility will contain any subset of this set x. In other words, a statement directly relevant to x will contain at least one of the terms defining x.

82

We shall expect relevant statements such as:

$$A_1 x_1 a_5 \qquad\qquad (5.1)$$

$$A_2 x_5 a_5 \qquad\qquad (5.2)$$

then although (5.2) contains no element of the set x, it has a link with x through (5.1).

This may be illustrated by a simple example:

Jill is Andrew's sister
Andrew is Irish

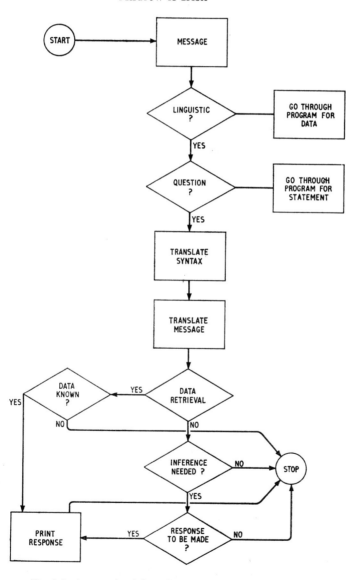

Fig. 5.1. A generalised flow chart for question identification

Since 'sister' implies at least the following rules (its *intension*, or something like it):

1. Andrew and Jill have the same parents
2. Andrew and Jill have the same nationality (where 'nationality' must be defined) so we can infer 'Jill is Irish'.

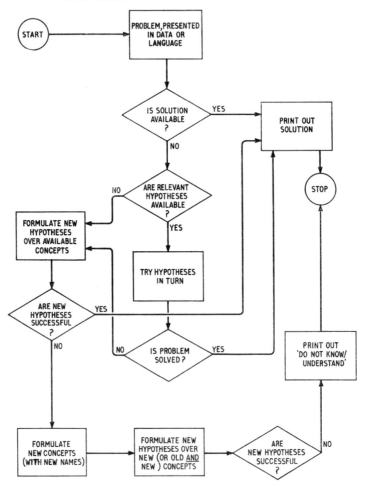

Fig. 5.2. A generalised flow chart for problem solving

Then, if we know that an Irish person is the local shopkeeper, it could be Jill, or Andrew.

The whole problem of relevancy depends upon building up a logical chain of arguments whereby it is possible to follow through from premises to conclusion. This is always implicit in human arguments, although not always made explicit. It is often easy for the human to accept 'jumps' in a logical chain, since the intermediate steps, making up the jump, are so obvious and so standard as not to need taking. In the computer program, this implicitness must be explicitly filled in.

We will next mention briefly the concept of reduction sentences and the field of scientific explanation. A scientific explanation of some event or events can take the form of reduction sentences, or other explanatory statements. Carnap[19] has suggested the form:

$$(x) [P(x) \supset Q(x) \equiv R(x)]$$

where x is *soluble* (R) (the concept to be explained) if, and only if, when it is immersed in water (P) it dissolves (Q).

This is a form of empirical description which comes to be an explanation, and in similar form can be used to analyse degrees of *confirmation*, degrees of *factual support*, etc., of scientific theories. The point to note is that this apparently takes us beyond problem solving, to the justification of the solutions to problems. The reason for its relevance is that in simulation we can only know solutions to be solutions by virtue of accumulating subsequent evidence. This is one aspect of the distinction between solution generating processes (discovery) and solution verifying processes (justification). When we try to describe an effective process to achieve the same ends, we cannot so easily maintain this distinction.

It is clear that definitions, as well as explanations, are part of the equipment needed to clarify, explain or solve a problem, in the sense of our specific examples.

Let us now return to thinking, or symbolised problem solving, which is a part of thinking. Our approach will be general, and we will first deal with the basic definitions and the beginnings of the problem.

VIEWPOINTS ON THINKING

Many experiments have been done on human beings and have been classed under the heading 'thinking'. Philosophers sometimes regard the word as being appropriate only to what we are 'consciously aware of'. This means, not that all of which we are consciously aware is thinking, but that all thinking is something of which we are consciously aware. Clearly this is a matter of semantics, but it seems preferable to take a broader view of thinking as a process involving internal organic modification, yet accompanied by symbolisation. This interpretation serves to assert that, while much of the process is conscious, some at least may be unconscious.

Problem solving by symbolising is part of what thinking entails. Price[20] has referred to thinking as 'cognition of the absent'; for him, thinking signified the process accompanied by images which were conscious and were not necessarily tied (or directly tied) to perception. We shall regard thinking as the capacity to be cognisant of both the absent and the present.

Thinking is closely related not only to learning, but also to problem solving. Problem solving is very much a part of learning, and also occurs with thinking. To this extent a whole mass of experiments comes within the scope of our subject, from classical conditioning[21] to instrumental conditioning[22] and Ruger's puzzles,[23] wherein the human subject has to disentangle bits of wire that are intertwined. Any scientist, mathematician or logician, in solving a problem, is trying to gather together evidence to provide a solution; and the gathering of the relevant evidence is very close to what we normally refer to as 'thinking'.

This distinction between thinking and problem solving is an important one; but on the other hand, the two processes share many similarities, and there are other points of view on the relationship between thinking and problem solving.

For example, there is the dual-process point of view as expounded by Wertheimer and Kohler, where there is an emphasis on 'seeing through the problem'; this really refers to the fact that 'insight' is taking place, but leaves us to explain what we mean by insight. There is indeed some obvious relevance in 'restructuring' a problem or becoming aware of new relationships. Bruner, Goodnow and Austin[26] have carried out a number of experiments on thinking in which they regard thinking as categorising behaviour. Categorisation, as they point out, has certain special advantages:

It reduces the complexity of the environment.
It is a means of identification.
It reduces the need for learning.
It is a means for providing action.
It permits the ordering and relating of classes of events.

All features of thinking are important and a series of experiments carried out by Bruner, Goodnow and Austin revealed what they termed 'strategies in concept attainment'. Their description is very similar to what we and Shaw, Simon and Newell[27] have called 'heuristics'.

The basis of the Bruner, Goodnow and Austin distinctions is between conception and perception; in spite of this distinction, these are usually recognised as being closely allied. The fact is, we usually invent categories and do not discover them, hence we encounter this difficulty between similarities and differences. This draws attention to the conventional nature of labelling or naming, even though labels may have long standing traditional backgrounds. Finally, concept attainment is not quite the same as concept formation, in that it is capable of being predicated of the absent as well as the present. Clearly, concepts are generalisations in some sense and are tested by virtue of their attributes—properties such as colour, weight, etc. The attainment of a concept depends on distinctions or discrimination—elephants are distinguished from tigers—and there is a validatory process, which is normally 'either-or', i.e. an item is either A or not A. In fact, of course, if the either-or distinction is not made, the categories make up a continuum.

A strategy is the set of decisions that leads to concept attainment, and can be thought of, in game-theoretic terms, as decisions governing a pay-off matrix. Various strategies are discussed by Bruner, Goodnow and Austin[26] and are called 'conservative focusing', 'focus gambling', 'successive scanning' and so on. For example, it is possible to find a satisfactory goal route through a maze by a trial-and-error method. Alternatively, one may do so by noticing only positive or successful results, by using negative instances of results, by formulating concepts or hypotheses that allow testing, and which involve either more or less risk. It is clear that one may in most test situations adopt a safe and slow or fast and risky technique and, indeed, there will generally be many other alternatives in between these limiting cases.

A concept is defined here as a network of sign-signific inferences by which one goes beyond a set of observed criterial properties exhibited by an object or event, to the class identify of the object or even in question; and thence to inferences about other unobserved properties of the object or event.

In contrast with this approach to concept formation, we have Bartlett's[28] definition of thinking based essentially on the same type of experimental problem solving situation:

'thinking is the extension of evidence in accord with that evidence, and this is done by moving through a succession of interconnected steps which may be stated at the time, or left until later to be stated'.

This definition, although perhaps unusually worded and perhaps also concerned with a limited aspect of thinking, could be easily interpreted to fit the concept formation activity described by Bruner *et al*. It is, we shall argue, a statement of induction, in that given some of the terms in, say, a mathematical series, one may propose a general rule for the generation of the series. This may, of course, involve decisions as to the base, and will be subject to validation by test.

In fact, we are assuming, following the above two views, that thinking is much the same as formulating inductive principles, which necessarily involves symbolisation. This does not mean that purely deductive inferences are irrelevant, but it may be assumed that the analogue of this operation in automata is relatively trivial. The main point is that the operation of categorising is itself what we shall call an inductive operation. Körner[29] has argued that conceptual thinking is typified, although not exhaustively illustrated, by the application and acceptance of ostensive rules. An ostensive rule is typified by a pointing operation accompanied by such a statement as 'this and this and everything like this is green.' This requires that bases for concepts are defined, and they may be defined in many ways, rather as co-ordinates can be chosen in many different ways to define a space.

The interesting problem that arises from Körner's work is that of the derivation of non-ostensive concepts and rules from either ostensive or non-ostensive bases. This represents another challenge: how can—if at all—a computer program be written so as to perform these sorts of operation? (It should be noted that this *may* involve no more than the ability to generalise, although this is a vital step and not easy to simulate over the same range as humans operate.)

Harlow[30] has discussed the relation of thinking to learning and perception and suggests that the sort of problem solving activity subsumed under the name 'thinking' is depicted in the following four steps:

1. Perception of a situation with incentive or goal inaccessible immediately, leading to

2. Elicitation of initial alternative responses, explicit or implicit, and ranging from unlearned responses to a limited number of highly organised response tendencies, these in turn leading either to

3. Problem solution (goal attainment) or failure (withdrawal).

4. Additional reaction tendencies, which again lead either to problem solution, withdrawal, or to the arousal of additional reaction tendencies. This approach, apparently ignoring symbolisation, seems useful in describing animal activities rather than human.

One last point should be mentioned in our brief survey on thinking. Price[20] noted that human beings do not always have their thinking operations tied closely to their perceptions. This is a possible objection to Harlow's argument above; the first stage may be a function of the input system but may not be tied directly to it; indeed, once the conceptual process has started, one state may presumably lead to another state without further perceptual steps being involved. This means that a man may sit in silence with his eyes closed and simply 'think' of one thing after another; he will ultimately reach a stage of thinking about something that is quite remote from his immediate surroundings at that moment.

Many of the people who have addressed themselves to this problem of thinking, like Körner, Price, Ryle and Wittgenstein, have not been concerned with the empirical facts as such, but with supplying a logical foundation for the development of propositions, and indeed for language in general. At the same time, those more connected with the empirical facts, such as Bartlett, Harlow, Hunt, Hovland and many others, have accepted that language plays a vital part in actual human thought.

In what way has our survey helped our own search? The answer is straightforward enough. Different people have studied thinking (and problem solving) for different reasons. Much of the work of philosophers has been one stage removed from that of a rigorous simulation of cognitive activity. Psychologists, who have been more nearly concerned with our problem, have not attempted a rigorous treatment. They do, however, supply empirical evidence which we can use as a basis for a working model, and help fit empirical data into that model.

Returning to our search for appropriate models, the first step is to look at some forms of sequential analysis. Sequential analysis is like the simulation of events with a view to formulating an algorithm or a heuristic; this is closely connected with the deductive and inductive processes, and almost everyone agrees that these processes are the core of thinking and problem solving.

SEQUENTIAL ANALYSIS

The kind of induction concerned with sequential analysis has, on the whole, received less emphasis than that concerned with atemporal induction. Some of the principles involved are relatively more simple; the easiest is perhaps that of conditional probabilities which refer to the sequence of events a, b, c, $\ldots$, n coupled to some *measure* of their frequency of occurrence:

$$\begin{aligned}
p(a/b) &= m_1/n_1 \\
p(a/bc) &= m_2/n_2 \\
p/(ab/c) &= m_3/n_3 \\
p(a/bcd) &= m_4/n_4
\end{aligned}$$

By taking longer and longer sequences (samples) we can, by use of the measure of conditional probabilities, refer predictively to events of greater and greater length. This is one method of discovering sequential patterns, and can be simulated on the computer by a naming and counting operation. By such means we arrive at new concepts derived from old, and empirical statements and hypotheses derived from concepts. Here, we should note that the processes or sets of events are to be thought identical *whether or not they are symbolised*. When symbolised, however, some details are omitted from the symbolisation (description) and thus in general a problem handled purely in symbolic terms is less complete than one handled directly (by acquaintance) in terms of direct, non-verbal, stimuli.

At this stage, we must ask ourselves whether or not all problems are tractable in terms of our suggested methods. The answer is uncertain, but for human beings most problems come within the logical (inductive-deductive) and linguistic complex, and in principle, we can see how these could be handled in a computer program.

Newell, Shaw and Simon[18] made a detailed study of what they called *creative thinking*; this dealt with those aspects of problem solving which required originality as opposed to explanation, definition, remembering, etc., all of which may come into the problem solver's day to day activities.

The work of Newell, Shaw and Simon has great importance because they were able to show by heuristic programming techniques how short cuts could be achieved in routes to goals (solution) by making assumptions that facilitated the problem solving process. The manner of approach is simple in principle and may be illustrated as follows. If you are an architect and asked to design a building and the building is intended for use as offices, then you can omit consideration of previous designs for private houses, garages, etc. When, however, you are performing the task algorithmically, you might try out every possible building type,, however irrelevant.

Newell, Shaw and Simon also refer to stages in problem solving involving incubation, illumination, etc., and these can all be simulated in some measure on the computer.

The same authors used *solution generators*, trial-and-error learning and then hypotheses, often involving working backwards from the solution (deducing sub-goals from goals) where the problem was to find a proof. They used *verifying processes* to justify their steps, and in this they made a distinction that parallels Reichenbach's[31] distinction between the context of discovery and the context of justification. Our own research differs from that of Newell, Shaw and Simon in its use of heuristics. Whereas they were concerned with simulating principles for theorem proving, and used human means of theorem proving, such as substitution, etc., we are more concerned with the delineation (through language) of a problem for which appropriate heuristics have to be sought (hypothesis formation by induction) and/or adapted to the needs of the situation.

Heuristics, as generalised rules of thumb or hypotheses, can be used in various ways. Newell, Shaw and Simon simulated the operations of the human problem solver, but Samuel[32] synthesised his heuristics by a set of polynomials from which appropriate heuristics were selected. Tonge[33] used heuristics to solve aspects of the line balancing problem, and the adaptivity of the heuristics was essentially pre-planned; a somewhat similar procedure was followed by Burstall.[34]

In addition to these uses, we would like to see heuristics employed in combination; heuristic generation occurring where no existing heuristic was appropriate.

From the computer viewpoint, heuristics are like sub-routines in a computer program, and they can be edited or strung together to form new heuristics, or plans; care must be taken, however, to distinguish adaptive from non-adaptive heuristics. This reflects a distinction similar to that between 'taking a set of hypotheses' as opposed to 'testing' and, if necessary, modifying those hypotheses as a result of circumstances, or even setting out 'new' hypotheses. This ability to adapt heuristics implies the ability to construct new (flexible) plans which in turn implies the ability to set up and reorganise sub-routines in computer programs.

It is in these terms that we ourselves see problem solving as a synthetic undertaking. Problem solving is the ability to construct or reconstruct sub-routines to solve problems, and to learn new sub-routines by experience, as circumstances demand, especially through verbal description. This synthetic approach would be of limited value were it not regarded as experimental; the whole purpose is to actually write and run such computer programs to discover the extent to which the programs do in fact synthesise, perhaps even simulate, the conditions in which we are interested.

It should perhaps be said that computers are universal machines, and they are the *only* machines capable of being constructed (programmed) to synthesise or simulate any system anywhere near as complicated as that involved in human problem solving. The possible use of computers in this context has hardly yet been touched upon, but we shall not discuss here their value relative to the alternatives such as comparative psychology or ethology; there is, though, an obvious and close parallel.

Finally, we will say a few words about the gulf which exists between a synthetic program and simulation program as a result of human emotions. We shall not discuss here the status of human emotions in detail, it will suffice to say that emotions are a biological necessity since they act as an alarm system. Without such an alarm system—essentially physiological in its origins and its effects—the human being, or any other animal, could hardly have survived. The fact that emotions lead to modified states of consciousness and to the exhibition of external signals is essentially incidental to, or a by-product of, their origin.

An important question to consider is whether the emotions can be simulated on the computer. The 'best' answer lies doubtless in chemical or colloidal chemical models, or computers. The nearest approach, by simulation, must lie in the weighting for emotional, and other purposes of rational processing. We can construct 'values' which we associate with different elements, then construct rules of associations and hence, manufacture a superstructure of values which help to determine the progress of the internal processing of the external environment.

In terms of computing, we have added a further dimension to our problem with the inclusion of emotions. The emotions allow associative, and sometimes irrational, weighting of events which means that a purely logical sorting is not wholly possible. The value of such weighting lies in the fact of being 'doubly careful' about events that threaten survival; such a step is partially simulated by the stage of Risk Analysis (a probabilistic weighting of the probable outcome of actions) which must always precede the final step of implementation of decisions based on computer processing.

All of what we have said suggests that we can string together sets of operations (computer procedures or sub-routines) which represent each step of the total decision making process; the 'mix', though, must be flexible. We need a system and indeed we can see, in principle, how a system can be constructed so that each and every problem (decision or plan) is dealt with on either a trial-and-error basis or on a hypothetical basis. If successful, this leads to the achievement of a goal, or sub-goals that lead to the goal.

The setting up of the generalised information (hypotheses or heuristics) that leads to the goals or sub-goals, is a problem that demands a process of recognition. Not only must patterns be recognised, but previously experienced patterns must be distinguished from 'new' patterns, and this leads to an association between the two; the general principle is easy enough; 'look for similarities among differences, and differences among similarities'.

CONCLUSION

We have covered a great deal of ground and have done it rather unevenly; but in this final section it is hoped to bring together the various features of our model.

First let us remind ourselves of the properties we know we can simulate: inference making and language. We can assume a sorting or classifying input (recognition); a process of weighted output (risk analysis); and we can assume also that thinking is a complex of inference making and symbolising; it is a partially conscious process, which enables a problem to be solved symbolically.

We should note that inference making is a very complex process, involving formal logic.[35] It is also very much a part of empirical logic (inference making within the context of factual axiomatic systems) and includes 'gestural' communication and an understanding of 'pictorial' relationships. In the light of this general comment, let us look briefly at the arbitrary assortment of problems we set out earliner.

The first one was 'How do we get from Bristol to Stratford-upon-Avon in the least time, on a Thursday afternoon?' This sort of question implies that problem solving can be thought of as a practical day-to-day activity, and methods which *optimise* over the data can supply a ready solution. The answer here though, is in general terms that this problem requires an empirical investigation. For example, questions need to be answered such as, 'What is the distribution of cars on the various possible routes from Bristol to Stratford-upon-Avon?' Through these optimisation techniques, an answer (probabilistic though it may be) can be derived; this sort of problem is reminiscent of Operational Research.

Our second question how to explain compiler languages, is clearly one of *explanation*. Our explanation must be couched in terms that are understandable to the computer, if it is a computer we are concerned with. Explanations are descriptions, although they may not refer to the present alone, and they may be general or particular.

The third question about breaking combination locks draws attention to the need for heuristics (hypotheses or rules of thumb). We have not got the Time to use an algorithm, so some sort of 'guesswork' or assumption is needed; then it is tested and is accepted or rejected.

Finally, algebraic equations and their solution demand both description and exemplification.

In coming to the end of this chapter, the author is conscious that he has covered just a few of the general features of certain aspects of problem solving. The hope is that some of these ideas will lead other people in the field to write computer programs to simulate other aspects of cognition. In the end, we shall gradually build up a more complete picture of the total, highly complicated process, which involves at least adaptation, learning, ability to generalise and thus effectively communicate both particularities and generalities. This implies the generation of heuristics, starting sometimes on a trial-and-error basis; the testing of the heuristic is to find whether it is adaptive, and if so, whether it can be optimised or at least improved upon. This is the central problem of cognition, and although inherently complex, one which, by the methods outlined in this article, we have gone some way towards solving.

REFERENCES

1. ASHBY, W. R., *Design for a Brain*, Chapman and Hall, London (1952).
2. WALTER, W. G., *The Living Brain*, Duckworth, London (1953).
3. HAYEK, S. A., *The Sensory Order*, University of Chicago (1952).
4. UTTLEY, A. M., 'The Classification of Signals in the Nervous System,' *Electroenceph. Clin. Neurophysiol.*, **6**, 479 (1954).

5. ROSENBLATT, F. H., *Principles of Neurodynamics*, Spartan Books, Washington (1962).
6. UTTLEY, A. M., 'The Conditional Probability of Signals in the Nervous System,' *R.R.E. Memo* No. 1109 (1955).
7. GEORGE, F. H., *Cybernetics and Biology*, Oliver and Boyd, Edinburgh (1965).
8. SUTHERLAND, N. S., 'Stimulus Analysing Mechanisms,' in *Mechanisation of Thought Processes*, N.P.L. Symposium (1959).
9. HEBB, D. O., *The Organisation of Behavior*, John Wiley, New York (1949).
10. THORNDIKE, E. L., *Animal Intelligence*, Macmillan, New York (1911).
11. KÖRNER, S., 'Ostensive Predicates,' *Mind*, **9**, 60, 80 (1951).
12. BANERJI, R. B., 'Computer Programs for the Generation of New Concepts from Old Ones,' in *Neure Ergebnisse der Kybernetic*, Eds. Steinbuch, K., Wagner, S. W., Oldenbourgh, Wien (1964).
13. GEORGE, F. H., 'Concept Formation on a Digital Computer,' paper given at the *Bionics Conference*, Dayton, Ohio (1966).
14. GEORGE, F. H., *Models of Thinking*, Allen and Unwin, London (to be published).
15. HUNT, E. B. and HOVLAND, C. I., 'Programming a Model of Human Concept Formulation,' in *Computer and Thought*, Eds. Feigenbaum, E. A., Feldman, J., McGraw-Hill, London (1963).
16. HILGARD, E. R., *Theories of Learning*, Methuen, London (1958).
17. HUNT, E. B., *Concept Learning: An Information Processing Problem*, John Wiley, New York (1962).
18. NEWELL, A., SHAW, J. C. and SIMON, H. A., 'The Processes of Creative Thinking,' *Rand Memo.*, P—1320 (1958).
19. CARNAP, R., 'Testability and Meaning,' *Phil. Sci.*, **3**, 419; **4**, 1 (1937).
20. PRICE, H. H., *Thinking and Experience*, Hutchinson, London (1953).
21. PAVLOV, I. P., *Conditional Reflexes*, Oxford University Press (1927).
22. HILGARD, E. R. and MARQUIS, D. G., *Conditioning and Learning*, Appleton-Century-Crofts, New York (1940).
23. RUGER, H. A., 'The Psychology of Efficiency: an Experimental Study of the Process Involved in the Solution of Mechanical Puzzles and in the Acquisition of Skill in their Manipulation,' *Amer. Psychol.*, **2**, 15 (1910).
24. WERTHEIMER, M., *Productive Thinking*, Harper Bros (1945).
25. KÖHLER, W., *The Mentality of Apes*, Kegan Paul, London (1925).
26. BRUNER, J. S., GOODNOW, J. J. and AUSTIN, G. A., *A Study of Thinking*, John Wiley, New York (1956).
27. NEWELL, A., SHAW, J. C. and SIMON, H. A., 'Empirical Explorations with the Logic Theory Machine; a Case Study in Heuristics,' in *Computers and Thought*, Eds. Feigenbaum, E. A., Feldman, J., McGraw-Hill, London (1963).
28. BARTLETT, F. C., *Thinking*, Allen and Unwin, London (1958).
29. KÖRNER, S., *Conceptual Thinking*, Dover Publications, New York (1959).
30. HARLOW, H. F., 'Thinking,' in *Theoretical Foundations of Psychology*, Ed. Helson, H., Van Nostrand, London (1951).
31. REICHENBACH, H., *Experience and Prediction*, University of Chicago Press (1938).
32. SAMUEL, A. L., 'Some Studies in Machine Learning using the Game of Checkers,' in *Computers and Thought*, Eds. Feigenbaum, E. A., Feldman, J., McGraw-Hill, London (1963).
33. TONGE, F. M., 'Summary of a Heuristic Line Balancing Procedure,' in *Computers and Thought*, Eds. Feigenbaum, E. A., Feldman, J., McGraw-Hill, London (1963).
34. BURSTALL, R. M., 'Computer Design of Electricity and Supply Networks by a Heuristic Method,' *Computer J.*, **9**, 3,263 (1966).
35. GEORGE, F. H., 'Inference Making on a Computer,' *E.S.D.Memo.* No. 14 (1967).

Chapter 6

Neurocybernetics (Communication and Control in the Living Brain)

W. Grey Walter, M.A., Sc.D. (Cantab.)
Director, Burden Neurological Institute, Bristol (U.K.)

SUMMARY

Having discussed the relationship between Wiener's work and his own, the author makes a critical study of the difference between cybernetics in theory and in practice. Misconceptions surrounding cybernetics are considered. The brain alpha rhythms and the processes of scanning and two-dimensional gating are then discussed in detail. The contingent coherent after-rhythm (COCAR) and the contingent negative variation (CNV) are described, as relating to brain activity. Finally, the author reviews the properties of the living brain, with particular emphasis on the thinking process, structural redundancy, memory and learning in the context of the role of cybernetics.

INTRODUCTION

My first meeting with Norbert Wiener was at the M.I.T. in 1946, when a frequency analyser of my design was being installed for Dr. Robert Schwab, of the Massachusetts General Hospital in Boston. This instrument was the commercial embodiment of a machine I had made during the war to quantify the spectrum of the complex intrinsic brain rhythms. By the standards of those days it was very elaborate and expensive, and the problems it was intended to clarify were poorly defined and quite intractable by visual analysis of the conventional records. The interest of this particular meeting was that I had, empirically and intuitively, hit on an electromechanical method of frequency analysis which generated a rough approximation to a Fourier Transform; and the parameters and characteristics coincided almost exactly with those recommended by Wiener on purely theoretical grounds. I was quite put out to hear Wiener holding forth about the theory and principles of frequency analysis applied to brain waves as if this were a novel and difficult concept, when my machine was ticking away almost next door, reeling off brain wave spectra automatically, every ten seconds, hour after hour. Wiener was more than a little affronted, too, because he had not been told what we were doing and when I gave my account of the empirical features, describing the design of the filters, the choice of a ten second epoch and the discoveries we had already made, he fell asleep at once—his habitual defence against competition. It was some time before we appreciated one another, but in later years we spent many happy and exciting days in one another's homes and at international meetings. I took several records of his own brain rhythms which proved, amongst other things, that his defensive naps were real deep sleep; he could drop off in a few seconds, but would awaken instantly if one spoke his name or mentioned any topic in which he was really interested.

For many years, Wiener's thinking and my experimentation kept converging and overlapping, almost without any direct collusion or collaboration. His notion of scansion by the alpha rhythms matured at almost exactly the same time as we had observed some sort of space-time transformation in analyses of real brain rhythms. Oddly enough, the artificial animals that I built at this time incorporated an elementary scanning receptor, while his model did not. My 'tortoises' are not confused by the dilemma of Buridan's donkey, while his 'moth' would trundle confidently midway between two targets, missing both. Wiener refers to some of the differences between the two models in both *The Human Use of Human Beings*[1] and in the second volume of his autobiography,[2] but without apparently appreciating the significance of space-time transforms as a possible resolution of the 'determinism free will' dilemma. This oversight seems all the more remarkable because of his intense interest in the reduction of philosophic verbalisms to operational hypotheses. Similar considerations apply to paradoxes such as those of Cantor and Russell which, as Wiener realised, can be resolved by attaching a time parameter to each statement. The automatic establishment of primacy confers special properties on a system which cannot be ignored in studies of the brain and organic behaviour; and the importance of temporal order in machine programming or process control cannot be exaggerated. Wiener's attitude to biological, social and political questions was radical and mechanistic, although not merely materialistic, yet in some of his theoretical propositions and conjectures he seemed deaf to practical observations and necessities.

CYBERNETICS IN THEORY AND PRACTICE

This peculiar gap between theory and practice is a feature of cybernetics, and may account for the disrepute which has accumulated around the term. So often has a cybernetic analysis merely confirmed or described a familiar phenomenon in biology or engineering—so rarely has a cybernetic theorem predicted a novel effect or explained a mysterious one. Physiologists are perhaps particularly sensitive to overstatement of claims by cyberneticians, since they were thinking in terms of 'feedback', that is reflexive action, long before mathematicians or engineers began to draw recurrent arrows around their black boxes. The term reflex is usually associated with Sherrington in the West, but it was in Russia that some of the most advanced ideas developed following the publication in

1863 of I. M. Sechenov's revolutionary monograph *Reflexes of the Brain*.[3] The observations and conjectures in this book are still providing a challenge to experiment, although most of them have been confirmed with techniques far more refined than those contemplated by Sechenov. Instrumentation owes a great deal to modern concepts of electronics and computation, but the theoretical approach is only beginning to develop from the state in which Sechenov classified reflexes as 'pure, passionate or psychic.'

Another criticism of cybernetics (which is both implicit in the classical study of behaviour and explicit in the rejection of naive animal-machine comparison) is that living systems exhibit some degree of 'spontaneous' or intrinsic activity. In the behaviour of whole animals, exploration is a common feature designated by I. P. Pavlov the 'Go and find out' or the 'What is it?' reflex. In the electrical activity of the brain, the most surprising and impressive characteristic is the abundance of persistent rhythms and discharges; these have preoccupied electro-encephalographers since their discovery by Berger in the mid-twenties. Sechenov —60 years earlier— supposed that the tonic activity of the higher centres was maintained by the incessant impact of signals from the environment. It was indeed puzzling to find that, on the contrary, the 'spontaneous' electrical activity seemed to be literally 'spontaneous'; the less the sensory inflow, the larger and more regular were the electrical rhythms. Wiener was well aware of this apparent paradox and devoted special attention to it in his later works.[4] These chapters provide an admirable example of the peculiar combination of ingenuity and ingenuousness in Wiener's mentality. He speaks confidently of the 'brain wave' (which he had often been told was a variable compound of many ingredients) and provides a figure of the 'spectrum of the brain wave' which is a gross parody of the crudest approximation to this function. He then proceeds to a detailed exposition of the results of fine structure analysis of this imaginary spectrum, with particular attention to the presence of a 'very narrow line' at 10 Hz which 'arises from a dip.' He compares this effect to the interaction of multiple a.c. generators on a loaded power line producing a frequency which fluctuates narrowly around a mean value, and asserts that the 'brain wave' is regulated in the same way and that this type of regulation would generate the specified spectrum with a central line in a dip in the continuous spectrum.

In support of this assertion, Wiener quotes various experiments in which the 'brain wave' can be driven by a flickering light (which is partly true) and by electrostatic induction from a 400 V 10 Hz generator. This latter procedure, he says, 'can actually drive the brain, causing a decidedly unpleasant sensation.' There is no reference to the source of this statement, and it is obvious that even if the experiment were performed, the electrostatic induction on the recording electrodes would be far greater than the potential of any brain wave that might be 'driven.' In effect, we are left with the impression that the explanation of an imaginary spectrum is supported by an imaginary experiment.

BRAIN ALPHA RHYTHMS

What, then, are we to make of the mathematical analysis in which these assertions are embedded? There is no doubt that the expressions Wiener derived would provide a spectrum of the form suggested, but the 'brain wave' does not in fact yield a line spectrum, although in some people the alpha band is quite narrow (± 0.1 Hz) and constant within this range over long periods. In other people, however, the frequency range is wide, with several distinct components within the alpha band, while in others again, there may be no alpha rhythms at all. The first serious discrepancy between physiologic fact and mathematical fiction, therefore, is *individual differences*. The relation of the central component to the 'dip' is even less satisfactory. The amplitudes of the brain rhythms vary constantly and even in those people who show a single constant component, amplitude modulation is a marked feature even when conditions are apparently unvarying. As is well known, amplitude modulation has the effect on a frequency spectrum of generating sidebands; this gives an appearance very similar to the humps and dip analysed by Wiener. This is certainly a necessary part of the explanation (since amplitude modulation is always present) and as far as can be ascertained, it is a sufficient one, since the amplitude and separation of the sidebands fluctuate rationally with the amplitude and mean frequency of the modulation.

This discrepancy between Wiener's interpretation and the observed relations seems unlikely to have arisen by chance. All the known facts about brain rhythms were accessible to Wiener either directly or through his colleagues, yet he selected certain features rather than others and from them derived an improbable and misleading solution. The feature which Wiener selected (because it impressed him as an unexpected property of a very complex system—the brain) was the degree of stability of some brain rhythms in some people; being a mathematician and not a biologist, he took this to be typical of the 'brain wave.' The relevant chapter of the second edition of *Cybernetics*[5] is entitled 'Brain waves and self-organising systems,' and he decides:

'We thus see that a non-linear interaction causing the attraction of frequency can generate a self-organising system, as it does, for example, in the case of the brain waves...... and in the case of the a.c. network.'

As further illustrations of this effect he quotes examples from virus molecules to fireflies, in which the tendency to non-linear interaction may account for the development of macro-systems of a higher order of stability than that of the individual elements.

One of the most serious mistakes that can be made in scientific controversy is implicit denial by assertion. In electrobiology, the classic case was the denial by Volta of Galvani's 'animal electricity' and by Galvani of Volta's 'metallic currents.' We know that both were right in their assertions and wrong in their denials; neither was able to perform the crucial experiments which would have reconciled their views. Yet from their experiments arose both electricity and magnetism on the one hand, and electrophysiology on the other. So it would be dangerous to deny all truth to Wiener's speculations. It seems unlikely that a well informed intelligence of the highest order would spend so much time fishing for red herrings, although Wiener could have been entangled in the elegance of his mathematical network. Is there some clue in his thinking that could indicate the true scent of his quarry? The answer may be in the relatively brief references (for example, in the chapter in *Cybernetics* mentioned above)[5] to the possible functions of the central alpha rhythm. The possibility of scansion has already been mentioned; scansion is a process of systematic two dimensional 'gating'. Rather surprisingly, in his last essay, Wiener refers to the alpha rhythm merely as a gating process; his more elaborate conception of a central scanning process antedates this and is far more interesting. In the same context he refers again

—also briefly—to the effect on the central frequencies of rhythmic stimuli at about alpha frequency. Here one cannot avoid an exclamation of deep regret that Wiener did not appreciate the true facts as they were at that time, and, still more, that we were denied the advantage of his analysis of the discoveries which were made shortly after his death.

The interaction between the intrinsic rhythms and incoming signals is even more intricate and suggestive than Wiener supposed. Some of the most illuminating developments have been promoted by the use of sinusoidally modulated light as a visual stimulus, suggested by De Lange in 1957[6] and adapted to the study of brain responses by van der Tweel[7] and Spekreijse.[8] These studies show that the interaction between sensory responses and the intrinsic activity of the brain depend on at least four systems. One of the most elegant demonstrations, which would have delighted Wiener, is linearisation of the non-linear features of the visual afferent system by the addition of irregular variations in light level, that is 'linearisation by noise.' (A paper by Wiener in 1942[9] was entitled 'Response of a non-linear device to noise'.) These experiments also showed the build-up and decay of brain responses to sine-modulated light typical of a resonant system, but again, this occurred only in certain subjects and in certain brain areas. In some people the apparent selectivity or Q-factor was as high as 15 at 10 Hz (that is, the rhythm took about 5 waves to fall to 37% of its original amplitude when the stimulus ceased). In other people the build-up and decay indicated no resonant features. The only phenomenon seen in nearly all people in these conditions was the appearance of responses at the second harmonic frequency, particularly with stimulation at lower frequencies. This indicates the intervention of a non-linear component in the eye-brain transmission line, and the analysis of its properties suggests a resemblance to an asymmetric full wave linear rectifier. Moreover, this element seems to be located at a relay station before the two eye fields are superimposed and is preceded in effect by a band-pass filter.

This analysis, elegant and conclusive though it is, lacks an essential feature of cybernetic discipline; the statement of a functional goal. This illustrates another aspect of cybernetics that often irritates conservative scientists—the implication of teleology. After all, the term means 'steersmanship' and a steersman must at least have a course to steer and preferably a destination. However exasperating, a cybernetic approach enforces consideration of the *purpose* of the system under study or design. In the case of the interaction between intrinsic rhythms and sensory responses in the brain, what are the likely functions of the elaborate filtering mechanisms identified by such analyses as those described above? This simple question can be answered only by considering the specific functions of the eye and brain as a visual recognition system. Thus, the cybernetician by asking 'What is it for?', forces the experimentalist to decide 'What does it actually do?'

Obviously, the answer to this question cannot be found in the experimental situation described above; the eye and brain are not generally required to detect the depth of modulation of a light source of constant mean brilliance. Even in much simpler animals the resolution of the visual system provides for specific responses to colour, distance, lines, edges, movement and most of the features of everyday patterns; in the human system, our subjective appreciation of intricate and rapidly changing patterns implies a delicate control of binocular eye position and movement, as well as an elaborate central timing process. It is in the latter connection that a cybernetic analysis would be most fruitful;

Wiener himself compared the problem with the difficulty of arranging an orderly flow of components in an automatic factory so that each element of the final product is delivered to the assembly at the right phase of production. This analogy is not particularly appropriate to the perceptual problem, since the essence of perception is novelty rather than repetitive assembly; a more helpful comparison is with the traffic control systems in a large city. The particular system that seems to have some of the properties of the sensory mechanisms of the brain is that common in Britain: sets of lights with a fixed stop-go cycle period but actuated also by approaching vehicles. When there is no traffic the lights operate rhythmically at the predetermined period and an observer would see regular twinkling of red and green signals. If the controls are synchronised along main thoroughfares, red and green waves would appear to pass along them at the expected speed of the imaginary traffic. When a vehicle enters the region under survey it will actuate the signal system and set the lights to green and this process will be repeated at each intersection, thus disrupting the regular stop-go rhythm along its path. When a number of vehicles interact with the system, the alternation of stop and go will become quite irregular over the whole area since the cycle period will rarely be completed before vehicle actuation occurs. In the imit, however, when all the pathways are full, the system must revert to the fixed cycle period since there is an equal probability of actuation in all directions.

These situations are in some ways comparable to the changes in appearance of the brain alpha rhythms in some people, first with the eyes shut, then with the eyes open viewing a patterned field, and then viewing an evenly illuminated but featureless field. In the first case the alpha rhythm tends to oscillate regularly at about 10 Hz, in the second the rhythm is disrupted, with occasional local transients, while in the third, the rhythm returns again as if the eyes were closed. The practical advantages of this system in the case of road traffic are obvious—in all situations every vehicle is given the best chance of finding a free path. When there is little traffic, solitary vehicles are not obstructed by arbitrary delays; yet when the system is congested, all vehicles have equal opportunities for movement whatever their provenance and destination.

This system of two dimensional gating is analogous to a process of scanning, but with the addition of a mechanism whereby an event can open a gate, and thus initiate the scanning process which wafts it on its way. In the familiar television scanner this would be seen as a serious fault, colloquially described as 'pulling on whites' due to the line ramp-generator being triggered by a 'bright' event in the video signal at the edge of the raster. A television receiver is required merely to display and not to 'perceive', but if in a particular application the occurrence of 'bright' events were of special importance, this interaction between afferent signals and intrinsic rhythms could be exploited to indicate when such a situation arose.

There seems a real possibility that the complex and consistent patterns of interaction between sensory signals and intrinsic rhythms in the brain may subserve this function of routing and timing information vehicles within the intricate network of cortical elements.

It is difficult to test this hypothesis directly with conventional techniques because the version of cortical activity seen on the scalp of normal subjects is an average compound over a large area—as though in our analogy, the traffic lights were seen from a great height through a London fog. However, the introduction during the last 10 years of surgical techniques for implanting in the human brain multiple small electrodes which can be left in place for several months has provided a means of penetrating this obscurity. Records can be obtained of the local rhythms arising in primary sensory cortex and the adjacent secondary and tertiary association areas; with suitable computation, the frequency, spatial distribution and relation to incoming signals can be ascertained with adequate precision.

COCAR—CONTINGENT COHERENT AFTER-RHYTHM

The most important general truth—which was suspected from superficial records—is that the alpha rhythms are multiple, and each rhythm is characteristic of a particular domain. Wiener postulated a multiplicity of alpha generators but supposed these to be close in frequency and liable to pull one another into phase by non-linear interaction. In fact, the various rhythms within the brain are very much less interactive than we had expected and, furthermore, their relations to sensory events are also more individual. Within a cortical volume of less than a cubic centimetre, some rhythms may be quite unaffected by a particular stimulus, others may be abruptly arrested by it, others again 'driven' by a rhythmic stimulus over a narrow frequency range, then blocked by it while an adjacent region picks up the changed rhythm. The impression is more that of a symphony orchestra than an assembly of a.c. generators—but where is the conductor and what tune are they all playing? One thing seems to be clear—no single analogy or simile or metaphor is adequate to describe these effects. Some of the regions in sensory cortex behave very like the traffic lights in the analogy, maintaining a steady period at rest, responding quickly to the arrival of a vehicle and resuming their intrinsic rhythms at saturation. Others seem almost indifferent to stimuli. In some regions (again in some people) a peculiar effect is seen when paired stimuli are received at critical intervals or when a single stimulus is assigned an arbitrary importance for the subject by association with a decision or action. This is a *coherent* after-rhythm, usually but not always at one of the alpha frequencies, starting a fraction of a second after the first response to the stimulus and lasting sometimes for 10 or 20 waves. This effect (which can sometimes be seen in scalp records) has been called 'ringing;' it is as though in these particular conditions the stimulus conjunction had rung the bell.

Because its appearance is contingent on some association of stimuli or stimulus and response, and because its coherence from trial to trial is so much greater than that of the free-running rhythms, this effect may be described as a Contingent Coherent After-Rhythm or COCAR. The relation of the COCAR to visual stimuli is almost absolute. Neither auditory nor tactile stimuli have been found to evoke a COCAR even when they are repeated or associated in precisely the same way as effective visual stimuli, or are associated with a subsequent visual stimulus. By appropriate manipulation of stimulus association it can be demonstrated in some people that appearance of a sustained COCAR depends on the probability of a visual signal being followed within one or two seconds by another event in which the person is in some way engaged. When this probability is diluted by interspersing meaningless visual signals among the significant ones the COCAR subsides, as though equivocation had muffled the bell.

CNV—CONTINGENT NEGATIVE VARIATION

The same considerations apply to the effect called the Contingent Negative Variation (CNV), (Fig. 6.1) a sustained rise in potential of the frontal cortex in the period between a conditional and an imperative stimulus.[10] The CNV is sometimes referred to as the 'expectancy wave'; it is not related to any specific

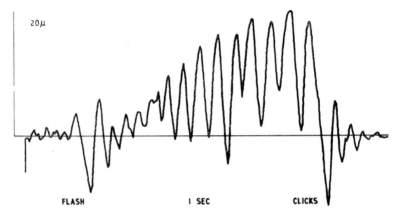

Fig. 6.1. Contingent negative variation. The development of a coherent after-rhythm or 'ringing' in the anterior brain regions of a normal subject following a conditional visual stimulus. The subject had been asked to press a button to stop the clicks which followed one second after the flash. The coherent rhythm is superimposed on a slow rise in potential

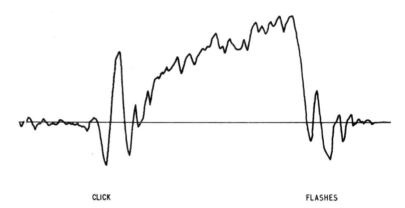

Fig. 6.2. Contingent coherent after-rhythm. This is the same subject in Fig. 6.1, but with inversion of stimulus order. The auditory conditional stimulus is followed by a slow rise of potential which terminates at the moment of decision when the visual stimulus appears, but there is no coherent rhythm. The total amount of rhythmic activity was the same in both conditions, but only the visual stimulus initiated coherence

modality of sensation or to intensity, only to the probability of association and subjective engagement. In the same terms the COCAR may be a sign of specifically visual expectancy—not expectancy that a visual event will occur, but expectancy that a visual event will have a significant sequel. Comparing the development and abrupt decline of a CNV with the simultaneous swell and subsidence of a COCAR, (see Fig. 6.2) one is reminded of another analogy—the unwinding of a spring and the ticking of an escapement. When the clock strikes, the awaited event will occur, a decision must be taken, an action performed.

PROPERTIES OF THE LIVING BRAIN

In many of the foregoing paragraphs descriptions of brain activity and conjectures as to their significance and origin have been qualified by the phrase 'in some people.' This is perhaps the most irritating, and yet the most exciting, aspect of human brain studies—the intrusion of gross personal differences. Oddly enough the only feature of brain electro-genesis which seems to be reasonably constant in the normal adult population is the one that was discovered most recently—the CNV. Alpha rhythms vary from 0 to nearly 100 μV in mean amplitude and from 8 to 13 Hz in frequency, with comparable diversity of spatial distribution and responsiveness. In normal people in specified conditions, the CNV has a mean peak amplitude of 20 μV between the top of the head and the sides, with a normal distribution varying from 16 to 25 μV between individuals, and only a few microvolts between occasions in a given subject. The waveform of this potential change, however, is individual and related to the mentality of the person and his attitude to the situation. The relative constancy of this effect is all the more surprising because its appearance depends on a high level integration of stimulus association and states of mind variously described as attention, intention, alertness, arousal, expectancy, motivation, conation, learning and decision. With so many ill defined ingredients, it is astonishing that the product should turn out so often with the same consistency. Does this mean that there are not really so many ingredients? May the higher nervous functions be simpler than we feared? This, of course, was always one of the main objectives of cybernetics—to prune away the barren growth of verbalism and encourage the setting of more substantial fruit. This needs more than the application of Occam's razor, however; cross-pollination between disciplines, so much easier to urge than to achieve, is the essential prelude to hybrid vigour.

CYBERNETIC THINKING

What are the prospects for a real revolution in thinking about thinking? For example, is the conjunction between refined neurosurgical procedures and computer techniques more than an accidental convergence? Direct access to the human brain and almost unlimited power to manipulate the information thus obtained have together opened the way to new prospects of understanding brain function, hence to more precise clinical diagnosis and more delicate therapy. But can this development be attributed directly or indirectly to cybernetics or described as a cybernetic procedure? The mere recognition of multiple reflexive pathways in the brain is certainly not a cybernetic discovery since, as already mentioned, this has been known for over a century; 'feedback' alone is not cybernetics, although a steersman must continually compare heading, course and tiller in an endless circuit of comparison and error correction. Neither, of course, is mathematical computation necessarily cybernetic in any useful sense. If there is a cybernetic aspect of such research it is in the way the problem is defined, particularly when the range of possible experiments is very wide and the amount of available information embarrassingly large.

In the case of brain research, where one is dealing with a richly connected 10,000,000,000 element system operating so that no event can have exactly the same effect on it twice, one can obviously use every source of advice and example in designing reasonable experiments. In this sense one can say that some recent developments in the understanding of what Russian physiologists call 'higher nervous activity' have had a cybernetic guide line. Nearly 20 years ago, to satisfy a long standing curiosity about the brain mechanisms of learning (which I had acquired while working under Pavlov on conditioning in dogs) I tried to work out an 'operational hypothesis' of simple learning by association.[11] At first this seemed simple enough—one had only to write down in logical sequence the necessary and sufficient events in the environment that would result in 'conditioning.' These might be the familiar bell ringing or light flashing followed by food or an electric shock. But even this is not as simple as it sounds. How long and how often must the bell ring and how quickly and regularly must the reward or punishment be presented? In the end I had seven separate and distinct operations specified, all of which seemed both necessary and physiologically plausible. Briefly these were: differentiation of the specific or unconditional stimulus; extension of a neutral stimulus; mixing of the overlap between these; summation of the areas of overlap; activation of a memory or storage system; preservation of the memory of summated significant overlaps; and finally, combination of this stored information with the action of a neutral stimulus, which thereby becomes 'conditional' and evokes a response similar to that evoked by the unconditional stimulus. This surprisingly intricate schedule of operations seemed difficult to embody in abstract or mathematical terms, yet worthy of testing in some way. The obvious solution was to crystallise these fluid concepts in a working model with electronic components whose functions could be defined accurately and were perfectly understood. When this was done it was found that the system could in fact 'learn' a simple association as prescribed, and it also displayed several emergent properties which had not been specified but were also characteristic of organic learning both in the laboratory and in free life.

EXPERIMENTAL WORK

These models were begotten before and independently of the publication of Wiener's *Cybernetics*;[5] they were the first viable artificial animals and still play a modest role in the teaching of biology to engineers and of engineering to biologists. They had a more significant function, however—they suggested what the signs of learning in the brain might be in electrical terms, and thus initiated a long and varied series of experiments, with human subjects and increasingly refined computational techniques, intended to discover these signs. Here, finally, a very interesting point emerged, typical of the way in which what we now may call cybernetics can both lead and mislead. Because of our general pre-occupation with intrinsic brain rhythms, and my related familiarity with the electronics of low frequency oscillators and resonators, the memory storage system of the model had been specified as a resonant circuit with a very long but adjustable time of decay. This circuit, once activated, stored information about significant associations as slow oscillations which decayed slowly (as organic memories do) if left undisturbed by subsequent activations. The elaborate technique of the

102

experiments designed to detect similar effects in the living brain was accordingly directed to the extraction of information about brain rhythms, and indeed a number of very interesting facts about these did emerge, among them the peculiar but disappointingly rare effect described as the Contingent Coherent After-Rhythm. If this had been a consistent accompaniment of conditioning in our subjects, the resemblance between the flesh and the metal would have been a complete corroboration of the original hypothesis but it was an exception, not a rule, and could not be accepted as a trustworthy sign of short term conditional association.

Later, when opportunities were presented for recording from inside the brain, using this same system, the situation was in no way clarified. The diversity and individuality of the rhythms encountered nearer their sources dispelled any idea that they could be related to the process of memory or learning. However, in spite of the system being designed to detect and enhance rhythm at the expense of slower irregular potential changes, in a few experiments, when the subject was penalised for a wrong response, a small slow wave was seen just before the penalty was to be expected. This was almost overlooked, but in laborious scrutinies of hundreds of photographs (with a comparator similar to that used by astronomers searching for small moving objects among fixed stars) this insignificant blob was found to be the only feature likely to be related to the state of learning. This was not a rhythm, but the remnant of a slow potential change, grossly distorted and attenuated by the carefully designed filters and display system of the apparatus. One might say that while listening for a tune we heard a distant drum.

It was some time before we discovered how to amplify and sustain this elusive effect, but in the end it emerged as the Contingent Negative Variation, described above as the most consistent feature in the electrogenesis of the brain in precisely the conditions specified for the operation of the Learning Machine. The lesson here is not merely that a scientist's powers of observation are limited as well as amplified by his equipment—this we can demonstrate with a magnifying glass—but a rather more subtle and two-edged one. The cybernetic approach, by which frustration in one discipline is relieved by facility in another, can open up an otherwise hopeless avenue of exploration, but at the same time it is very likely to introduce distraction by meretricious detail. A familiar example of the generality of this effect is the way in which the early computers suggested how certain functions of the brain, otherwise inscrutable, might be considered as *computations*. This is an encouraging and fertile notion—but at the same time the dependence of the computers on binary logic misled many theorists into supposing that the brain must operate in the same way. (In fact, transmission in peripheral nerves is in a sense digital—which seemed excellent confirmation of the idea.) This naturally suggested that brain functions were likewise logical (in the algebraic, not the literal sense) and that every aspect of behaviour, from peripheral reflexes to human imagination, could be resolved into a progressive series of yes-no statements and dichotomies. Attention was therefore concentrated on those features of central nervous function which do approximate to binary decisions. The participation of graded, probabilistic processes was ignored or dismissed as a trivial analogue embroidery on the basic fabric of digital computation.

In fact, of course, both classes of operation exist in the brain and interest in one of them does not preclude appreciation of the other. There seems to be some resemblance to the development of ideas about the properties of matter.

The term 'gas' was derived from 'chaos' because matter in this state had no form or shape. Nevertheless, the laws relating pressure, volume and temperature, as every student learns, can be defined theoretically with great precision. But these are statistical laws, dealing with very large populations of molecules. When great accuracy is needed in a practical case, the existence of molecules with different sizes and velocities has to be taken into account. The essential statistical laws cannot be derived from observation of a few individual molecules and when only a few are present—as in outer space—the familiar concepts of temperature and pressure are no longer realistic. The space traveller must expect to meet molecules with enormous 'temperatures' in 'the wind that blows between the worlds it cut him like a knife.' On the other hand, in a practical application on earth, for example, the specification for a pneumatic tyre which ensures constant pressure per unit area to carry a given weight, the behaviour of individual molecules is irrelevant and the schoolroom gas laws are an adequate guide.

In the brain, we must consider both the individual elements—the neurons and their appendages—and at the same time, if possible, the statistical behaviour of large populations. The latter, theoretically, should be the whole nervous system, since there is no *a priori* justification for excluding interaction between any part of it and any other; but this is obviously impracticable, and one of the prime questions in such investigations is how restricted can the brain population be without falling between the two stools of unit precision and statistical significance.

REDUNDANCY IN THE BRAIN

One property of the human brain that is encouraging in this respect is its apparent structural redundancy; large amounts of cortex can be removed without serious impairment of intelligence, personality or function. One patient obtained a good university degree following a total right-sided hemispherectomy for persistent fits and behavioural disturbances. His intellect was well above average, his complaints were alleviated, and the irreversible left-sided hemianopia and paresis caused only mild inconvenience. Bilateral lesions of the frontal lobes —for example, those resulting from leucotomy—may actually improve total function by relieving anxiety or compulsive thinking.

This feature of high redundancy has suggested a number of explanations for the versatility and functional robustness of the brain as a reliable machine made with unreliable components. In fact, the reliability of the higher structures, where redundancy seems greatest, is not as impressive as the reliability of the more peripheral structures, where there seems to be greater economy. Deficiencies and breakdowns in higher nervous activity, that is mental subnormality, neuroses and psychoses, are at least as common as disorders of the spinal cord and peripheral nerves, and it seems possible that at the highest level the redundancy is more apparent than real; its function may be to provide a very large temporary storage capacity for moment to moment information, that is, to act as an input buffer in relation to a general learning programme. The evidence for this view is derived from observation of the brain responses to sensory signals during the conditioning paradigm designed to ascertain the electrical accompaniments of learning in human beings, during which the CNV was discovered. A preliminary part of this procedure involves the presentation of isolated sensory stimuli, without association, first slowly at irregular intervals, then more rapidly and at regular intervals then again slowly and irregularly. This is to assess the rate and extent of 'habituation', that is, the decline in the evoked responses as novelty diminishes with monotonous repetition. In Pavlovian terms this would be called 'Extinction of the Orientating Response.'

This effect is almost invariable and quite familiar; it seems at first sight a simple process, similar to fatigue or accommodation, but a number of features suggest that it is more complicated. The most peculiar one is that when a response has declined to, say, 10% of its original size following 50 or 100 regular presentations, it can recover its original extent and amplitude at once if there is a change in any parameter of the stimulus, even a *reduction* in its intensity or the omission or interposition of a single stimulus in the series. This seems to imply that all the characters of the predictable stimulus are stored progressively and as the stored trace accumulates detail, less and less of the cortex is engaged in the response (recorded amplitude being a function of synchrony and spatial extension to the cortex). When the representation of the stimulus in cortical terms, presumably an electrochemical engram, is complete, it is used as a recognition template; subsequent stimuli which match the template fall through into oblivion. But whenever a mismatch is detected, in any parameter, an error signal is emitted and a novelty response appears once more.

This description (which could, of course, be the basis of a computer program) sounds quite simple, but the amount of detail to be accommodated to provide for the observed degree and versatility of the process is enormous. Even in a single modality, the amount of selective information that must be accepted and stored (for example, in the habituation to a particular pictorial stimulus to ensure that a response reappears if a fresh detail is added or one omitted) is very large indeed and nearly all of this information is by definition useless in itself. It is difficult to avoid concluding that this extravagant system must require a very large reserve of temporary cortical storage space with arrangements for erasure or transfer to the long term core according to whether the signal pattern concerned turns out to be trivial or to have an important implication. This decision is the critical transition between habituation and learning and in the living brain there is, indeed, an indication of this in the growth of the CNV following a significant signal and its abrupt discharge with decision or action

BRAIN STORAGE SYSTEMS—MEMORY

Reverting to the simple learning machine that was the artificial origin of many of these natural observations, the oscillatory memory which served both as guide and decoy in the search for signs of learning in the brain is not the only storage system in the circuit. There is also a series of slow potential changes, initiated by the congruence of conditional and specific signals, an analogue of their observed overlap. This storage system, surprisingly like the real CNV, is described in the original diagrams as 'Memory 2' the cumulative indication that two events are occurring together more often than would be expected by chance. It is strange that one could have drawn this diagram and then ignored it, searched for another pattern and then rediscovered the rejected figure in real graphs drawn by the brain itself years later. Following the vogue for the Haiku one could write sadly:

> Scientist's nightmare—
> To look at the right angle,
> And then miss the point.

The designation of the artificial potential changes as Memory 2 is a significant detail. In all computers, whether flesh or metal, there must be two main classes of mechanism, clocks and stores; and except in the very simplest cases, there are several of both, in series and parallel. A computer designer arranges his stores —which he may call buffers, accumulators, cores or memories according to the function assigned to them—so as to provide the most satisfactory compromise between capacity, permanence, accuracy, versatility and accessibility. An optimum arrangement is difficult to achieve and a wide variety of systems has been tried. Early computers like the learning machine used mechanical or electrostatic oscillatory systems; more recently magnetic stores, both dynamic and static, have found favour but these in turn may be superseded by electromagnetic wave or micro-chemical systems. It would not be surprising if a comparable diversity of structure and mechanism were to be found in the brain—it is one of the propositions of cybernetics that ponderous organic evolution by natural selection is likely to follow steps similar to the more hectic fumbling of human invention—the differences in scale of size and time are interesting but not fundamental.

In the brain, oscillatory systems have been proposed, occasionally found, but rejected as a universal storage mechanism. (Additional evidence against this hypothesis is the complete survival of human memory after cooling of the brain to 10°C for several hours during heart operations; all electrical activity ceases and the organ would be considered as dead—but on re-warming the patient revives with all his souvenirs intact.) The CNV looks very like Memory 2 (Memory 1 being the mere prolongation of the effect of a possibly significant signal). The time range of the CNV (as seen on the scalp) is from about 0·5 sec to perhaps 1 minute. This is the sort of time in which a new phone number can be remembered—but is forgotten for dialling immediately afterwards. A characteristic feature of the CNV is its abrupt fall on each occasion a decision is taken or an action performed, thus resembling the discharge of the short term phone-number type of memory. This pattern would suggest a 'destructive writeout'; the store is cleared as soon as the operation to which it is related is accomplished. The write-out may not be completely destructive, however. In the conditioning in which the CNV develops, it seems more likely that with each termination of the potential rise some information is transferred to a more durable storage register—the subject remembers for a long time that he did something unusual that day, although he often forgets exactly what, and may never have appreciated the true relations between the signals.

The question then arises, what is the nature of the long term store—that which we may call Memory 3? Compared with Memory 2, this system has a very large capacity and long persistence, but is less precise, particularly in its relation to 'real time' (it must be supplemented by external clocks and calendars for everyday human use). Access to it is erratic, often requiring a playback of long sections and various mnemonic devices in order to retrieve a specified item. In computer terms this sort of store would be something like a rather roughly coded library of magnetic tapes. Is there anything like a jumble of tapes in the brain? Ignoring the question of scale (which even in computers is diminishing rapidly almost to invisibility) the discoveries of molecular biologists suggest that there is indeed just this, not only in the brain but in every living cell—the neatly double-coiled molecules of the nucleic acids that are presumed to hold and transmit specifications for the construction of every cell of every animal. The scale of information capacity is apparently adequate (bearing in mind that we can perhaps dispose of not merely the 10,000,000,000 neurons but also of the even more numerous neuroglial structures that are particularly rich in nuclear material). But how are the bits of information about individual experiences and actions, each perhaps associated with something like a CNV, transferred from the electrical fields in the cortex, each according to its conditional significance, into the patterns of molecular arrangement within the cells? And which cells?

There are two problems here: first, are there regions or systems in the brain that one can consider as the transducer (corresponding to the write and read heads in a magnetic tape transport); and, secondly, is there any evidence as to exactly where the 'tape' runs and where it is stored? Such questions are obviously naive, particularly in the context of the human brain, but they are probably worth asking because evidence being accumulated from simpler creatures is already indicating that specific neural circuits and chemical processes are involved in the cerebral classification and storage of information. The studies of learning in octopus by Young and his school,[12] and the cytochemical analyses of Hydén in rats[13] support the notion of an intelligible mechanism even in our own brains, particularly since we have the advantage of subjective appreciation of our own mnemonic powers and failings.

MEMORY FAILURE

The fallibility of human memory is not a trivial consideration—much can be learned about the nature of a machine from the ways in which it breaks down. The great mass of clinical observation provides clear evidence supporting the concept of various grades of memory; a knock on the head may destroy very recent memories irreversibly, but the long term store can be disrupted only by generalised toxic processes which inflict demonstrable cytochemical injury, particularly on the structures connecting the temporal lobes to midline nuclei. Positive interference with these regions by electrical stimulation in normal brains produces lapses of time-sense and confusion of recall and in some epileptics, Penfield and his colleagues[14] have observed the evocation of prolonged and often stereotyped and detailed memories during stimulation of temporal cortex. Within the temporal lobes the hippocampus (one of the strangest conglomerations of old and new cortex, curved like a race track and unique in its abundance of peculiar enzymes and cell foliage) is essential for the inscription of current experience and recall of recent memory. In this region also, regular electrical rhythms appear during learning, shifting phase and frequency according to success or failure of achievement. Is this perhaps the 'write-read' head of the brain's tape-deck? And the tape itself, the vast congregation of coded nucleotides within the cells—is this perhaps distributed over the whole convoluted surface of the 'silent areas' where electric stimuli are ineffective and lesions destroy no specific item of intelligence? Some arrangement must certainly be made in such a system for structural redundancy, and the degree of apparent redundancy in the human 'silent areas' is impressive. Such conjectures are still beyond the range of verification by present techniques. We cannot see how the widespread electrochemical wave patterns related to momentary experiences are condensed into intracellular molecular templates, or how these latter can be used to re-establish a specific behaviour relevant to the original contingency.

PROBABILISTIC OR LOGICAL?

Implicit in such speculations and explicit in many experiments now being performed is the concept of the higher nervous system as a probabilistic machine rather than a logical one—a system adapted particularly to the recognition of resemblances and similarities, rather than identities. Such a system has all the faults with which we are familiar—frequent lapses of memory, the creation of spurious constellations in a chaotic firmament, trivial fancies, illusions, hallucinations. Where there is little reason, we generate mnemonic rhyme, and this may be the literally poetic function of cybernetics; to impose an operational prosody on the babble and jargon of diverging disciplines.

REFERENCES

1. WIENER, N., *The Human Use of Human Beings*, Houghton Mifflin, Boston (1950).
2. WIENER, N., *I am a Mathematician*, Doubleday, New York (1956).
3. SECHENOV, I. M., *Reflexes of the Brain*, Moscow (1863).
4. WIENER, N., *Non-Linear Problems in Random Theory*, M.I.T. Press and John Wiley, New York, Chapman and Hall, London (1958).
5. WIENER, N., *Cybernetics*, M.I.T. Press and John Wiley, New York, 2nd ed. (1961).
6. LANGE, H. de, *Attenuation Characteristics and Phase Shift of the Human Fovea-Cortex Systems in Relation to Flicker-Fusion Phenomena*, Thesis, Delft University, Netherlands (1957).
7. TWEEL, L. H. van der, 'Some Problems in Vision Regarded with Respect to Linearity and Frequency Response,' *Ann. N.Y. Acad. Sci.*, **89**, 829 (1961).
8. SPEKREIJSE, H., *Analysis of E.E.G. Responses in Man Evoked by Sine-Wave Modulated Light*, Thesis, Amsterdam University (1966).
9. WIENER, N., *Response of a Non-linear Device to Noise*, Rep. No. 129, Radiation Laboratory, M.I.T. Press Cambridge, Mass. (1942).
10. WALTER, W. GREY, COOPER, R., ALDRIDGE, V. J., MCCALLUM, W. C. and WINTER, A. L., 'Contingent Negative Variation: an Electric Sign of Sensori—Motor Association and Expectancy in the Human Brain,' *Nature*, **203**, 380 (1964).
11. WALTER, W. GREY, *The Living Brain*, Duckworth, London (1953); Penguin Books (1961).
12. YOUNG, J. Z., *The Memory System of the Brain*, Oxford University Press (1966).
13. HYDÉN, H., 'The Neuron in the Cell,' Volume 4, *The Cell*, Eds. Brachet, 0 and MIRSKY, 0, Academic Press, New York and London (1960).
14. PENFIELD, W. and PEROT, P., 'The Brain's Record of Auditory and Visual Experience,' *Brain*, **86**, 595 (1963).

Chapter 7

Medical Cybernetics

J. H. CLARK, M.A., M.B. (Cantab.), D.P.M. M. Inst. C. Sc.
Senior Lecturer, Department of Psychology, University of Manchester (U.K.)

SUMMARY

Medicine is analysed in terms of a teaching system; two people participate, the doctor and his patient, alternating the roles of teacher and pupil. Cybernetic medicine is then described as medicine approached by way of this analysis at many different levels. Examples of such analyses are given, together with references to other work in the field from which each example is taken.

The examples include Dr. J. L. Gedye's use of teaching machines in diagnosis; Dr. A. H. Bottomley's work on mechanical muscles in prosthetics; computer diagnosis; computer data retrieval; Mr. H. S. Wolff's work on data display and transducers; the automation of laboratories; patient monitoring systems; travel aids for the blind; and the author's own work on hypnosis.

The author believes that the computer will change medicine radically. He foresees an increase of polyclinics in towns and of computer links for doctors who are isolated geographically; all aspects of medicine will be changed, it will become more efficient and more readily available.

But at the heart of medicine, the author sees a conversation between the doctor and his patient. This, he believes, will not change, being already a profound and satisfying cybernetic system.

INTRODUCTION

Cybernetics is the art and science of government; not just the government of nations but of any system whatsoever. The insights of cybernetics are as old as the fantail on windmills[1] and the Watt governor on steam engines. Yet, it is only in the last three decades that these insights into feedback, information and purpose have been made explicit and generalised.[2, 3, 4] This period has also seen the development of the computer, enabling us to simulate complex systems.

109

(Simulation by writing a computer program is a modern version of testing a theory.)

Our ordinary language, being linear, is not entirely satisfactory for describing cybernetic systems. It can describe sequences very well,[5] but when a system loops back on itself in time our language is not so efficient. All feedback systems have such loops and the systems are more clearly understood if they are set out as diagrams with all their interconnections marked. These can then be appreciated at a glance (see, for example, Fig. 7.1).

A doctor is a maintenance engineer looking after a biological learning machine, man, of which he has incomplete knowledge. He must therefore seek constantly to increase this amount of knowledge so that he may apply it more effectively. The situation is complicated by the fact that the doctor himself belongs to the group he is investigating. Thus, a psychiatrist, who specialises in maintaining the computer of the learning machine, has such a computer inside his own head. He is a man, the most complex piece of the universe we know, puzzling over a fellow complexity. In this chapter I shall discuss some ways of stepping back from this complexity so that we may try to cope with it.

Medical cybernetics is the application of cybernetic thinking to any system encountered in medicine. Such systems occur at many levels. We can consider, for example, the relationship between a doctor and his patient or the hypnotist and his subject; we can consider the homeostatic mechanisms of the body at a physiological level,[6] or the genetic system at the level of molecular biology. At all levels we seek an analysis in terms of circular, purposive, feedback systems. We also, at all levels, seek to simulate the systems we have analysed, either by using special purpose machines or, more generally, by writing programs for digital computers. At the highest level, the search for artificial intelligence echoes the ancient preoccupation with the robot or Golem.[7] At lower levels, simulation is being extended to organ after organ, limb after limb; we have long had wigs, false teeth and spectacles—now we have artificial kidneys, lungs and hearts.

The literature covering medical cybernetics will be found in many journals, especially those concerned with bioengineering and computers. The references in this chapter will give an indication of where to look. There is an International Society for Medical Cybernetics which holds regular congresses and publishes a journal called *Cybernetic Medicine* (No. 1 was published in 1967). The Secretariat of this Society is at 348, Via Roma, Naples, Italy. The President is Prof. Aldo Masturzo of the University of Naples.

THE CHANGES TO COME

We are perhaps now in a position to speculate fruitfully on the future development of medicine as the cybernetic revolution gains momentum. The heart of medicine is a doctor talking to his patient. This will continue to be the heart. But what may change is the whereabouts of the doctor, his relationship to fellow doctors, to hospital services and to medical information. The increasing complexity of medicine may encourage the development of polyclinics, attached to hospitals. As a young doctor, I spent six months as a Junior Casualty Officer at the Westminster Hospital. Each day, along with my colleagues, I saw patients in the Casualty Department. Had we also gone on visiting-rounds in the surrounding streets of Pimlico, we would have been members of a polyclinic. We had specialist advice always at hand, and the facilities of a hospital immediately available.

We must also, however, envisage the doctor practicing in a remote country district far from any colleagues. But imagine that instead of relying solely on his case of medical books in the consulting-room, he has a typewriter keyboard and a TV screen. Our imaginary lone doctor is now connected to a vast store of clinical information, advice and case records kept in a central computer miles away.

There is no aspect of medicine that will be untouched by the computer in the next decade or two. I think that the influence of the computer, with the inevitable rationalisation of the systems it serves, will be benign. Patients will be better diagnosed, they will be admitted to hospital more efficiently, they will be better fed, they will be more safely observed and they will be better treated for their illnesses.

These are some of the possible directions in which medicine may move. Computerisation of medical literature, case records and laboratory reports is already beginning to transform the doctor's life. I expect my reader will think of many other possible developments as he reads this chapter.

None of this would serve much purpose if the patient of the future were to feel himself merely an object of an impersonal, albeit effective, system. People want their doctors to be human as well as efficient. I am glad to say that I think the computer will help doctors to be human. By relieving them of routine, automatic and tiring jobs they will be freed to establish the human relationships which give the patient confidence and which make medicine such a satisfying profession.

MEDICINE AS A TEACHING SYSTEM

TEACHING AS A CYBERNETIC SYSTEM[8]

The simplest description of a teaching system which I can devise is shown in Fig. 7.1. The pupil is confronted by a task to be learnt with the assistance of a teacher. The task is divided into a series of subtasks, arranged in a logical order so that later tasks depend on earlier ones being understood.[3] Each subtask, 1, 2, 2A, 3 and so on, can be considered to consist of an assertion, such as water boils at 100°C. This in turn can be rewritten as a question Q together with its correct answer CA. We can now describe the process of teaching as follows:

1. The task sends a question Q to the pupil.
2. The pupil sends an answer A to that part of the teacher which is a comparator.
3. The task sends the correct answer CA to the comparator.
4. The comparator compares the answer A with the correct answer CA and computes an error score S which is sent back to the pupil and which is also sent to the other part of the teacher which is the instructor.
5. The comparator also notes the nature N of any error and sends it to the instructor.
6. The instructor tells the task to send the next question Q and, if necessary, modifies M the task.

7. The instructor sends information about the task to the pupil. Such information is shown as the contents of a subtask Q, CA.

The above notation, using Q and A should not be taken too literally. Often Q is not a question grammatically, and it may not be verbal. My aim is to get away from the stimulus S, response R notation, which is equally inadequate, while still avoiding the rather cold 'input I, output O' notation.

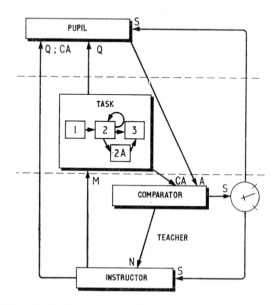

Fig. 7.1. A feedback system (teaching) expressed diagrammatically

The reason these notations are inadequate is because there is an intrinsic ambiguity in all teaching systems. Who can say at any moment who is the teacher who the taught? Bearing in mind its limitations, I think the above notation is worth using for the light it casts on the many medical situations which have the form of a dialogue, that is to say, which are cybernetic.

THE STAGES OF MEDICINE

I find it helpful to analyse medicine in terms of the above teaching system.

At first it might appear that the doctor is the teacher and the patient is the pupil, and that is certainly true some of the time. However, on closer examination we find that these roles alternate with the medical process.

The stages of medicine are:

1. History, physical examination and special investigation.
2. Diagnosis.
3. Treatment.

While taking the patient's history, the doctor is the pupil. His task is the patient's life story and, in particular, those aspects of it bearing upon his illness.

As the doctor learns this task the patient, in his role of teacher, checks that the doctor is getting it correct, supplies additional information and modifies the presentation of subtasks. The doctor remains the pupil during his physical examination of the patient. Now his task is the state of the patient's body as open to the doctor's senses. The doctor extends the use of his senses by using various instruments, and when such instruments are elaborate, the examination is called a special investigation; examples include X-rays, laboratory tests and biopsies.

The psychological test is an interesting case of the special investigation in which, within the general situation the doctor is the pupil; but within this situation, the doctor sets up a second system in which the patient is the pupil in a specific learning situation. The doctor wishes to learn how the patient behaves in the learning situation (see p. 118).

Diagnosis is the next stage. This does not require the presence of the patient, but is a comparative procedure which takes place inside the doctor. He compares the information gathered from the patient with similar information gathered from other patients. Very often such information falls into recognisable patterns and these patterns, in turn, are given names. The process of diagnosis is facilitated by the training which the doctor has received and by his textbooks and sources of reference. He may also have access to specialist colleagues and large medical libraries. (The place of the computer in diagnosis is discussed on p. 121).

The last stage in medicine is treatment. The doctor now adopts the role of teacher and the patient that of pupil. Under the instructions of the doctor, the patient is taught to cope with a task. The task is the changed environment in which the doctor places the patient. It is changed with respect to the amount of time spent in bed, the presence of special drugs, alterations in the diet, surgical operations, exercises and so on. The process of adapting to this task is the process of treatment, and the doctor supervises the patient's progress through it. When successful, the process of treatment restores the patient to his normal trajectory of health from which he was displaced by illness.

We may summarise the above analysis, as shown in Table 7.1.

Table 7.1. THE STAGES OF MEDICINE

Stage of medicine	The role of the doctor	The role of the patient
1. History Physical examination Special investigation	Pupil	Teacher
2. Diagnosis	—	—
3. Treatment	Teacher	Pupil

MEDICAL EDUCATION

TEACHING MACHINES

An interesting side effect of research into teaching machines is that it has made authors more conscious of the need to organise their material as a logical sequence of subsections (or, with reference to Fig. 7.1, sub-tasks). Indeed, it has even been suggested that the best policy would be to prepare a teaching machine programme (or programmed textbook) and then turn it back into ordinary prose. Research into the exact role of teaching machines is continuing, and there are some interesting papers on their use in medical education, such as those by Owen, Hall, Anderson and Smart,[9] and Weller, Greene and Geis.[10]

The development of very elaborate teaching machines, controlled by digital computer, is being carried out in the U.S.A. These machines can have multiple consoles so that many students may be taught at once. Each student sits opposite a small screen on to which is projected the instructional material; the student responds by way of a control-box connected to the screen.[11, 12, 13]

BIOLOGICAL ENGINEERING

One of the problems of medical education is communication between doctors and the engineers who design the machines which are becoming such a prominent feature of medical life. How can doctors and engineers talk together? It is uneconomical for doctors to try to be engineers and vice versa. Nevertheless, *some* doctors must learn to talk some of the language of engineering and some engineers must reciprocate. This problem is being tackled by the formation of medical engineering clubs and by the publication of medical- and bio-engineering journals.

One technique which may be helpful is to know how to draw logical circuits in the form of flow diagrams. An engineer can then translate these diagrams into the latest kind of electronic engineering (logic is presumably timeless). Such logical circuits are needed in most machines and skill in designing them might become a valuable part of medical education for at least some students.

With the increasing use of analogue computers in the simulation of biomedical systems (see p. 129), medical students may also find it very useful to become acquainted with the 'feel' of such systems in the laboratory. I think the 'discovery' element in education could be encouraged by letting students literally 'play' with these devices.

MEDICAL COMPUTATION

In the U.S.A., medical computation has become a medical specialty in its own right; doctors specialise in it as a career. This information comes from the revealing survey on medical computing in the U.S.A. by Dr. D. E. Clark.[4] From his survey it appears that 'all medical schools in America seem to have at least one computer.' It is also 'anticipated that by 1980 half of the medical graduates would have a knowledge of computing science, mathematics and electronics.'

Dr. D. E. Clark's survey indicates that England is lagging in this vital field. His voice, like that of Mr. Heinz S. Wolff (see pp. 117 and 122) is radical and prophetic.

RESEARCH IN MEDICAL EDUCATION

In the U.S.A. there is a *Journal of Medical Education* and in 1966 a similar journal, the *British Journal of Medical Education,* was founded. The Royal Society of Medicine founded a Section of Medical Education in 1966. The Annual Conferences on Research in Medical Education publish their *Proceedings* in the *Journal of Medical Education*. This journal also publishes bibliographies on medical education compiled by Medlars (see p. 116).

MEDICAL ADMINISTRATION

A possible design for a typical hospital ward of the future has been suggested by Dr. L. C. Payne.[15] The beds are arranged in an arc around a central nursing station and a mobile semi-automatic sub-pharmacy. The nursing station contains a console for the patient-monitoring system which measures the patient's pulse rate, respiration rate and blood pressure continuously. A closed circuit television camera enables the house-doctor to show the patient to a consultant at a distance. Dr. Payne makes the point that, since it is impossible to predict the demands that future developments of medical technology will make upon space and facilities, it is wisest to leave the plans of our new hospitals as flexible as possible. He also suggested that in the forthcoming era of hospital building, attention is paid to modern planning methods which can be assisted by the computer, for example, critical path programming. (Details of network analysis generally are given in reference 16.) A similar point is made by Dr. D. E. Clark.[14] In his survey of medical computing in the U.S.A. (referred to above) he found that the design of a modern hospital was preceded by an extensive use of computer aided operational research; this was thought to be an essential stage of planning.

There are many aspects of medical administration where the computer and its attendant systems can be used. For example, in the field of computerised menu planning techniques, Dr. D. E. Clark[14] reports that in the U.S.A., the cost of food had been cut by amounts varying from 10% to 25%, and that a bed utilisation system raised the bed usage in a children's hospital from 85% to 95%. Other fields are blood bank inventories and nurses' time-tables.

MEDICAL INFORMATION

CASE RECORDS

According to Stacy and Waxman,[17] '. . . the medical record is a morass of irregularly entered 'soft' data.'

Professor Alwyn Smith[18] has discussed how the computer could transform the above unsatisfactory situation. He envisages first the transfer of all patients' records to a computer store and secondly the possibility of linking individual hospitals to a national library of medical records. Much research and development would be required to realise these systems. Another interesting account of an electronic medical records system will be found in Chapter 2 of Dr. L. C. Payne's very readable book, *An Introduction to Medical Automation.*[15] In this, he makes the distinction between Class 1 data, which are 'enumerable', such as a patient's number, age, sex, occupation, blood group, or blood pressure, and Class 2 data, which are 'innumerable', such as doctors' notes, X-rays, EEGs, etc. He notes the tendency for Class 2 data to be converted into Class 1 with the progress of medical science, which quantifies more and more data.

Record Linkage

Every individual gathers a series of numbers during his life, such as his National Health Service number and Birth Registration entry number. Prof. A. Smith[19] has described the problem of record linkage as that of '... being able to link two or more records of vital or medical events occurring in the same individual'. There is also the problem of linking the records of an individual to the records of his parents, his wife and his children. The same author looks ahead to the future possibility of a central medical file for each individual in the community.

Other papers on record linkage will be found in Session 2 of the Medical Research Council Conference.[20]

STORAGE AND RETRIEVAL

Turning from the patient's case records and other personal data to another aspect of information, let us consider how medical knowledge in general is stored and retrieved. The method employed traditionally was the article in the learned journal, and the book. This system, at any rate as deployed in conventional libraries, is breaking down as the printing press gives way to the computer. *The present age is not just one of change but of change in the rate of change.* Ledley[21] shows a histogram of the increase in bio-medical research. This doubled from 1950 to 1955 and again from 1955 to 1960 and it goes on increasing.

Medlars

To cope with the concomitant outpouring of medical literature many abstracting and indexing systems have been developed over the years. These have themselves been computerised in recent years and, in particular, the monumental *Index Medicus* has been computerised and has been rendered more accessible by a computerised search system called MEDLARS (Medical Literature Analysis and Retrieval System). This system has budded off an experimental U.K. MEDLARS Service,[22] which uses a copy of the computer tape containing the index. The fundamental change in retrieval technique embodied in MEDLARS is the use of standard 'index heading words'. These are allotted to each journal article (from the World Medical Literature, as contained in 2,800 journals) by a team of indexers who scan each article for about 5–15 minutes. The point is that the information is being indexed at the level of the *concepts* used in the article and not just at the level of its title and author and the name of the journal. Such index heading words are called *descriptors* or *key-words*.

116

A similar technique is being used in the FAIR project[23] which is being applied specifically to the field of biomedical engineering in Mr. H. S. Wolff's department at the National Institute for Medical Research at Hampstead.

SPECIAL INVESTIGATIONS

LABORATORY AUTOMATION

There are three main ways in which automatic methods may be applied to special investigations. First, they may be applied to the data obtained from existing investigations such as the electroencephalograph (EEG) and electrocardiograph (ECG).[24] Other typical applications are in blood counts and X-ray analysis. Secondly, automatic analysis may be applied to the data produced by investigations introduced recently such as the counting and classification of the human chromosomes.[21, 25]

Thirdly, new techniques have been introduced to produce and elaborate certain data. In particular this applies to the laboratories of clinical biochemistry. The demands made on these laboratories have expanded so rapidly in recent years that automation, both of the tests and of the data produced by the tests, has become essential.[26] The trend today is away from testing single specimens or small batches and towards the routine and regular testing of each patient for a wide range of variables. Apart from such a 'cold' laboratory, a 'hot' laboratory must be maintained for emergency tests which must be done out of the flow of the routine testing. Dr. Whitehead[26] shows how a computer can be used to cope with the data produced by a clinical biochemistry laboratory using the continuous testing system called the autoanalyser. Other automatic laboratory systems exist but from all of them ensue several consequences. First, a mass of data builds up on all the patients and by appropriate techniques such as cumulative summing, discrepancies due to test error can be spotted and corrected early. Secondly, a more accurate range of 'hospital normal' values can be established with which the individual patient's value can be compared.

DISPLAY OF INFORMATION

Mr. H. S. Wolff admits[27] that the presentation of data is a particular hobby-horse of his. He points out that the human brain is not good at spotting trends in a mass of tabulated data. Yet data are often presented to the doctor in this form, for example, clinical laboratory results. Mr. Wolff makes the interesting suggestion that data should be presented in a way which takes advantage of the highly developed human ability to recognise and remember shapes. By arranging a series of results along a set of axes in a sort of rose and joining them with straight lines, an outline emerges in the form of a loop which will take up characteristic shapes for different diseases. The normal shape could be kept to a circle by adjusting the scales along each axis (see Fig. 7.2). Characteristic loops should emerge for different diseases and, for a given patient, his progress from day to day should show up as the loop changes with his condition.

Doctors are already trained to observe the characteristic facial changes accompanying various diseases. If Mr. Wolff's method was adopted, they would be able to learn the biochemical equivalent.

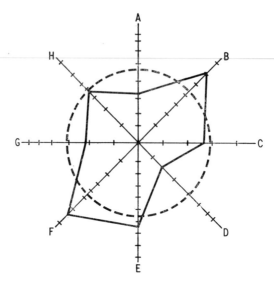

Fig. 7.2. Visual display of information

PSYCHOLOGICAL TESTING

There is a dilemma in psychology between 'vitality of material' and 'precision of measurement'.[28] On the one hand, there are tests typified by Raven's *Progressive Matrices*,[29] in which 'objectivity' is maintained by scoring the test according to the subject's choice from a limited set of prepared answers. On the other hand, we have 'clinical' interviews in which, at the cost of 'subjectivity', the interchange between the observer and the subject seems to be richer and more human. Both methods are in use but both have disadvantages, and that is the dilemma. (The solution put forward by Dr. Bannister[28] is the method devised by Kelly[30] as part of his 'Personal Construct Theory.')

Another resolution is embodied in the radically new approach of Dr. J. L. Gedye.[31]

This is a cybernetic method which sets up a system analogous to the doctor-patient system, but then observes the system objectively. It substitutes for the doctor a teaching machine which has considerable flexibility in its performance. This method goes towards resolving the dilemma as stated above. It combines the flexibility of the interview with the objectivity of a standardised test.

Dr. Gedye has made the important point that the work of a psychologist can be divided into two parts. There is a human part in which a patient's confidence is gained and personal information is obtained. The methods used here are the characteristic human skills of conversation and observation. There is also a more automatic part which can be reduced to a fairly rigid, though branching, routine. It is these automatic parts which, he says, should be automated, since they lend themselves to the process and such automation frees the psychologist for the other, more human, skills in relation to his patients.

THE NON-PARTICIPANT OBSERVER

In terms of the analysis of the teaching system (Fig. 7.1), the teaching machine takes over the function of the teacher, presenting a standard task in an adaptive manner according to each patient's (pupil's) responses. The teacher is a participant-observer. Then a second observer studies the 'conversation' between the teacher and the pupil without taking part in it. This observer is external or non-participant, he overhears messages as they pass from teacher to pupil but does not send any to either.

When a doctor makes his diagnosis, he is really studying the 'conversation' between himself and his patient during the history, physical examination and special investigations. This is literally true in psychiatry, where much of the data as to the patient's 'mental state' is derived from a critical examination by the doctor of the nature of their actual conversation, as it was conducted in ordinary language. The teaching machine used by Dr. Gedye replaces the doctor (or psychologist) in the role of participant-observer. The doctor (or psychologist) is then able to 'step back', as it were, into the passive role of observer (non-participant).

This is a most significant advance in the methodology of psychology. For when, as previously, the doctor or psychologist tries to be *both* participant *and* non-participant observer, he is likely to be unable to perform the second function with enough detachment, and is liable to vary in his performance with regard to the first, thus making his behaviour adaptive but not standard with each patient. (Compare the two observers on p. 130). The terminology used here of 'participant observer' and 'external observer' derive from Professor Colin Cherry's book[32] *On Human Communication* (see his Fig. 3.2 on p. 89).

Method

In the reference above, Dr. Gedye[31] was testing old people in hospital for brain damage. He got them to learn a simple task with the aid of a teaching machine from Educational Systems Ltd. (E.S.L.). The machine, a modified 't.m. 1024', has

Fig. 7.3. Dr. Gedye's Machine: testing arrangement

a 9 in square screen on which 35 mm filmstrip is back-projected. The subject has two colour-coded push-buttons (see Fig. 7.3). Each 'frame' (sub-task) of the program demands a response from the patient—either the left or the right button has to be pressed. The response made and the time taken to respond is recorded and punched on paper tape, ready for computer analysis.

The task

The task is a paired-associate learning task. It is divided into a set of units called 'filters', each of which contains four successive problems. Until the patient has solved all four problems correctly, he cannot proceed to the next filter. An error leads to a correction stage. Should he get this wrong, he is demoted to the next lowest filter. The general plan of the filters is shown in Fig. 7.4. Each filter tests a particular aspect of the task, and thus, the particular level at which the patient stops tells something about the nature of his brain damage.

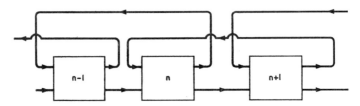

Fig. 7.4. Dr. Gedye's Machine: arrangement of filters

Nearly all of the patients enjoyed using the teaching machine. The approach uses the 'worst-case' design. That is, the program is designed to cope with the worst pupil likely to be encountered. All the pupils who require *less* help can thus be assessed in terms of this amount of help.

Results

Different patients were able to achieve different levels of proficiency in the task and took varying times to achieve these levels. By analysing their path through the branching task, some insight could be gained into the nature of their brain damage.

The interesting feature of this approach is that the test is a standard one. It is objective, yet each patient takes his own path through the branching task, receiving varying amounts of assistance from the teaching machine. In every case the machine tries to optimise the patient's performance so that the best possible level of achievements is attained. This adaptive yet standard behaviour on the part of the machine is what makes it similar to the behaviour of a human psychologist who adapts his behaviour to a patient in a test situation while presenting a standard test so far as he is able. Such adaptive behaviour can be better controlled and measured when performed by a machine. Emphasising the point yet again, the use of a teaching machine in psychological testing represents a radical new approach which attempts to resolve the old dilemma between precise yet objective tests which seem rather lifeless, and tests which are more vital yet suffer from subjectivity.

DIAGNOSIS

The process of diagnosis, as we have already seen (p. 113), is a comparison 'within the doctor' between the pattern of data collected from his patients and other patterns available to him from his medical knowledge and his access to medical literature. The good diagnostician is one who thinks of all the possible diagnoses and then selects, on the basis of the probabilities, the most likely one.

COMPUTER DIAGNOSIS

Clearly, the process of diagnosis should be capable of mathematical formulation and hence of automation. Until recently this was not done, and diagnosis remained a mysterious art to be learnt by a sort of 'osmosis' by contact with the famous doctors at one's teaching hospital. However, the germ of automatic diagnosis can be detected in two quite early books—French's *Differential Diagnosis*[33] and Savile's *Textbook of Medicine*.[34] Both start with a particular symptom and discuss in a logical manner what other symptoms, signs and special investigations should be considered in the search for a diagnosis. Moreover, in recent years attempts have been made to mechanise particular diagnostic problems.

The first complete logical analysis of diagnosis was made by R. S. Ledley[21] and L. B. Lusted.[35] Dr. Ledley, whose chapter on this topic is a most lucid and elegant piece of work, analyses diagnosis in terms of Boolean algebra and displays his ideas as a series of matrices in which symptoms and diseases are shown linked in various combinations. The logical set of possible diagnoses is thus set out clearly and explicitly. To arrive at a particular diagnosis, the body of medical knowledge is applied to this total matrix and reduces it in size as various combinations of symptoms are eliminated because they do not in fact, occur.

Dr. Ledley then discusses how Probability Theory may be applied to make the final diagnosis when more than one diagnosis is possible. The whole of his method is suitable for computerisation and he discusses how this might be done to provide a diagnostic service to the doctor over the telephone (MEDIAC).

DIAGNOSTIC CATEGORIES

The effect of computerisation on diagnostic thinking is to make us examine the nature of diagnostic categories. These are *patterns* of symptoms, signs and special investigations. Until fairly recently they have not been specified very exactly nor have the relations between categories been very explicit. Computer diagnosis will demand a clarification of these points. More exact data will be needed from the clinician and the laboratory, and new methods of describing patterns and their relations will emerge.

At the M.R.C. Conference on Mathematics and Computer Science in Biology and Medicine,[20] Session III was devoted to these topics and included a paper by I. J. Good on the 'Categorisation of Classification.' Two other papers in this field are by Baron and Fraser[36] and Fraser and Baron.[37]

TREATMENT

INTENSIVE PATIENT CARE

There is a spectrum of patient care. At the one end, is the patient who largely looks after himself, at the other is the completely helpless patient. This spectrum has always existed, but in recent years the intensive care of the severely ill patient has become the topic of special study. Hospitals are setting up Intensive Care Units where patients suffering from medical and surgical emergencies, post-operative conditions, burns and accidents can be treated with the greatest efficiency. Such patients require constant observation and often need the simultaneous use of complicated techniques with respirators, artificial kidneys,[38] transfusions and so on. The *Post-Graduate Medical Journal* devoted an issue[39] to a 'Symposium on Intensive Therapy'. It is in intensive care that patient monitoring finds one of its principal applications.[40]

PATIENT MONITORING

Mr. H. S. Wolff, the head of the Division of Biomedical Engineering of the M.R.C.'s National Institute for Medical Research at Hampstead, describes[41] four years' work on a major research project into patient monitoring. The outcome was the 'Monitron' system. This system consists of multiple transducers, attached to the patient and leading to a modular bedside unit which sends signals to chart-printers and visual displays. Much thought has gone into these displays, which indicate very clearly when a particular variable is outside the preselected alarm levels, high or low.

Before this project, little work on patient monitoring had been done in Britain. The whole question of the biomedical instrumentation industry and its relationship to the Health Service is discussed in another characteristically vigorous article by Mr. Wolff.[42] Details of the 'Monitron' and other systems will be found in Dummer and Robertson[43], which contains a bibliography of medical electronics. It should also be noted that *Excerpta Medica* have introduced a new section, Section 27, on 'Medical Instrumentation'.

ANAESTHETIC MACHINES

Anaesthetic machines have been devised in which the amount of anaesthetic reaching the patient is determined automatically. These machines assess the 'depth' of anaesthesia in the patient by an analysis of his electroencephalograph (EEG). This information is fed into the control system of the machine which then adjusts automatically the flow of anaesthetic to the patient.[21, 44]

X-RAY THERAPY

Computers are being used to work out the dosage of X-rays needed to treat deep-lying tumours.[45, 15, 17]

BEHAVIOUR THERAPY

The form of treatment known as behaviour therapy is still being assessed and compared with other forms of treatment.[46] It is, however, of particular interest in the context of this chapter because it can be analysed as a teaching system[8] (Fig. 7.1).[8]

In behaviour therapy the task is known as the 'anxiety hierarchy.' This is a set of stimulus situations arranged serially in order of the amount of anxiety they arouse in the patient. Consider, as an example, the patient who has a phobia for cats. He is, perhaps, presented first of all, with the word cat written very small on a piece of paper which is placed on a table on the other side of the room. He proceeds from this to more realistic stimuli such as a photograph of a cat or a toy cat until, eventually, he can bear the presence of a real cat in the room. These stimuli Q (see p. 111) evoke responses A in the patient in the light of which the therapist as teacher moves him on to the next stimulus, removes the stimulus or gives more of the accompanying progressive relaxation treatment which counteracts the anxiety produced by the stimuli. The desired or correct response CA is a low level of anxiety. Session by session the therapist moves the patient up the 'hierarchy' until the phobia is removed.

The accompanying progressive relaxation can be interpreted as information Q, CA which allows the patient to deal with the task successfully.

OCCUPATIONAL THERAPY

It has long been a principle of medicine that patients get well more quickly if they are kept pleasantly amused and occupied, during their stay in hospital.

To help them achieve this happy state there are, in many hospitals, Departments of Occupational Therapy (O.T.) where patients can take part in a wide variety of activities such as games and crafts. (Referring to Table 7.1, p. 113, O.T. is a treatment, with the patient as the pupil.)

As a contribution to this field, I produced a device which would play a game with a patient much as a human partner would do. The idea was that such a device would take some of the burden of keeping patients happily occupied from human shoulders. I was particularly interested in applying this idea to the occupation of psychiatric patients.

The Horses Game

Dr. Gordon Pask kindly helped me with this project and he designed an entertaining device called the 'Horses Game'[8] which I built. The Horses Game was tried out at the York Clinic, Guy's Hospital, in 1959. Twenty-five patients and twenty-five other people played the Horses Game and nearly all found it absorbing and entertaining. It consisted of a teaching machine similar to S.A.K.I.[47] The teaching machine included a display and a keyboard. The patient sat down in front of the display (see Figs. 7.5 and 7.6) and was able to modify it by operating the keyboard. The display showed a 'field' with eight 'points' in it indicated by a variable food light (shown as a cross in a circle) whose intensity represented the amount of 'grass' at that point in the field. Two 'horses' wandered about in the field. One was a green horse and the other was red (shown in Fig. 7.6 as black

123

and white). They were represented by a green light and a red light at each of the eight points. Only one of the eight green and one of the eight red lights was lit up at any moment, so there was an illusion of the red and the green horses moving about the field. Their paths were very limited, but at four points they could move off in one of two possible directions. When the machine was switched on, the horses started to move along their paths and at each point they 'ate' the grass

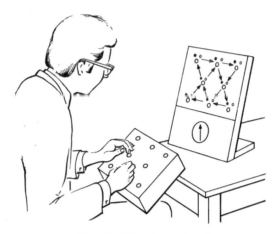

Fig. 7.5. 'The Horses Game'

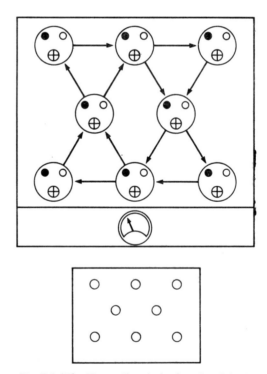

Fig. 7.6. 'The Horses Game': keyboard and display

available. This was seen by the grass light dimming. As a certain grass level was reached the horse would move on to the next point. If left alone the two horses tended to separate at once and pursue different paths around the field, sharing the available grass.

The game consisted of influencing the horses' behaviour by putting extra food in their way. This was done by pressing one of the eight buttons on the keyboard. When one of the buttons was pressed, a pile of hay was said to have been placed at that point on the field and this was shown by the appropriate variable food light increasing in its intensity.

Since the horses made their choice of path according to which offered more food, it was possible, by dumping hay ahead of a horse to influence its behaviour. The horse also had a simple memory which biased it to continue along the path, left or right, which in the recent past had contained more food.

The patient was encouraged to play with the 'Horses Game' and the object of

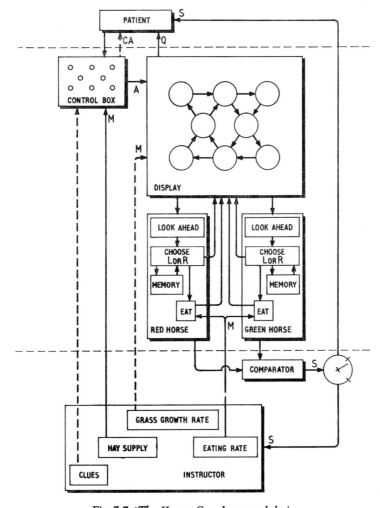

Fig. 7.7. 'The Horses Game': general design

the game was explained to him. It was to keep the two horses moving around together, instead of wandering separately about the field. The patient soon found how easily this could be achieved. All he had to do was to dump several loads of hay a few steps ahead of both horses and at once they slowed up, ate the hay and joined together in harness, as it were.

However, being a *Paskian* teaching machine the device adjusted itself rapidly to such successful play. A score was computed and as a result of continuous high scoring, the game became more difficult. The horses ate much faster and dashed ahead again, and the portions of hay available became smaller. As a result of this *negative feedback*, the successful player soon found himself being 'paced' by the teaching machine which requested a more skilful performance from him if he were to maintain his score and, more important, his feeling of mastery.

If, then, the difficulty overwhelmed the player, his score would rapidly fall as the horses separated. But the teaching machine would then again respond with negative feedback and the game would become less difficult to play. The horses would eat more slowly and the piles of hay would get bigger.

Thus, *alternately paced and encouraged*, the patient was helped to play the game skilfully and was neither frustrated nor bored since the teaching machine constantly adjusted the game to the player's performance. 'Clues' (Fig. 7.7) were not realised but would be in the form of lights coming on inside the 'Correct' buttons.

This game, though very simple, opened up a field of very entertaining devices which could keep patients of all types occupied.

POWERED ARTIFICIAL LIMBS

Medicine and its allied crafts have long repaired the ravages of time and accident by supplying us with spectacles, wigs, false teeth, hearing-aids, crutches, peg-legs and hooks. More recently, artificial limbs have achieved a high degree of mechanical excellence, and a nearly normal gait can be achieved with artificial legs.

The *hand* is more difficult to replace since it performs more delicate operations. The arm, too, must rotate at the elbow in addition to making simple hinge-like movements. The first problem is that of simulating the hand at the cosmetic level. This has been solved with considerable success by very life-like artificial hands complete with skin-ridges. Next we come to the mechanical problem, how to produce the intricate movements of the hand and arm. This has been tackled by the use of 'artificial muscles,' i.e. mechanical devices which move the artificial limb just as real muscles move our normal limbs. Such artificial muscles may be pistons worked by compressed gas, or they may be electric motors running off batteries carried by the patient. These batteries are nowadays very compact and long-lasting.

Once artificial muscles have been added to artificial limbs, the problem arises of how to *control* these muscles. At first, switches were employed which could be operated by the patient. To do so the patient used his sound limb. This method, however, has the disadvantages that the sound limb cannot itself be employed usefully when it is operating the switches on the artificial limb. Another disadvantage is that artificial muscles, controlled by switches, tend to move jerkily. They also make movements which are too violent for a particular job, such as gripping a glass of beer.

An ingenious solution to the first problem has been found. Instead of using the sound limb, it has been found possible to use what remains of the defective limb, in other words, the stump muscles after amputations or the muscle remnants in paralysed limbs. These muscles, however small or feeble, are nevertheless capable of producing an electrical signal which is picked up by electromyographic (EMG) electrodes on the skin above the muscles. Thus, suppose the patient wishes to move his limb. Although his own muscles are incapable of doing so, they produce a wave of electrical excitation which can be picked up. This in turn can be used as a control signal to operate the power-source which supplies the artificial muscles. As the patient tries to raise his arm, say, he generates potentials which regulate the power supply to the artificial muscles in his artificial limb. The arm rises.

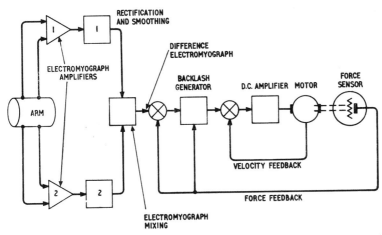

Fig. 7.8. The myo-electric powered hand, developed by The Medical Research Council and St. Thomas's

The other problem, of jerky and violent movements, can be solved by having sensing devices which moderate the force of a grip, and smoothing devices which avoid jerky movements. Such feedback elements can be incorporated in a small control device which receives the EMG signals and puts out executive signals to the artificial muscles.

Norbert Wiener himself was very concerned with these problems and spoke about them at the Medical Cybernetics Congress held at Amsterdam in 1962.[48] Groups in Britain, the United States, Yugoslavia and Russia are working to try and find solutions to these problems.

As an example of progress in this field, I would like to describe the work of Dr. Alastair H. Bottomley at the Medical Research Council Centre for Muscle Substitutes, West Hendon Hospital, London, and at the Bio-Mechanical Research and Development Unit, Roehampton, London.[49-55] The particular example of this work which I should like to discuss in more detail is described in reference 50. In this paper, the control system for the Medical Research Council/St. Thomas's myo-electric powered hand is described. This is a prosthesis for the mid-forearm and it ends in a power-operated split hook.

The control system is shown as a block diagram in Fig. 7.8. From the arm, two pairs of electromyograph (EMG) electrodes pass to their respective amplifiers. The paper discusses the requirements of these amplifiers needed to overcome the fluctuations in the skin resistance which may occur at any time. From the amplifiers, the signals are rectified and smoothed and then passed to a device which measures the difference between the two signals. The object of this is to cancel out the 'crosstalk' which occurs when some of the signal picked up by each pair of electrodes (placed over the biceps and triceps respectively) comes from the other muscle by conduction through the arm. The signal from the muscle actually contracting always predominates, so that the difference signal can be used as the control signal to operate the split hook. This signal passes by way of a backlash generator and a d.c. amplifier to the motor. The purpose of the backlash generator is to allow for the random variations which occur in the signal as a result, probably, of the sampling error of the surface EMG electrodes. The system contains three feedback loops. A force sensor sends a signal back which is compared with the myo-electric signal. When it is less than the myo-electric signal the force is increased, and vice versa (the signal is also fed back to the backlash generator which adjusts its preset limits as the force increases). A velocity feedback allows the speed of the hook-closure to be related to the myo-electric signal. These feedbacks allow the user to control the speed of movement before grasping an object and afterwards to control the strength of his grip, both by varying his effort.

Research is continuing into these devices, with the aim of producing ever more complete prostheses with increasingly ingenious control systems.

TRAVEL AIDS FOR THE BLIND

Traditionally, blind people use sticks to feel their way around the world. Sometimes they tap objects as they pass, and listen to the noise, and sometimes they can tell something about the path ahead from the changing echo of their own footsteps. Deprived of the dominant sense of distance, i.e. their sense of vision, the blind thus sometimes use their hearing as an alternative. However, many blind people do not have sufficiently sensitive hearing to do this, and in any case it is not a very accurate method.

To help blind people detect what lies in their path, some mechanical substitute for vision is required. A considerable amount of work has been done on this problem and the answer seems to be a device which uses the 'radar-like' properties of an ultra-sound beam or of a low energy laser beam. These beams bounce back off the objects in the blind person's path and are received and translated into an audible note, or a vibration under the fingers, which tells him about the distance and nature of the objects. In 1966, St. Dunstans held a conference on 'Sensory Devices for the Blind' in order to bring together research workers in this field. At this Conference, Professor L. Kay[56] described a *Monaural Sonic Aid* for the blind.

The Monaural Sonic Aid is in the shape of a torch, and is held in the hand. A two-dimensional effect is obtained by hand-scanning and by the blind person memorising the signals so produced to form a 'picture' in his mind of the immediate environment. Amplitude variations and Doppler shifts add to the complexity of the signal. The user can learn to interpret this complexity and thus enrich his mental picture. The Monaural Sonic Aid has two 'windows' at the end. One transmits the ultra-sonic beam, the other receives the reflected beam. Inside the handle of the instrument, the signals received are converted into signals in the audible range. A hearing aid-type earpiece and lead convey these signals to the

128

user's ear. The handle of the instrument contains the power source, a nickel-cadmium cell.

Another aid, the *Binaural Sonic Aid*, is in the form of spectacles which conceal a wide-angle transmitter and two wide-angle receivers spaced apart and connected one to each ear. The binaural spectacles provide a more complex system, since signals reaching the two receivers can vary in amplitude, time of arrival and frequency. The subject learns to use these differences and they enable him to build up an even more realistic 'picture' of the world.

Also described at the St. Dunstans Conference was the *Bionic Instruments Travel Aid*, presented by T. A. Benham.[57] This device works in a similar fashion to the previous ones but instead of a sonic beam there is a laser beam. This is incorporated in a cane which also contains receiving devices to pick up the reflections. These in turn are converted into vibrations detected by the user's hand and into audible sound detected as a note.

MEDICAL RESEARCH

Every section of this chapter deals with research, but here I wish to focus on the new type of research which has been made possible by cybernetic thinking and the computer.

Operational research (OR) upon a specific process, leading to its simulation by a machine, is the pattern of modern industry. Operational research is only the old 'scientific method' brought up to date and applied to the problems of war and commerce. This powerful approach is now being reapplied to science. A wide selection of typical examples will be found in Dr. Ledley's encyclopaedic book[21] especially in Chapter 9, 'Synthesis of Biomedical Systems: Simulations' other examples are given by Brandt[58] and other papers dealing with OR will be found in the *Proceedings of the International Congress on Medical Cybernetics*, for example Gatev's paper[59] on the development of control over eye movements in the child. The President of the International Society for Medical Cybernetics (see p. 110) has put forward his concept of dysnomic diseases.[60]

An important trend is the use of analogue computers in these biomedical simulations.[17] A new international journal called *Computers and Biomedical Research* was published for the first time in March, 1967.

HYPNOSIS: A CYBERNETIC ANALYSIS

'*. . . for if the imagination fortified have power, then it is material to know how to fortify and exalt it.*'

Francis Bacon
The Advancement of Learning, 1605

My own research[8, 61-63] has been in the field of hypnosis, where I have tried to perform a cybernetic analysis of the relationship between the hypnotist and his subject.

The language of hypnosis has been curiously neglected. In a recent survey of suggestion, Evans[64] noted this and himself put forward a tentative classification of hypnotic sentences based on voice and mood. Although the neglect of hypnotic language follows from the astonishing neglect of hypnosis in general by psy-

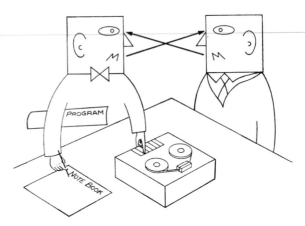

Fig. 7.9. The traditional hypnotic situation—the participant observer

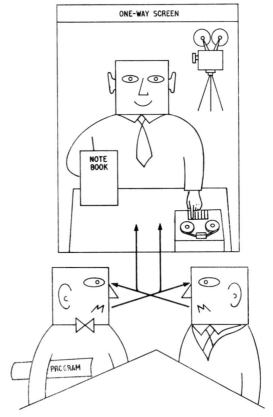

Fig. 7.10. A new hypnotic situation—the non-participant observer

chologists,[65] I think there is another reason for it. The study of hypnosis has traditionally been in the hands of medical men, from Mesmer onwards. Because of this, hypnosis has been studied and described mainly by participant observers, the doctors, who are both *in* the conversation and observing it. It is my contention that a person performing a skill involving adaptive behaviour, such as hypnosis, cannot be an *efficient* observer at the same time.

This criticism applies I believe, to nearly all psychological experiments. There should, in these cases also, be a non-participant or external observer who is outside the system and who only receives outputs from it.[32] He may know quite a lot about one or both the participants (the may, indeed, have built one of them as an automaton). Another point about the observation of complex learning systems, that has been made very forcibly by G. Pask,[47] is that we interact in it—they are observing us back. Only a cybernetic analysis can cope with this situation. My own study of hypnosis has been made mainly with myself as a non-participant observer. At other times I have been the participant observer, the hypnotist. I have also been the subject. Thus I have at one time or another played all three roles shown in Fig. 7.14 on p. 134.

We can represent the traditional kind of observation by Fig. 7.9 and the new kind by Fig. 7.10. (Another example of this method is given on p. 118.)

THE HYPNOTIC SITUATION

The hypnotic situation is a sort of conversation, but it is a very asymmetrical one. Consider first an ordinary conversation (Fig. 7.11)—both persons speak, both listen, both move and both watch. (In a *polite* conversation, they speak one at a time.)

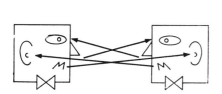

Fig. 7.11. Ordinary conversation

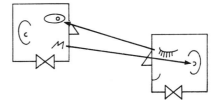

Fig. 7.12. Hypnotic conversion

The hypnotic conversation is quite different (Fig. 7.12) for here, only the hypnotist talks while only the subject listens, but only the subject moves while only the hypnotist watches (the subject *may* talk but need not do so).

HYPNOSIS AS A TEACHING SYSTEM

The curious asymmetry of this situation has an important consequence It renders feasible the automation of hypnosis (see p. 139). Consider the hypnotic situation as a teaching system in which the procedures of hypnosis are seen as a serial task, that is to say, as a piece of programmed instruction (see Fig. 7.1). Note that the pupil is the hypnotic subject. He receives verbal inputs Q from the task under the control of the hypnotist, who is seen here as the teacher. The task is formalised as a series of steps linked together in a branching network. Each step consists of an input Q together with its expected correct response CA. For every Q the hypnotist hopes to obtain the CA and in the case of a 'deep' subject he does so. The teaching system can be described as follows:

1. Hypnotist sends an input Q and a description of the correct response CA to the subject, for example, 'When I say your eyes are heavy Q they will begin to droop CA.'
2. Hypnotist sends input Q to the subject 'Your eyes are heavy.'
3. Subject responds non-verbally with a response A. For example, the subject's eyes droop.
4. Hypnotist receives the response A and compares it with the correct response CA sent from the task to the comparator. The comparator sends an error score S to the instructor and also sends a message about the nature N of any error. In the light of S and N, the instructor modifies M the task if necessary, and causes the next input Q or Q, CA to be sent to the subject. For example, if the subject's eyes had not drooped there would have been an error score S and the instructor would probably have told the task to send as the next input Q, to the subject, the same input again.

The Stanford Hypnotic Susceptibility Scale 'C'

The above analysis of the hypnotic situation applies quite well to the Stanford Scale. Although this is a *test* which is scored S as it proceeds, it is also a typical hypnotic session and demonstrates admirably the features of hypnotic language. Consider this scale. It has a traditional 'induction procedure,' which is optional, followed by 12 sections, which I shall call procedures; these are arranged in order of difficulty, starting with easy ones like hand lowering and going on to very difficult ones (which few subjects are 'deep' enough to pass) like negative visual hallucination. Each subject is taken through the scale and is given a score, at the end.

The order of increasing difficulty, in which the procedures were arranged, was established by experiment.[66] Clearly, the procedures form a serial task, with the subject passing systematically from 0 to 1, to 2 and so on to 12 under the hypnotist's instructions (Fig. 7.13).

Each procedure has an overall topic which distinguishes it from the others. The more detailed structure of a procedure will be examined later. The next section deals with the vital subject of suggestion.

THE LOGIC OF SUGGESTION

Weitzenhoffer[67] has discussed suggestion at length and puts forward several definitions. I prefer the one on page 272 of his book, where he implies that a suggestion in some way *stands for* something else. This is the line along which I myself have attempted to define suggestion.[61]

Suggestion is a Trojan Horse. A sentence is spoken and received by someone else, whereupon it gets to work inside that person under the cover of its outward appearance. The harmless horse conceals soldiers. The etymology of the word suggestion is revealing: *sub* meaning 'under' and *gerere* meaning 'to carry'. In particular, *gerere* is associated with *bellum* meaning 'war', as in the phrase to 'carry on' or 'wage' war. Thus the word 'suggestion' has the connotation, ety-

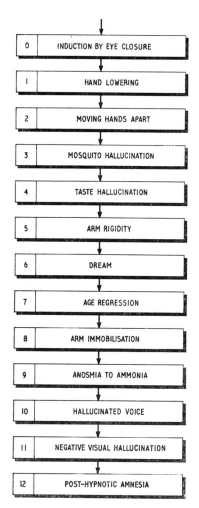

0	INDUCTION BY EYE CLOSURE
1	HAND LOWERING
2	MOVING HANDS APART
3	MOSQUITO HALLUCINATION
4	TASTE HALLUCINATION
5	ARM RIGIDITY
6	DREAM
7	AGE REGRESSION
8	ARM IMMOBILISATION
9	ANOSMIA TO AMMONIA
10	HALLUCINATED VOICE
11	NEGATIVE VISUAL HALLUCINATION
12	POST–HYPNOTIC AMNESIA

Fig. 7.13. The procedures of hypnosis on the Stanford Hypnotic Susceptibility Scale 'C'

mologically, of getting something across, of doing something under cover, perhaps even something underhand (its adjective 'suggestive' has even seedier connotations).

The World of the Subject: A Semantic Classification

Fig. 7.14 shows a hypnotist and his subject, and a nonparticipant observer. I have indicated, inside the subject's head, a small 's' for 'subjective,' meaning the subject's private world of sensations, thoughts and emotions (or, his 'mind'). Outside the subject is the 'public' world labelled 'p'. This contains the hypnotist, and the non-participant observer and a potted plant. In between the public world 'p' and the subjective world 's' is a frontier zone, the world of the subject's 'behaviour', labelled 'b'. The behaviour in this situation is, clearly, closing the eyes, breathing and moving a limb. These pieces of behaviour are the visual messages along the non-verbal feedback channel to the hypnotist, shown in Fig. 7.12. The world of behaviour is a frontier zone because behaviour '*b*' belongs both to the public world '*p*' and to the subjective world '*s*'. If the subject takes a deep breath, this is a public act visible to the hypnotist and to the non-participant observer. It is also a subjective act with its concomitant sensations.

We now have three categories '*p*', '*b*' and '*s*' defined in relation to the subject. Using these categories we may classify any sentence uttered by the hypnotist. Thus, the sentence 'your hand is rising' refers to the behavioural world '*b*',

Fig. 7.14. Semantic classification

whereas 'you feel sleepy' refers to the subjective world '*s*', and I shall touch your arm' refers to the public world '*p*'. These categories relate to the meaning, albeit only to one aspect of the meaning, of the sentences uttered by the hypnotist. They are therefore semantic categories.

The Sentences of the Hypnotist: A Syntactic Classification

Next let us consider the hypnotist's sentences from the point of view of syntax. It is possible to classify these sentences as questions Q, assertions A or commands C. For example, 'Are you ready?' is a question Q. 'You are breathing deeply' is an assertion A, and 'Relax!' is a command C. (These letters must not be confused with those used in Fig. 7.1.)

THE MATRIX OF SUGGESTION

We are now in a position to put together these two sets of categories and form a matrix of suggestion as represented in Fig. 7.15. Each cell can be labelled, and I have adopted the practic of putting the semantic category first, using a lower-case letter for it, thus: (*pQ*), (*bA*), (*sC*) and so on. Using this matrix, we can analyse every sentence uttered by the hypnotist. For example, 'You are breathing deeply' is a behavioural assertion (*bA*) and 'Relax completely!' is a subjective command (*sC*). The sentence (as spoken by the hypnotist) is then plotted by putting a circle (representing his open mouth, speaking) in the appropriate cell.

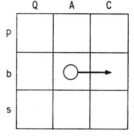

Fig. 7.15. *Matrix of suggestion*   Fig. 7.16. *'You are breathing deeply', as*
expressed on a matrix of suggestion

The next thing to be plotted is an *imaginary* sentence. This is obtained by observing the subject's behaviour, and by knowing the hypnotist's intentions. I know the hypnotist's intentions because I have been a hypnotist. When the hypnotist says 'You are breathing deeply' (*bA*), he is deliberately making a false assertion. But given time, during which the sentence is *repeated* and *varied*, most subjects *do* breathe deeply. The assertion, originally false, becomes retrospectively true. I then write down the simplest sentence which, *had the hypnotist uttered it*, would have led to the eventual behaviour at once. (I assume any co-operative subject.)

In this case the sentence is 'Breathe deeply' a behavioural command (*bC*). I plot this on the matrix by adding an arrow from the circle to the cell in which 'Breathe deeply!' falls (Fig. 7.16).

The question may be asked, Why does the hypnotist take all this time? Why does he not say simply 'Raise your arm' in the first place? The answer is that while everyday language is used to obtain immediate results in everyday life; it is the very fact that the hypnotist uses *peculiar* language, over a period of time, to produce unusual results, that acts on the subject's brain and hypnotises him. Taking the analysis of hypnosis put forward by Miller *et al.*[65] I assume that this peculiar conversation bypasses the subject's own *planning* and substitutes the *plans* of the hypnotist.

The Arrow of Suggestion

Having plotted the two sentences, that is, the one spoken and the imaginary one which would have led to the subject's behaviour at once,' we have a notation which represents suggestion as the *relationship between two sentences*. The analysis of a sentence like 'You are completely relaxed,' a subjective assertion (*sA*), is not easy because it does not lead to behaviour. However, I argue by analogy that it acts as a subjective command (*sC*) Relax! and so I represent the suggestion as in Fig. 7.17. I also argue by experience, since I have been a hypnotic subject.

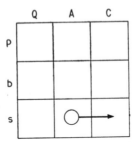

Fig. 7.17. 'You are completely relaxed', as expressed on a matrix of suggestion

SUB-PROCEDURES

Let us now look again at the procedures of hypnosis. When we look more closely at any procedure we find a new kind of structure; each procedure can be analysed into a set of what I call sub-procedures. The authors of the Stanford Hypnotic Susceptibility Scale do this analysis, to some extent, implicitly, by the way they organise the text. However, my own interest in this structure has led me to be more explicit and to give names to the sub-procedures. My reasons for doing so will emerge as this section continues.

Consider, therefore, one particular procedure, procedure 5, called *arm rigidity*. When we examine this we find that it can be analysed into the following sub-procedures (note that in my analysis I do not adhere strictly to the Stanford text):

5.1. Set up new posture
5.2. Produce stiffness
5.3. Challenge to bend
5.4. Stop challenge to bend
5.5. Remove stiffness
5.6. Restore original posture

It is sometimes said that hypnotists use 'suggestions'. They do, but not all the time. Let us examine these six sub-procedures more closely.

The Types of Suggestion

Each sub-procedure has a distinct task to perform, each requiring a distinct type of suggestion. At once we meet the paradox that the hypnotist, at times, uses ordinary language. Consider the first sub-procedure, 5.1, 'set up posture'. The hypnotist wants the subject to put out his arm straight in front of him. He *could* achieve this by the prolonged repetition and variation of suggestions such as 'Your arm is rising and will soon stretch out in front of you.' But, in practice, he does not. He uses an ordinary, everyday behavioural command (*bC*) 'Put your arm out!', the subject recognises this for what it is and obeys at once. In this case suggestion has not occurred. A sentence has been used which acts, as itself, at

136

once. There is no arrow of suggestion. I represent this type of sentence by plotting the sentence spoken and leaving it at that. It belongs to the zero class of suggestion (Fig. 7.18).

Next consider sub-procedure 5.2, 'produce stiffness'. Here the classic type of hypnotic suggestion is used. The hypnotist says 'Your arm is getting stiff' (*bA*). He repeats and varies this in a style familiar to all who have seen or read about hypnosis; 'Your arm is getting stiff, stiffer and stiffer. It is getting more and more stiff. More stiff, more and more rigid, like an iron rod . . . . .'. (This type of variation will be discussed briefly on p. 139).

With time, according to the hypnotic susceptibility of the subject, the subject's arm begins to become stiff, *as if* he were obeying the sentence 'Stiffen your arm!' (*bC*). So we can plot the suggestion as in Fig. 7.19. This familiar kind of suggestion I call a Class 1 suggestion. (Compare Figs. 7.16 and 7.17.)

Next, look at sub-procedure 5.3, 'challenge to bend'. Here the hypnotist says 'You can't bend it' (*bA*) and then goes on to say, 'Try to bend it!' (*bC*). The 'deep' subject is unable to bend his arm at this point, although he may some times be

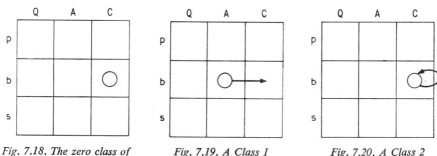

Fig. 7.18. *The zero class of suggestion*   Fig. 7.19. *A Class 1 suggestion*   Fig. 7.20. *A Class 2 suggestion*

seen to try to do so. It seems as if 'You can't bend it' (*bA*) acts as 'Don't bend it!' (*bC*) (compare Fig. 7.16), and that 'Try to bend it!' (*bC*) acts as 'Don't bend it!' (*bC*). This last can be shown as in Fig. 7.20.

The rather strange suggestion 'Try to bend it!' (*bC*) acting as 'Don't bend it!' (*bC*), I call a Class 2 suggestion to distinguish it from the more familiar Class 1 and from Class 0. Compare the concept of the double-bind.[68]

The sub-procedure has now done its job; the subject has either bent his arm or not. Before the hypnotist can move on to the next procedure he must restore the subject's muscle tone and posture to normal, *in that order* (after first carrying out sub-procedure 5.4, 'stop challenge to bend'). The next sub-procedure therefore, is 5.5, *Remove stiffness*. The hypnotist says, 'Your arm is no longer stiff' (*bA*), which acts as 'Relax your arm!' (*bC*), a Class 1 suggestion (Fig. 7.19.)

Finally, the hypnotist 'Restores the original posture' with sub-procedure 5.6. He just says 'put your arm back on the chair!' (*bC*) which acts as itself, a zero class suggestion (Fig. 7.18).

The Order of the Sub-Procedures

The order in which the procedures are arranged is determined empirically, whereas the order of the sub-procedures is a logical one. You cannot alter this order without upsetting the procedure as a whole. Thus, one cannot challenge a suggested stiffness of the arm without first producing the stiffness.

Each sub-procedure has a distinct part to play and each employs a distinct kind of suggestion, suited to that particular part. Moreover, ordinary language is used where it is more economical; for example, suggestions of Class 0 are in ordinary language (Fig. 7.18).

Flow Diagram

Another aspect of the sub-procedures is that not only are they arranged in a logically determined order they are also arranged in a branching flow-diagram of varying complexity (as apposed to a single linear succession.) For procedure 5.0, 'Arm rigidity', the diagram is quite simple (Fig. 7.21).

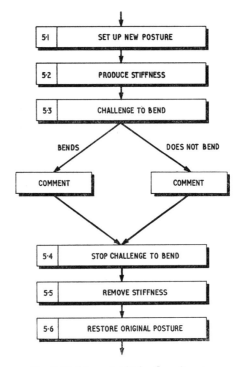

Fig. 7.21. 'Arm rigidity'—flow diagram

For other procedures, e.g. 10·0, 'Hallucinated voice,' the flow chart is much more complex. Clearly we are dealing here with branching teaching programmes. We have already noted that the series of procedures form a *linear* serial task; on looking more closely, we see that the constituents of each procedure, the sub-procedures, form a *branching* serial task. The branches allow for subjects of varying hypnotic susceptibility to react differently and to be dealt with adaptively by the hypnotist.

The hypnotist has a number of methods by which he may adapt to the subject. He may omit or add whole procedures. He may alter the duration of sub-procedures. To do this he may vary the number of sentences he uses. Naturally, if a sub-procedure becomes very lengthy, the hypnotist runs the risk of boring the subject and thus losing his attention. To avoid this, the hypnotist tends to employ the device of 'elegant variation.' For example, 'Your arm is getting stiff, stiffer and stiffer. Your arm is getting more and more stiff. It is getting so stiff it is like an iron rod. It is getting stiffer and stiffer. Stiff, like an iron rod, like an iron rod...'

THE GENERATION OF HYPNOTIC TEXT

We do not know the rules by which sequences of sentences are generated. The ability to perform this is one of the sub-skills of being a hypnotist. I have a tentative theory which supposes that each passage of text, as above, is generated by applying various grammatical rules to a theoretical entity which I call the *basic sentence*. Thus in the above passage the basic sentence is 'Your arm is stiff!' The problem is to specify the rules required to generate such text from such basic sentences. John C. Marshall and I[63] have made a start on the problem with our attempt to analyse the Eysenck Body Sway Gramophone Record.[69]

HYPNOTISING MACHINE, MK. I

This is now in use, based on Fig. 7.1. see Ref. 70.

POSTSCRIPT FOR PUGWASH

There is an old belief that for every harmful agent, Nature provides, close at hand, the antidote. Thus children, if stung by a nettle, look round at once for a dock leaf.

Let us hope that the cybernetics of world government will be applied in time to stop us all being blown up by atoms, poisoned by bacteria or paralysed by nerve gas. There is no point in this book if it is not.

Shall we send Mozart to the Moon?

It might be just as well to take a few precautions anyway. Could we not enclose a masterpiece in each vehicle that lands on the Moon? It seems such a pity to risk wasting all that lovely evolution.

ACKNOWLEDGEMENTS

Fig. 7.1 (which has been slightly modified) and Fig. 7.6 (drawn from the photograph) were previously published as Figs. 7 and 9 in 'Nerve, Brain and Memory Models,' *Progress in Brain Research*, Vol. 2, pp. 226 and 231, edited by Wiener, N. and Schadé, J. P., Elsevier Amsterdam (1963).

Fig. 7.2 was previously published as Fig. 3A on p. 347 of the *Post-graduate Medical Journal*, **43**, April (1967).

Figs. 7.4 and 7.3 are taken from Figs. 2 and 8 on pp. 374 and 383 of 'Aspects of Educational Technology', *Proceedings of the Programmed Learning Conference* held at Loughborough, 15–18 April, 1966. Methuen London (1967).

Fig. 7.8 was previously published as Fig. 3 in the *Journal of Bone and Joint Surgery, British Number*, **47B**, No. 3, 1965, in the article 'Myo-electric Control of Powered Prostheses'.

I am grateful to Dr. David Stafford-Clark, Physician in Psychological Medicine, Guy's Hospital, for his permission to try out the 'Horses Game' at the York Clinic.

The cybernetic analysis of hypnosis was started during my tenure of a Medical Research Council Clinical Research Fellowship and continued while I was working at the former M.R.C. Psycholinguistics Research Unit at Oxford.

I am most grateful to the staff of the Medical Library of Manchester University for their help in obtaining many of the books to which I refer.

My colleague, Mr. Ian. P. Christensen, kindly read the chapter in draft and made some very helpful suggestions.

Finally, I am very grateful to the Secretarial Staff of the Psychology Department, Manchester University, for typing the various drafts.

REFERENCES

1. WAILES, R., *The English Windmill*, Routledge and Kegan Paul, London (1954).
2. WIENER, N., *Cybernetics*, John Wiley, New York (1948).
3. ASHBY, W. R., *Design for a Brain*, Chapman and Hall, London (1952).
4. SHANNON, C. E. and WEAVER, W., *The Mathematical Theory of Communication*, University of Illinois Press, Urbana (1949).
5. MCLUHAN, M., *Understanding Media*, Routledge and Kegan Paul, London (1964).
6. CANNON, W. B., *The Wisdom of the Body*, W. W. Norton, New York (2nd ed.) (1939).
7. COHEN, J., *Human Robots in Myth and Science*, Allen and Unwin, London (1966).
8. CLARK, J. H., 'Adaptive Machines in Psychiatry,' in *Nerve, Brain and Memory Models*, Eds. Wiener, N. and Schadé, J. P., Elsevier, Amsterdam (1963).
9. OWEN, S. G., HALL, R., ANDERSON, J. and SMART, G. A., 'Programmed Learning in Medical Education. An Experimental Comparison of Programmed Instruction by Teaching Machine with Conventional Lecturing in the Teaching of Electrocardiography to Final Year Medical Students,' *Post-Grad. med. J.*, **41**, 197 (1965).
10. WELLER, J. M., GREENE, J. A. JR. and GEIS, G. L., 'Programmed Instructional Material for a Medical School Laboratory Course,' *J. med. Educ.*, **42**, No. 7 (1967).
11. UTTAL, W. R., 'Computer Teaching Machines: Real Time Simulation of the Tutorial Dialogue,' *Proc. IVth Int. Cong. Cybernetic Medicine*, Nice (1966).
12. COULSON, J. E., 'Computers in Research and Development on Automated Instruction,' *Proc. IVth Int. Cong. Cybernetic Medicine*, Nice (1966).
13. BITZER, D. L., LYMAN, E. R. and EASLEY, J. A. JR., 'The Uses of PLATO: a Computer Controlled Teaching System,' *Audiovisual Instruction* (Jan., 1966).
14. CLARK, D. E., 'Medical Computing in the U.S.A.,' paper given at the Symposium on *The Collection and Handling of Medical Data*, University of Salford, 6th May (1967).
15. PAYNE, L. C., *An Introduction to Medical Automation*, Pitman Medical Publishing Co., London (1966).
16. BATTERSBY, A., *Network Analysis*, Macmillan, London (1964).
17. *Computers in Biomedical Research, Volume* **1**, Eds. Stacy, R. W. and Waxman, B. D., Academic Press, New York (1965).
18. SMITH, A., 'Automation of Medical Record-Keeping,' *Lancet*, 395, 22nd Feb. (1964).
19. SMITH, A., 'Automatic Linkage of Medical and Vital Registration Records,' *Br. J. prev. soc. Med.*, **17**, No. 4 (1963).
20. *Mathematics and Computer Science in Biology and Medicine*, Conference of the Medical Research Council, H.M.S.O., London (1965).
21. LEDLEY, R. S., *Use of Computers in Biology and Medicine*, McGraw-Hill, New York (1965).
22. HARLEY, A. J., *U.K. MEDLARS. Information Retrieval Service. A Handbook for Users*, National Lending Library for Science and Technology, Boston Spa, Yorks (1966).
23. PICKFORD, A. G. A., 'FAIR (Fast Access Information Retrieval) Project: Aims and Methods,' ASLIB *Proc.*, **19**, No. 3 (1966).

24. *Computers in Biomedical Research, Volume 1*, Chapters 12 and 16, Eds. Stacy, R. W. and Waxman, B. D., Academic Press, New York.
25. HILDITCH, J. and RUTOVITZ, D., 'Techniques of Computer Recognition of Chromosomal Patterns,' paper given at the Symposium on *The Collection and Handling of Medical Data*, University of Salford, 6th May (1967).
26. WHITEHEAD, T. P., 'Computers for Laboratory Services,' *Hosp. Mgmt Plan. Equip.*, (Dec., 1966).
27. WOLFF, H. S., 'Signal Received but not Understood'.
28. BANNISTER, D., 'A New Theory of Personality,' in *New Horizons in Psychology*, Ed. Foss, B. M., Penguin Books, London (1966).
29. RAVEN, J. C., *Progressive Matrices*, H. K. Lewis, London (1938).
30. KELLY, G. A., 'A Theory of Personality,' Chapters 1, 2 and 3 in *The Psychology of Personal Constructs*, Norton and Co., New York (1963).
31. GEDYE, J. L., 'A Teaching Machine Programme for Use as a Test of Learning Ability,' in *Aspects of Educational Technology*, Proceedings of the Programmed Learning Conference, Loughborough, 1966. Methuen, London (1967).
32. CHERRY, C., *On Human Communication*, John Wiley, New York (1961).
33. FRENCH, H., *Index of Differential Diagnosis*, Wright, Bristol (1912).
34. SAVILL, T. D., *A System of Clinical Medicine*, London (1903).
35. LUSTED, L. B., 'Computer Techniques in Medical Diagnosis,' in *Computers in Biomedical Research, Volume 1*, Eds. Stacy, R. W. and Waxman, B. D., Academic Press, New York (1965).
36. BARON, D. N. and FRASER, P. M., 'The Digital Computer in the Classification and Diagnosis of Diseases,' *Lancet*, 1066, 20th Nov. (1965).
37. FRASER, P. M. and BARON, D. N., 'Computer-Assisted Classification and Diagnosis of Liver Disease,' *Proc. R. Soc. Med.*, **59**, No. 8, 776 (1966).
38. BLAGG, C. R., 'The Management of Acute Reversible Intrinsic Renal Failure,' *Post-grad. med. J.*, **43**, 290 (1967).
39. JONES, E. S., 'The Organisation and Administration of Intensive Patient Care,' *Post-grad. med. J.*, **43**, 339 (1967).
40. CLIFFE, P., 'Measurement and Recording during Intensive Patient Care,' *Post-grad. med. J.*, **43**, 195 (1967).
41. WOLFF, H. S., 'The Monitron Project,' *Br. Hosp. J.*, Oct. 21st. (1966).
42. WOLFF, H. S., 'The Biomedical Instrumentation Industry in Britain,' *Biomedical Engng*, (Nov., 1966).
43. DUMMER, G. W. A. and ROBERTSON, J., *Medical Electronics Equipment 1966–1967*, Pergamon Press, Oxford (1966).
44. WODOLAZSKY, L. A. and RABINOVITCH, N. E., 'Indicator of Anaesthesia Stages (by means of EEG),' *Proc. IVth Int. Cong. Cybernetic Medicine*, Nice (1966).
45. EMERY, E. W., 'Computer-Assisted Radiation Treatment Planning,' paper given at the Symposium on *Progress in Medical Computing*, Elliott Medical Automation Ltd., London (1965).
46. WOLPE, J., 'Behaviour Therapy and Psychotherapeutic Goals,' in *The Goals of Psychotherapy*, Ed. Mahrer, A. V., Appleton-Century-Crofts, New York (1967).
47. PASK, G., *An Approach to Cybernetics*, Hutchinson, London (1961).
48. *Progress in Biocybernetics, Volume 1*, Eds. Wiener, N. and Schadé, J. P., Elsevier, Amsterdam (1964).
49. BOTTOMLEY, A. H., 'The Control of Muscles,' in *Progress in Biocybernetics, Volume 1*, Eds. Wiener, N. and Schadé, J. P., Elsevier, Amsterdam (1964).
50. BOTTOMLEY, A. H., 'Myo-Electric Control of Powered Prostheses,' *J. Bone Jt Surg.*, **47B**, No. 3 (1965).
51. BOTTOMLEY, A. H., 'Amplifier Design and Signal Processing for Myo-Electric Control of Powered Prostheses,' *Digest 6th Int. Conf. Med. Electron. and Biol. Engng.*, Tokyo (1965).
52. BOTTOMLEY, A. H., 'Control Methods for Powered Prostheses,' *Proc. R. Soc. Med.*, **59**, No. 1 (1966).
53. BOTTOMLEY, A. H., 'A Pressure-Demand Valve for Use in the Control of Pneumatic-Powered Prostheses,' *Bio-Med. Engng* (1966).

54. BOTTOMLEY, A. H. and COWELL, T. K., 'An Artificial Hand Controlled by the Nerves,' *New Scientist*, No. 382, March (1964).

55. BOTTOMLEY, A. H., KINNIER WILSON, A. B. and NIGHTINGALE, A., 'Muscle Substitutes and Myo-Electric Control.' *J. Br. Instn Radio Engrs*, **26**, No. 6 (1963).

56. KAY, L., 'Ultrasonic Spectacles for the Blind,' paper given at St. Dunstan's International Conference, *Sensory Devices for the Blind* (1966).

57. BENHAM, T. A., 'The Bionic Instruments Travel Aid,' paper given at St. Dunstan's International Conference, *Sensory Devices for the Blind* (1966).

58. BRANDT, E. N. JR., 'Symposium on Computers in Biomedical Research,' *Clin. Pharmac. Ther.*, **8**, No. 1, pt. 2 (1965).

59. GATEV, V., 'Ontogenetic Development of the Oculomotor Control System,' *Proc. IVth Int. Cong. Cybernetic Medicine*, Nice (1966).

60. MASTURZO, A., 'La Cybernétique des Maladies dites Dysnomiques,' *Proc. IVth Int. Cong. Cybernetic Medicine*, Nice (1966).

61. CLARK, J. H., *The Logic of Suggestion*. Unpublished paper (1964).

62. CLARK, J. H., 'The Induction of Hypnosis,' *Proc. IIIrd. Int. Cong. Cybernetics*, Gauthier-Villars, Paris (1961).

63. CLARK, J. H. and MARSHALL, J. C., 'The Generation of Hypnotic Text,' *Proc. IVth Int. Cong. Cybernetic Medicine*, Nice (1966).

64. EVANS, F. J., 'Suggestibility in the Normal Waking State,' *Psychol. Bull.*, **67**, No. 2, 114 (1967).

65. MILLER, G. A., GALANTER, E. and PRIBRAM, K. H., *Plans and the Structure of Behaviour*, Henry Holt, New York (1960).

66. WEITZENHOFFER, A. M. and HILGARD, E. R., *Stanford Hypnotic Susceptibility Scale, Form C*, Consulting Psychologists Press, Palo Alto, California (1962).

67. WEITZENHOFFER, A. M., *Hypnotism*, John Wiley, New York, (1953).

68. BATESON, G., *et al.*, 'Toward a Theory of Schizophrenia,' *Behavl. Sci.*, **1** (1956).

69. EYSENCK, H. J. and FURNEAUX, W. D., 'Primary and Secondary Suggestibility: and Experimental and Statistical Study,' *J. exp. Psychol.*, **35**, 485 (1945).

70. CLARK, J. H., 'The Simulation of the Human Hypnotist by a Teaching Machine' *Proc. Int. Fed. Information Processing Congress*, Edinburgh (1968).

PART 3

CYBERNETICS AND ARTIFACTS

'The competition of the world has become a competition of intellect'

Lyon Playfair (1885)

Chapter 8

Cybernetics and Information
(Information Theory Problems)

A. M. ROSIE, M.Sc., Ph.D.

Lecturer, Department of Electrical Engineering, Queen's University, Belfast (U.K.)

SUMMARY

Information theory grew up as an attempt to provide a unified foundation for the study of communication systems. Basic to any such theory is the need to measure the quantity ('information') transmitted by any such system. The transmission of information bearing signals would be a very simple matter if it were not for the effects of interference ('noise') which causes the received signals to differ in exact form from those transmitted. This distortion means that sometimes a received signal is interpreted erroneously and mistaken for some other possible signal. However, it has been shown theoretically that it is possible to transmit information, in the presence of noise, with no errors, as long as the rate of information transfer is below a certain maximum limit.

INTRODUCTION

Taking Wiener's definition of cybernetics as 'the science of control and communication in the animal and the machine,' we see that this includes the study of the many artificial methods of communication devised by man since his earliest known history. In modern times, these artificial methods of communication are almost all electrical in nature; but this was not, of course, always the case and we can trace a path of communications starting from the early bonfire beacons, through such systems as smoke signalling and semaphoring with wooden arms and flags, to the world- and space-wide methods of today, which send electrical signals either over wires and cables or by the propagation of electromagnetic waves.

Information theory is the result of attempts to provide a unified structure for studying the performance of communication systems. Traditionally, as new sys-

145

tems have been devised, various claims have been made to justify their introduction, and the estimation of the comparative merits of different systems has been very difficult. It was hoped that information theory would supply the common framework necessary to allow assessment of their relative efficiencies (using the word in a very broad sense).

The first attempts to estimate the capabilities of systems for transmitting intelligence appear to be those of Nyquist[1] and Hartley[2] in the 1920's. They were concerned with telegraphy and estimations of the maximum signalling rates possible over limited bandwidth cables. They did not, however, consider the effects of interference on the transmitted signals and it was not until the publication of Shannon's early work[3, 4] in 1948 and 1949 that real interest in the subject was aroused. He studied the properties of information sources and the communication channels used to transmit the outputs of these sources, and derived theoretical results bounding the rate at which information could be conveyed over a channel of a certain bandwidth in the presence of a certain level of interference ('noise'), when the signal is subject to a certain mean power limitation.

To estimate the performance of a communication system it must be possible to measure the quantity being transmitted by the system. This is called the *information*, but the word is used in a sense that differs slightly from its usual connotation, and, for example, no attempt is made to estimate the semantic content of a sentence. We shall return to this question of measuring information shortly, and in the meantime we shall consider two other important topics—the interference to which all signals are subject and reasons why two-level or binary signals are favoured in many communication systems.

NOISE

Noise is the term applied to any unwanted voltage or current that is combined with the desired signal in its passage from the transmitting to the receiving end of a communication system. Such interference cannot be eliminated completely and hence received signals are not faithful replicas of those transmitted. Some types of noise, for example, that due to interference from the ignition systems of motor car engines, are eliminable but there are two basic noise producing mechanisms which are not. These mechanisms produce *thermal* and *shot* noise respectively.

Thermal noise appears as random voltages and currents in conductors at any temperature above absolute zero. It arises because free electrons in any conductor have a random motion because of their thermal energy. The amplitude probability density distribution of thermal noise is gaussian and its spectrum is flat up to frequencies at which quantum restrictions become significant.

Shot noise is also subject to a gaussian amplitude probability density distribution and arises because the flow of charge carriers constituting the current in any active device (e.g. a transistor or a thermionic valve) exhibit statistical irregularity. For example, suppose that the average or direct current flowing between anode and cathode of a valve is 10 milliamps. This implies that 6.25×10^{16} electrons leave the cathode per second, or 62,500 per picosecond (10^{-12} of a second). In one particular picosecond, however, only 62,400 may leave, while in another picosecond 62,600 may leave; it is these variations that give rise to the noise component of the current.

Unwanted currents and voltages are referred to as noise, because they produce a continuous background sound in the loudspeaker or earpiece of an audio communication system.

146

If it were not for the effects of noise, communication (at least in theory) would be a very simple business. Signals could be sent over very long distances and reproduced faithfully by amplification. In practice, however, when a signal is attenuated to a very great extent (by sending it over a long distance) it becomes so small that it may be masked by the noise produced in the amplifying device and become unrecognisable.

MODEL OF A COMMUNICATION SYSTEM

A general model of any communication system is shown in Fig. 8.1. The source is the initial information producing device, and its output is usually referred to as the message. The purpose of the coder is to transform the message into a signal (usually electrical) suitable for transmission over the channel which might be a wire, cable, electromagnetic wave propagation space or similar medium. The

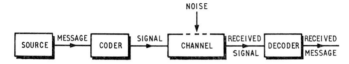

Fig. 8.1. Model of a communication system

decoder examines the received signal and reconstructs the message from it. In a system that can only transmit a finite number of distinct messages (e.g. Morse telegraphy) the coder may include a decision mechanism that decides which of the possible transmitted signals the received signal resembles most closely; it then delivers the appropriate received message. In systems using continuous wave-forms (e.g. telephony or television), the final message is a noisy version of the original message.

The noise is shown in Fig. 8.1 as being injected into the channel, but in practice it may arise in the receiver (decoder). For the purposes of our model, however, the assumption is always justified. The received signal is also taken to be the sum of the transmitted signal plus the noise, it being assumed that any attenuation of the signal while passing through the channel is compensated for by amplification in the decoder.

BINARY SIGNALLING

In modern communication, two-level or binary signals are used extensively. Figure 8.2 (a, b and c) shows three different kinds of binary signals. In the first and second kinds, the information-bearing parameters are the length and position of the binary pulses respectively, while in the third the message is coded into binary form (as in a digital computer), and the binary digits 1 and 0 are represented by a pulse and no pulse respectively. As Fig. 8.2 (d, e and f) illustrates, binary signals have good tolerance to noise because, as long as the noise peaks do not exceed $\pm \frac{1}{2}$ V volts, signals of magnitudes 0 and V can be reconstructed exactly by a process of tight clipping or slicing (passing them through an amplifying circuit which saturates on application of small inputs above or below the mean of $\frac{1}{2}$ V).

The term 'binary' is often used to denote only the type of signal shown in Fig. 8.2(c), in which the significant property is the presence or absence of a pulse, the exact length or position of a pulse being of no importance. The first two types of signals are then usually referred to as length modulated and position modulated pulses respectively. The term 'binary signalling', therefore, from now on will, be taken to imply constant duration pulses representing the binary digits 1 and 0.

In addition to having good noise combating properties, binary signals are generated and processed relatively easily. The linearity of the electronic circuits used is not critical and in fact, very non-linear circuits having two stable states are employed frequently.

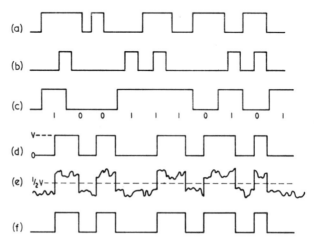

Fig. 8.2. *Communication signals (a) Length modulated binary pulses, (b) Position modulated binary pulses, (c) On/off binary pulses, (d) Binary pulse train, (e) Signal of (d) plus noise, (f) Signal reconstituted by slicing*

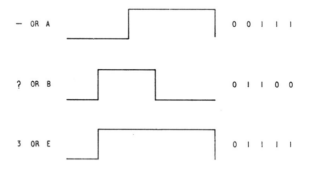

Fig. 8.3. *Three typical code groups*

A common telegraphic code uses combinations of five binary digits to represent the letters *A* to *Z*, the numerals 0 to 9 plus an assortment of other useful symbols such as commas, spaces, etc. Some typical code groups are shown in Fig. 8.3.

The uncertainty as to which of the two possible symbols is denoted by a combination, for example, whether 0 1 1 1 1 means *E* or 3, is resolved by having two combinations 0 0 0 0 0 and 0 0 1 0 0 called 'letters' and 'figures' respectively. Sending one of these indicates that all succeeding groups should be interpreted appropriately until receipt of the other indicates a switch of interpretation.

Binary communication is being used increasingly in fields other than telegraphy. It is ideally suited to data transmission links where the data originate frequently in digital computers and are already in binary form. Telephony by pulse code modulation is also expanding rapidly. In this system speech signals are encoded into binary form for transmission.

MEASUREMENT OF INFORMATION

As was pointed out earlier, if any assessment is to be made of the performance of a communication system, it must be possible to form a measure of the quantity of information being conveyed by the system. As it would be extremely difficult to measure information in the everyday sense of the word—we all know people who can talk for ten minutes or more without increasing their audience's enlightenment—the semantic meaning of messages is disregarded, and it is assumed that the amount of information is proportional to the time of communication.

If we consider a system that conveys a finite number of discrete messages rather than continuous waveforms, some of the initial concepts are simpler. Telegraphy is a discrete system in which the message may be regarded either as the letters plus numbers and punctuation marks, or as the words and numbers of the language used; telephony, on the other hand, is usually regarded as a continuous system.

The effect of the reception of a message is to change the state of knowledge of the recipient and the amount of this change is a measure of the information conveyed. We see at once, therefore, that less likely messages convey more information than more probable ones. If we tell someone something of which he is already 99 % sure, his knowledge does not increase very much; but when we inform him of the occurrence of some highly unlikely event we pass on much more information. Thus, we see that the nature of information is statistical and the information content of a message is a function of the reciprocal of the probability that this particular message is sent. The set of probabilities governing the frequencies of occurrence of the various messages of a communication system is usually termed the *a priori* or prior probabilities. Another set of probabilities to be considered concerns the authenticity of the information. Due to the effects of noise, the received signal may look more like some other possible signal than the one actually transmitted and hence may be misinterpreted. An analogy to this effect in conversation is the truthfulness of the speaker. If a person who is known to be absolutely reliable says 'the two largest ships in the world collided yesterday and both sank', the listener gains much more information than he does when a similar statement is made by an inveterate liar. The appropriate probability of authenticity is called the *a posteriori* or posterior probability. In the case of a discrete system sending messages A, B, C, D, etc., this is defined as the probability after the message is received that the transmitted message (which is not known with certainty at the receiver) was the one actually transmitted. For example, if D is sent but due to noise is misinterpreted as B, then the appropriate *a posteriori* probability, $P(D_i/B_j)$, is the probability—knowing B is received—that D was sent (The subscripts i and j denote the transmitting and receiving ends of the system respectively.) In any particular case this probability cannot be estimated at the receiver, since the fact that D was sent is not known there. If no noise is present no errors occur in transmission and all the posterior probabilities are unity. We see that information gained increases with this probability and therefore is some function F of the ratio of posterior to prior probability.

$$I = F\left(\frac{a\ posteriori\ \text{probability}}{a\ priori\ \text{probability}}\right)$$

$$I = F(P)$$

We still have to choose a suitable function F and we define one that suits our intuitive idea that information should be linearly additive. This means that if we obtain 2 units of information from one message and 3 units from another, we should expect to gain 5 units from the two messages.

If P_1 and P_2 are respectively the *a priori* probabilities of two messages, then the *a priori* probability of both messages being sent is P_1P_2. If we assume for simplicity that no noise is present and hence all *a posteriori* probabilities are unity we see that we have to choose F such that:

$$F\left(\frac{1}{P_1P_2}\right) = F\left(\frac{1}{P_1}\right) + F\left(\frac{1}{P_2}\right)$$

A simple function satisfying this relationship is the logarithm and hence we define information gained as:

$$\log \frac{a\ priori\ \text{probability}}{a\ posteriori\ \text{probability}}$$

The base of logarithms is still open to choice and is most commonly taken as 2, followed by natural logarithms and then the base 10; the units of information are as shown in Table 8.1.

Table 8.1. UNITS OF INFORMATION CORRESPONDING TO BASES OF LOGARITHMS

Base of logarithms	*Unit of information*
2	bit
e	natural unit
10	hartley

The 'bit' is the amount of information associated with each binary digit in a sequence where the occurrence of both kinds of digits is equiprobable and successive digits are independent. The *a priori* probabilities of 1's and 0's are then both $\frac{1}{2}$

and

$$\log_2\left(\frac{1}{\frac{1}{2}}\right) = 1 \text{ bit}$$

As noted above, the definition of *a posteriori* probability does not seem very practical, as it means that this quantity cannot be estimated for any particular transmission. However, since information is statistical in nature, it is more important to be able to estimate an average rate of conveyance of information than the specific amount gained by any one particular transmission.

As an example, suppose (1) that a system can transmit the three messages *A*, *B* and *C*; (2) that these occur at the transmitting end with relative frequencies of 2, 1 and 1 respectively; and (3) that the various transition probabilities of correct or erroneous interpretation are as shown below. It is desired to estimate the average amount of information received per transmission.

$$A \rightarrow \begin{matrix} A & \frac{5}{8} \\ B & \frac{1}{4} \\ C & \frac{1}{8} \end{matrix} \qquad B \rightarrow \begin{matrix} A & \frac{1}{4} \\ B & \frac{1}{2} \\ C & \frac{1}{4} \end{matrix} \qquad C \rightarrow \begin{matrix} A & 0 \\ B & \frac{1}{4} \\ C & \frac{3}{4} \end{matrix}$$

All the possible transmissions are listed in Table 8.2, together with the appropriate *a priori* and *a posteriori* probabilities, the information associated with each transmission and the probabilities of these transmissions.

Table 8.2. DATA REQUIRED FOR ESTIMATING THE AVERAGE AMOUNT OF INFORMATION RECEIVED PER TRANSMISSION

Transmission	P_1 a priori probability	P_2 a posteriori probability	$\dfrac{P_2}{P_1}$	I Information $\log_2 \dfrac{P_2}{P_1}$	P Probability of transmission	$P \times I$
$A \rightarrow A$	$\frac{1}{2}$	$\frac{5}{6}$	$\frac{5}{3}$	0·737	$\frac{5}{16}$	0·2302
$A \rightarrow B$	$\frac{1}{2}$	$\frac{2}{5}$	$\frac{4}{5}$	$-0·322$	$\frac{2}{16}$	$-0·0403$
$A \rightarrow C$	$\frac{1}{2}$	$\frac{1}{5}$	$\frac{2}{5}$	$-1·322$	$\frac{1}{16}$	$-0·0826$
$B \rightarrow A$	$\frac{1}{4}$	$\frac{1}{6}$	$\frac{2}{3}$	$-0·585$	$\frac{1}{16}$	$-0·0366$
$B \rightarrow B$	$\frac{1}{4}$	$\frac{2}{5}$	$\frac{8}{5}$	0·678	$\frac{2}{16}$	0·0848
$B \rightarrow C$	$\frac{1}{4}$	$\frac{1}{5}$	$\frac{4}{5}$	$-0·322$	$\frac{1}{16}$	$-0·0201$
$C \rightarrow A$	$\frac{1}{4}$	0	0	$-\infty$	0	0
$C \rightarrow B$	$\frac{1}{4}$	$\frac{1}{5}$	$\frac{4}{5}$	$-0·322$	$\frac{1}{16}$	$-0·0201$
$C \rightarrow C$	$\frac{1}{4}$	$\frac{3}{5}$	$\frac{12}{5}$	1·263	$\frac{3}{16}$	0·2368
						0·3521

The *a posteriori* probabilities and the probabilities of the various transmissions are easily found by considering the following diagram in which each column represents an equally likely happening:

transmitted *A A A A A A A A B B B B C C C C*

received   *A A A A A B B C A B B C B C C C*

Twice as many *A*'s are sent as either *B*'s or *C*'s so the top row contains eight *A*'s but only four *B*'s and four *C*'s. Five (i.e. five-eighths) of the *A*'s remain *A*'s while two become *B*'s and one is received as a *C*. The *a posteriori* probability of, for example, the transmission *B* → *C*, is the fraction of the received *C*'s which started off as transmitted *B*'s, and this is easily found from the diagram.

To obtain the average information per transmission, the information from any particular transmission is weighted by the appropriate probability of that transmission and the result summed for all possible transmissions giving 0·352 bits per message.

It is interesting to note that a negative amount of information is gained in some cases when a message is received incorrectly.

ENTROPY

If we consider the average information output of a source producing discrete outputs, it is found that the expression obtained is very similar to one used in statistical thermodynamics for the entropy of systems and hence the average information produced by the source per symbol output is referred to as the *source entropy*.

If the source can produce *k* discrete independent outputs and these occur with probabilities $P(1), P(2), \ldots, P(k)$ then the information associated with the production of the *i*th output or message is:

$$\log \frac{1}{P(i)} = -\log P(i)$$

It is assumed that no noise is present and hence the *a posteriori* probability is unity.

To obtain the average information output of the source the above expression must be averaged over all possible values of *i* giving:

$$\text{average information per output} = -\sum_{i=1}^{k} P(i) \log P(i) \tag{8.1}$$

This is the expression which is similar to the one for thermodynamic entropy and which gives rise to the use of the term entropy for average information content. Whether there is any closer connection between thermodynamic entropy and the entropy of information theory is a question which has been discussed at considerable length. They are both, in a general sense, a measure of disorder. A certain volume of a gas at some temperature has a higher entropy than the same gas if it is separated into various parts according to the individual energies of its molecules. If it were possible to separate the molecules into three (say) vessels having low, medium and high energies these would have low, medium and high temperatures respectively and greater entropy than the original gas. The more ordered arrangement corresponds to the lower entropy state.

If the outputs of an information source are ordered in the sense that they are known in advance, obviously no information is gained when they occur and the source entropy is zero.

When we consider sources that produce continuous waveforms instead of discrete outputs, we find that by manipulating expression (8.1) carefully, we obtain an analogous answer of:

$$\int_{-\infty}^{\infty} p(v) \log p(v) \cdot dv \qquad (8.2)$$

In this case the waveform is a function $v(t)$ subject to a probability density distribution $p(v)$ as shown in Fig. 8.4.

Equation (8.2) gives the entropy of a continuous signal if it is examined at one specific instant. Obviously, if a waveform does not contain very high frequencies it cannot change to a value independent of its value a very short time before,

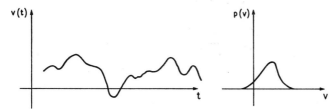

Fig. 8.4. Waveforms and associated probability density distribution

and therefore we should expect some relationship to exist between the minimum time necessary for a waveform to attain a value independent of its value at some previous instant, and its spectral content. The form of this relationship was expressed by Shannon[4] in his statement of the *Sampling Theorem:*

'If a function $F(t)$ contains no frequencies higher than W cycles per second (Hertz), it is completely determined by the values of its ordinates at a series of points less than $\dfrac{1}{2W}$ seconds apart.'

This theorem gives the justification for the many communication systems in use today in which continuous signals are effectively conveyed from transmitter to receiver although, in fact, only the values of these signals at regular intervals are sent. For example, if a speech signal of nominal bandwidth 200 hertz to 4 kilohertz is sampled at a rate of 8 kilosamples per second, the value of each of these samples can be sent in a time of 1 microsecond leaving intervals of 124 microseconds between samples. These intervals are used to send samples of other signals, thus allowing many different messages to be conveyed over the same channel. This process of interleaving of samples is referred to as *Time Division Multiplexing.*

Another interpretation of the Sampling Theorem is that $2W$ samples per second is the maximum sampling rate which gives substantially independent samples. If the rate is higher, more samples are being taken than are necessary for reconstruction and hence these cannot be independent.

Since the entropy of a continuous signal at one sampling point is $\int p(v) \log p(v) \cdot dv$ the entropy rate or average information per second is:

$$2W \int p(v) \log_2 p(v) \cdot dv \quad \text{bits per second}$$

REDUNDANCY

A very important concept in communications is that of *redundancy* which can be defined as the presence of any superfluous detail in a source, message, signal, channel or system.

An example of a redundant source is someone who repeats everything he says twice. Inherently all languages are redundant as all possible combinations of letters of alphabets do not form meaningful words and all combinations of words do not make up intelligible sentences. If all letter combinations were permitted, then a much smaller alphabet than 26 letters would be sufficient to make up the total number of words found in the average English dictionary (about 30,000). In fact, if all words were of 5 letters, an alphabet of 8 letters would be enough.

The effect of redundancy in an information source is to reduce the source entropy to a lower value than that obtainable from a maximum entropy source producing the same set of outputs. It can readily be shown that a discrete source has maximum entropy when all its outputs occur independently and with equal probability. The first of these conditions is fairly obvious, as the presence of intersymbol influence or dependence between successive outputs would mean that some information concerning future outputs could be obtained by studying past outputs. The second condition, that maximum entropy is obtained when all source outputs are equiprobable, is not so obvious but seems intuitively reasonable from consideration of a limiting case. If the probability of one output becomes much greater than that of the remainder (i.e. it tends to 1) then the information associated with it tends to zero ($\log 1 = 0$). A large amount of information is derived from the very infrequent occurrences of the other outputs, but on the average this also tends to zero since, for P tending to zero, $-\log P$ tends to infinity at a lesser rate, so the product $P \log P$ tends to zero.

If a source produces outputs with less than maximum entropy and these have to be coded for transmission over a binary channel then, by suitable coding, it is effectively possible to transmit the information at a rate approaching the maximum that the channel can handle. Procedures for doing this will be considered later in the chapter (p. 157).

It might seem at first sight that the reduction of redundancy is always a desirable objective but this is not invariably so, and in some situations the introduction of redundancy helps to give reliable performance in the presence of noise. On high frequency radio telegraph links, redundancy of receiving equipment is common. Two receiving aerials spaced apart are used to give a *space diversity* receiving system. When propagation conditions are such that the signal strength is fading severely, it is unlikely that this will happen simultaneously at both aerial sites and by selecting the stronger signal at any one time, much more reliable reception is achieved.

The inherent redundancy of language also helps to give noise protection. When conversing over a noisy telephone circuit, it is often possible to guess accurately the various words that are not received intelligibly. If there was no redundancy in language all possible other words would form meaningful sentences and the absence of the missing words would render the communication valueless.

ERROR DETECTION AND CORRECTION

Redundancy is frequently introduced deliberately in binary communication to give protection against noise. This is accomplished by adding extra binary digits (called *check digits*) bearing special relationships to the original *information* (or *data*) digits. Errors in transmission then disturb these relationships and hence enable the presence and sometimes the locations of the errors to be identified.

The simplest example of this type of procedure is a *single* parity check code. The sequence of binary information digits is broken down into blocks and an extra digit (either a 1 or 0) is added to the block to make the total number of 1's in the complete block even. This is referred to as an even parity check on 1's. Alternatively, the number of 0's could be counted and the check digit chosen to make this total even or odd. Examples of these procedures for a total block length of seven digits are shown in Table 8.3.

Table 8.3. SINGLE PARITY CHECK CODE—EXAMPLE OF PROCEDURE FOR A BLOCK LENGTH OF SEVEN DIGITS

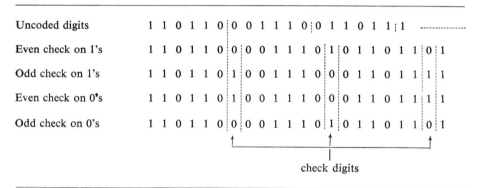

Uncoded digits	1 1 0 1 1 0	0 0 1 1 1 0	0 1 1 0 1 1	1 ------
Even check on 1's	1 1 0 1 1 0 0	0 0 1 1 1 0 1	0 1 1 0 1 1 0	1
Odd check on 1's	1 1 0 1 1 0 1	0 0 1 1 1 0 0	0 1 1 0 1 1 1	1
Even check on 0's	1 1 0 1 1 0 1	0 0 1 1 1 0 0	0 1 1 0 1 1 1	1
Odd check on 0's	1 1 0 1 1 0 0	0 0 1 1 1 0 1	0 1 1 0 1 1 0	1

check digits

At the receiver the number of 1's or 0's in each block is counted and if the check tallies it is assumed that no error has occurred. Failure of the parity procedure implies the presence of a wrong digit. It is obvious that the presence of two, four, six or any even number of errors in a block will not upset the parity relationship and hence will not be detected. For this reason a single check digit gives a *single error detecting code*. Fortunately, the probability of more than one error is usually very much lower than the probability of a single error occurring in a group or block and therefore the chance of undetected errors is small. If the error probability of a single digit is E and is independent of whether preceding digits are correct or in error, then the probability of a single error in a group of n digits ($n-1$ data and 1 check digit) is $nE(1-E)^{n-1}$ and the probability of 2 errors in the group is $^nC_2E^2(1-E)^{n-2}$. For the case where $n = 7$ and $E = 10^{-4}$, these probabilities are 5×10^{-4} and 21×10^{-8} respectively. A very common radio telegraph system uses a similar single error detecting code and achieves error correction, on detection of an error, by sending a signal back to the original transmitter asking for a repeat of the wrong block. This simple system makes very good use of the redundancy, as this latter quantity increases with the number of repeats transmitted and is low when noise conditions are favourable. An analogous vari-

155

able redundancy situation occurs in everyday conversation when the listener says 'pardon' (or 'what') when he fails to understand the talker.

By adding greater redundancy than one check digit per group it is possible to make binary coding schemes that are inherently self correcting. One such code is shown in Table 8.4. This code uses groups of four data digits; three check digits

Table 8.4. A BINARY CODING SCHEME THAT IS
INHERENTLY SELF-CORRECTING

Data Digits				Check Digits			
A	B	C	D	P	Q	R	
1	1	0	1	0	0	0	*P* checks *A B C*
1	0	0	1	1	1	0	*Q* checks *B C D*
							R checks *C D A*

are required to give single error correction. The four data digits are labelled *A*, *B*, *C* and *D* and each of the three check digits checks three of them. When an error occurs in one digit (either a data or check digit), all checks covering that digit fail when examined at the receiver and a unique combination of failing checks occurs for each possible single digit error. These combinations are shown in Table 8.5.

Table 8.5. COMBINATION OF FAILING CHECKS FOR
EACH POSSIBLE SINGLE DIGIT ERROR

Digit error	Failing check
If *A* is wrong	*P* and *R* fail
If *B* is wrong	*P* and *Q* fail
If *C* is wrong	*P*, *Q* and *R* fail
If *D* is wrong	*Q* and *R* fail
If *P* is wrong	*P* fails
If *Q* is wrong	*Q* fails
If *R* is wrong	*R* fails

This is a single error correcting code as the occurrence of two wrong digits produces a combination of failing checks that indicate a single error in some other digit. For example, if digits *A* and *P* are in error, only check *R* fails indicating a single error in position *R*.

By adding more check digits, it is possible to make codes detect and/or correct greater numbers of errors. The noise combating properties of codes are expressed readily in terms of *Hamming distance*. This is defined as the minimum number of digits in which two code groups differ. For example, if the groups of a code are always different in at least three digits, then a single error cannot make a group more similar to another group than to the original group and, therefore, it can be identified with the latter.

Suppose that the original group is 1 0 0 1 0 1 and one error occurs in the third digit making it 1 0 1 1 0 1. It is still more similar to 1 0 0 1 0 1 than to any other group (say 1 1 1 0 0 1) and hence the error can be located and corrected. Error detection but not correction is possible when a wrong group is halfway between two allowed groups. Table 8.6 summarises the properties of codes for various Hamming distances.

Table 8.6. THE PROPERTIES OF CODES FOR VARIOUS HAMMING DISTANCES

Hamming distance	Typical pair of groups	Noise combating properties
1 (no redundancy)	1 1 0 0 1 0 1 1 1 0 1 1 0 1	None
2	1 1 0 0 1 0 1 1 1 1 1 1 0 1	Single Error detecting
3	1 1 0 0 1 0 1 1 0 0 0 0 0 0	Single Error correcting
4	1 1 0 0 1 0 1 0 0 1 1 1 0 1	Single error correcting + double error detecting
5	1 1 0 0 1 0 1 1 0 1 1 0 0 0	Double error correcting
6	1 1 0 0 1 0 1 1 0 1 1 0 1 0	Double error correcting + triple error detecting

CODING TO MATCH SOURCE INFORMATION RATE AND CHANNEL CAPACITY

If the outputs of a redundant source have to be transmitted over a digital channel, the source redundancy may not be in a form suitable for giving protection against noise and if a simple coding scheme is used, information may be transmitted over the channel at a much lower rate than that which the channel can actually handle. Suppose, for example, that a source produces four independent outputs which we may refer to as *A, B, C* and *D* having respective probabilities of occurrence of 0·6, 0·3, 0·08 and 0·02. The entropy of the source is found from the formula $-P \log P_p$ to be 1·37 bits per output. These outputs could be encoded for transmission over a quaternary or four-level channel by representing each one by one of the four levels of signal. This, however, would be an inefficient use of the channel, as each digit has a potential information carrying capacity of 2 bits. Similarly, if each output is represented by a group of two binary digits, for transmission over a binary channel, the actual information transmission rate would be less than the maximum possible (again 2 bits per group). In both of these cases the coding efficiency is:

$$\frac{1\cdot37}{2} = 68\cdot5\%$$

Coding efficiency is defined as the ratio of actual rate of transmission to the channel capacity, which is the maximum possible rate the channel can handle.

The philosophy of more efficient coding schemes is that the more probable outputs are represented by shorter code groups than the ones occurring infrequently. Taking this reasoning to the extreme it might seem that an efficient binary code would be:

$$A \quad B \quad C \quad D$$

$$1 \quad 0 \quad 11 \quad 01$$

The average number of binary digits required to represent a code group is $1(0 \cdot 6 + 0 \cdot 3) + 2(0 \cdot 08 + 0 \cdot 02) = 1 \cdot 1$ corresponding to a coding efficiency of $1 \cdot 3/1 \cdot 1$ or 118%. This code is useless, however, as it has no synchronising properties allowing the end of one group to be distinguished from the start of the next. For example, the sequence of received binary digits 11001010001101 could be interpreted as *AABBADBBDAD* or *CBDDBBBCBA* or in some other fashion. This difficulty could be surmounted by inserting some distinctive synchronising group of digits between each information carrying group but, of course, this increases the redundancy again. Any code in which the groups are of equal length

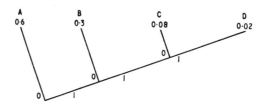

Fig. 8.5. Encoding by the Shannon–Fano method

presents no synchronising difficulties, but again it has a higher redundancy. It turns out that the maximum efficiency that can be obtained from a useable code is, reasonably enough, 100%.

Two principal methods are available for constructing efficient codes. These are usually referred to as Shannon–Fano codes and Huffman codes respectively and, in general, the latter can provide slightly higher efficiencies than the former.

To encode by the Shannon–Fano method, the outputs are arranged in descending order of probability and divided into two parts of as nearly equal probability as possible. These two groups are similarly subdivided, and this is repeated until each probability is on its own. At each division one sub-group is allocated the digit 1 and the other the digit 0. The coded form of each output is given by the appropriate sequence of binary digits proceeding from start to finish of the subdividing procedures. Representing the above example as in Fig. 8.5, this gives the code:

$$A \quad B \quad C \quad D$$

$$0 \quad 10 \quad 110 \quad 111$$

Huffman's procedure is to arrange the probabilities once again in descending order, add the two lowest and replace them by this joint probability, rearranging the sequence if necessary to keep it in order of descending probability. The new two lowest are then added and so on. At each addition one of the pair is allocated the symbol 1 and the other 0. Our example above is then represented as in Fig.

8.6, giving the code:

$$A \quad B \quad C \quad D$$
$$0 \quad 10 \quad 110 \quad 111$$

which we see is the same as that obtained by the Shannon–Fano method for our simple example.

The average number of binary digits per code group is $1(0{\cdot}6)+2(0{\cdot}3)+3(0{\cdot}08+0{\cdot}02) = 1{\cdot}5$ giving a coding efficiency of $1{\cdot}37/1{\cdot}5$ or $91{\cdot}2\%$.

No synchronisation is needed as in no instance does one group form the start of another group.

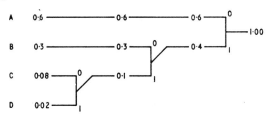

Fig. 8.6. Encoding by Huffman's procedure

To obtain more efficient encoding it is possible to take the source outputs in pairs and treat each of these pairs as a new symbol with appropriate probability, e.g. *AA*, *AB* and *DC* have respective probabilities of $0{\cdot}36$, $0{\cdot}18$ and $0{\cdot}0016$. The complexity of the procedure is much greater, however, and if it is desired to increase the efficiency still further by taking the outputs in threes, the process becomes very unwieldy.

If the source has to be matched to a channel that handles other than binary signals, an efficient coding procedure is to code initially into binary, using the Shannon–Fano or Huffman procedures, and then to recode to suit the channel. For example, if the channel handles quaternary or four-level signals, the recoding procedure is merely the simple one of taking the binary digits in pairs and replacing each one of the four possible combinations by one of the four quaternary digits, e.g.:

binary	00	01	10	11
quaternary	0	1	2	3

As the maximum possible information contents of one quaternary digit or two binary digits are both two bits, the recoding process introduces no extra redundancy and hence causes no loss of efficiency.

In many cases, however, the recoding procedure cannot be carried out without a reduction of efficiency. Suppose that a five-level channel is available; four of these could be used to represent the four pairs of binary digits but the fifth would be unused. A more complicated scheme would be to take the binary digits in groups of 14 (there are 16,384 groups) and represent each of these by one of the 18,125 groups of 5-level digits taken 6 at a time. This would still introduce some redundancy, as 1,761 of the latter groups would not be used.

IDEAL MAXIMUM COMMUNICATION RATE

It might appear on first sight that an error free communication system is impossible in the presence of noise, as there would always seem to be a finite probability that the noise could cause a transmitted signal to become more similar to some other signal, and hence cause misrecognition. In practice this is so, but Shannon[3,4] showed that it is theoretically possible to transmit information in the presence of noise with an error rate that tends to zero as long as the rate of information transmission does not exceed a certain maximum value. This limit to the rate of error free transmission is given by the expression:

$$C = W \log_2 \left(1 + \frac{P}{N}\right) \quad \text{bits per second}$$

where C is the communication rate of information
W is the bandwidth of channel (and signals)
P is the average signal power
and W is the average noise power

Shannon first showed[3] that this expression gives an upper limit to the rate of information transmission. In another paper,[4] he demonstrated that this rate should be attainable with an error rate that tends to zero. The first part he proved by considering the entropies of the received signals and the noise and showed that, to achieve the maximum rate, the transmitted signals must have amplitude probability density distributions that are of gaussian form; in other words, the signals must look like random noise. This arises from the fact that a waveform, limited to a certain mean power, has maximum entropy when its statistics are gaussian.

To show that the maximum rate should be attainable with a negligible error rate, Shannon used a multi-dimensional space representation of a communication system. Every signal of duration T seconds and bandwidth W hertz can be represented by $2TW$ samples, (strictly a waveform limited to a time T has an infinite bandwidth and one limited to a bandwidth W must extend for all time, but as long as TW is large, waveforms limited in both domains may be postulated). The magnitudes of each of these samples is plotted as a co-ordinate distance in a space of $2TW$ dimensions. This means that each signal is represented by a point in the space or by the vector joining the origin to the point. Points near to each other represent signals which are similar to each other and, in fact, the cosine of the angle between two vectors is a measure of correlation between the signals represented by the vectors. If it is assumed that all signals have the same mean power, then they all lie on the surface of the same multi-dimensional sphere.

Shannon estimated the maximum communication rate by calculating how many signals could be accommodated on the surface of such a sphere, without them being so close together that their chance of being misrecognised when perturbed by noise became appreciable. To keep this error probability negligible, he found it necessary to make the duration of the signals tend to infinity. This immediately shows why no practical system has ever been constructed with a performance reaching that of the theoretical maximum. If signals of duration T are used, there is a delay of T at the transmitter after the output from the information source is obtained, and before the encoding operation is complete. At the receiver, all the signal must have been received before it can be compared with all the possible signals and a decision made about its identity. If the information source is continuous and sections of its output, T seconds in duration, are encoded into signals T seconds long, there is a delay of $2T$ seconds between the information input at the sending end and its output at the receiver.

The use of signals of finite duration always introduces a finite error rate. Rice[5] estimated that if a system is to have an error probability of 1% and is to transmit information at a rate 97% of the ideal maximum, it requires to have a 'vocabulary' of 10^{2408} signals, which is clearly impractical. This brings out the point that Shannon's formula is useful, not so much as a target for the performance of actual systems, but rather as a help in the understanding of the processes of communication and as a general yardstick.

If it is rewritten in the form:

$$I = TW \log_2 \left(1 + \frac{P}{N}\right)$$

where the total amount I of information communicated is equal to the product of the communication rate C and the time of transmission T, then we see that T, W and P/N are interchangeable in the sense that a certain amount of information may be communicated by using a noisy channel for a long time or a less noisy channel for a shorter time (if W remains constant). Correspondingly, bandwidth may be exchanged with time and signal-to-noise ratio.

In practice, time is exchanged for bandwidth and signal-to-noise ratio in the systems sending back pictures of the moon from lunar probes. The scan rate of the pictures is very low, hence the signals have a small bandwidth and are received reliably. In everyday life, time and signal-to-noise ratio are traded when one spells out the name of the desired exchange to a telephone operator. In this case a more time-consuming form of coding is being used to reduce the output signal-to-noise ratio and hence increase the reliability of transmission.

If we apply the maximum communication rate theorem to speech communication we find than information is being transferred at a very much lower rate than the theoretical maximum. A typical telephone circuit has a nominal bandwidth of about 3,400 hertz and a fairly poor signal-to-noise power ratio, possibly of the order of 3. An ideal channel with these parameters would have a maximum error free communication rate of:

$$3,400 \log_2 (1+3) = 6,800 \quad \text{bits per second}$$

The actual rate of transferring information by conversation is very much less than this. For the English language, with an alphabet of 27 characters (the letters A to Z plus a space), maximum entropy would be obtained if these were all equiprobable, when it would be about 4·7 bits per letter. In fact, the redundancy of language is very considerable, first of all because not all characters are equiprobable and more importantly because only a very small fraction of possible letter combinations are used. As was pointed out earlier when discussing redundancy (p. 154), 5 letter words formed from an alphabet of 8 letters provide sufficient combinations to form 30,000 words. Similarly, only a very small proportion of possible word combinations form meaningful sentences. By a process of showing people sections of text with portions missing and asking them to fill in the blanks, Shannon[6] estimated the redundancy of English and decided that the actual entropy of English is about 1 bit per letter.

From this, and taking the length of an average word to be 6 letters (5 plus a space) and the average speaking rate to be about 2 words per second, we see that the average conversational information rate is about:

$$6 \times 2 \times 1 = 12 \quad \text{bits per second}$$

which is very much less than the ideal telephone channel communication rate of 6,800 bits per second.

Even if the inherent redundancy of language is neglected, there is still a difference of two orders of magnitude between the ideal error free rate and the actual rate of $12 \times 4 \cdot 7$ or $52 \cdot 4$ bits per second. This discrepancy demonstrates that it should be possible, by suitable encoding of speech, to utilise transmission channels much more efficiently and a considerable effort has been devoted for many years to perfecting speech bandwidth compression methods.

We see, therefore, that in spite of the impossibility of having a practical communication system with a performance approaching that of Shannon's ideal, the rate theoretically obtainable from the latter is of great importance. It forms the main cornerstone of Information and Communication Theory and much of the later work has been built upon it.

REFERENCES

1. NYQUIST, H., 'Certain Factors Affecting Telegraph Speed,' *Bell Syst. tech. J.*, **3**, 324 (1924).
2. HARTLEY, R. V. L., 'Transmission of Information,' *Bell Syst. tech. J.*, **7**, 535 (1928).
3. SHANNON, C. E., 'A Mathematical Theory of Communication,' *Bell Syst. tech. J.*, **27**, 379, 623 (1948).
4. SHANNON, C. E., 'Communication in the Presence of Noise,' *Proc. I.R.E.*, **37**, 10 (1949).
5. RICE, S. O., 'Communication in the Presence of Noise,' *Bell Syst. tech. J.*, **29**, 60 (1950).
6. SHANNON, C. E., 'Prediction and Entropy of Printed English,' *Bell Syst. tech. J.*, **30**, 50 (1951).

Chapter 9

Learning and Teaching Systems

G. PASK, Ph.D., M.A.

Systems Research Ltd., Richmond, Surrey, and Institute of Cybernetics, Brunel University (U.K.)

SUMMARY

This chapter describes some early work in the field of 'learning machines' (hardware embodiments for moderately detailed models of a learning process). Our chief aim in constructing these artifacts and performing experiments with them, was to design a complementary 'teaching machine'. The same design principles were used to construct teaching machines capable of instructing subjects in a variety of skills. After giving an account of the equipment, I have described a number of experiments on the simulation of animal and human learning processes (the teaching paradigm is derived from a consideration of these results).

INTRODUCTION

Inspired by Wittgenstein's insistence upon the primacy of relations, C. E. G. Bailey, T. R. McKinnon Wood and I set about the task of building a machine capable of learning the relationships between events in its environment. In parallel with this project, we devoted some effort to teaching the machine a subset of useful or desirable relationships and concluded that a further mechanism was needed for that purpose. We embodied this mechanism in another piece of hardware and C. E. G. Bailey christened the learning system 'EUCRATES' (the original sorcerer's apprentice).

There were several EUCRATES systems. The first of these, represented diagrammatically in Fig. 9.1, was commissioned by the Solartron Electronic Group and was exhibited in the Physical Society Exhibition of 1955 in London. The finally engineered version, illustrated in Fig. 9.2, is an analogue computer for use in designing adaptive teaching machines by examining their interaction with a simulated student, and was completed by Solartron in 1960. These systems have been mentioned in the literature[1-4] and they were reported extensively. So far,

163

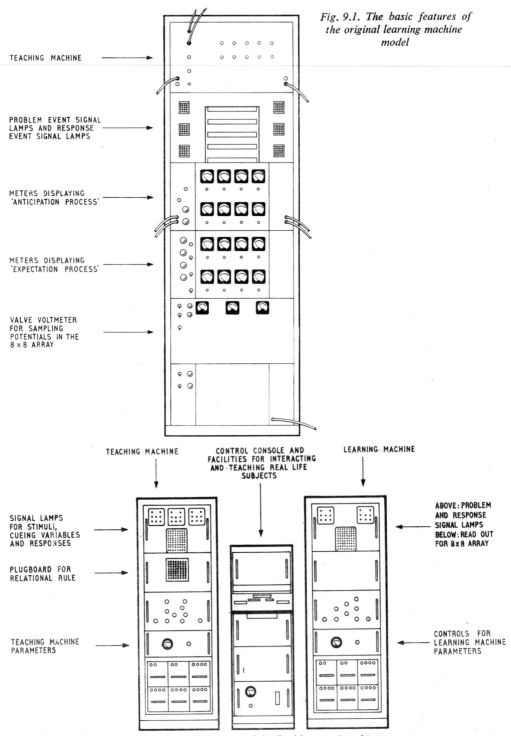

TEACHING MACHINE →

PROBLEM EVENT SIGNAL
LAMPS AND RESPONSE
EVENT SIGNAL LAMPS →

METERS DISPLAYING
'ANTICIPATION PROCESS' →

METERS DISPLAYING
'EXPECTATION PROCESS' →

VALVE VOLTMETER
FOR SAMPLING
POTENTIALS IN THE
8 × 8 ARRAY →

Fig. 9.1. The basic features of the original learning machine model

TEACHING MACHINE

CONTROL CONSOLE AND
FACILITIES FOR INTERACTING
AND TEACHING REAL LIFE
SUBJECTS

LEARNING MACHINE

SIGNAL LAMPS
FOR STIMULI,
CUEING VARIABLES
AND RESPONSES →

PLUGBOARD FOR
RELATIONAL RULE →

TEACHING MACHINE
PARAMETERS →

ABOVE: PROBLEM
AND RESPONSE
SIGNAL LAMPS
BELOW: READ OUT
FOR 8×8 ARRAY

CONTROLS FOR
LEARNING MACHINE
PARAMETERS

Fig. 9.2. The basic features of the final learning/teaching system

however, they have not been described technically and this paper is an attempt to remedy the situation; it concentrates upon the learning machine, since it turns out that an effective teaching machine is a stochastic inverse of it. I believe it is worth writing about this machinery, even though the work is a dozen years out of date, because in some respects the design is still quite 'modern' and because the fabrication and manipulation of these devices gave rise to a programme of work that is still in progress in my own laboratory.

THE MACHINE

PHILOSOPHY

Basically, EUCRATES is a reflex 'learner' which is sensitive to rewarded relations between the stimuli it receives and the responses it produces. In this respect, its design owes a great deal to the pioneering work of Uttley,[5,6] with conditional probability learning machines. In addition, however, EUCRATES contains a mechanism interpretable as an expectancy mechanism and another which simulates response anticipation (or, at any rate, something akin to Thorpe's[7] specific action potential). Further, EUCRATES is designed around concepts to do with 'curiosity' and 'attention' (it has a primitive curiosity system and there is a sense in which its attention must be occupied). Briefly, EUCRATES is a machine which looks for problems and, having found one, is impelled to learn how to solve it. This property is so basic to the design of the system that if the machine is placed in a situation that prevents the exercise of 'curiosity', then it becomes functionless.

The action of the machine can be analysed in several ways. We might, for example, adopt the elegant techniques developed by Steinbuch[8] in connection with his learning matrices (which are special types of conditional probability machine). For the present purpose, however, we can analyse the activity quite satisfactorily by saying what the machine does and how it does it, without going into mathematical niceties.

OVERALL PLAN

The layout of the machine is shown in Fig. 9.3. It consists of a stimulus unit with components $I_1...I_8$, an output or response unit with components $J_1...J_8$ and an array of 8×8 analogue storage devices (retaining the values of variables θ_{ij}, $i = 1, 2, ..., 8$ and $j = 1, 2, ..., 8$). In the first machine to be constructed, this 'array' consisted of 64 capacitors with read in, read out and lock facilities provided by clamp diodes. (Read out, even into a high impedance, modifies appreciably the state of an individual store.) In later machines, this rather crude arrangement was replaced by 64 capacitors, each of which was associated with a Miller Integrator, amplifier and impulse circuits for read in, so that the state of a store is substantially unchanged by an interrogation.

Stimulus Unit

The circuitry of the stimulus unit is shown in Fig. 9.4. The output of the unit is a vector, X, of 8 binary variables x_i, each of which is associated with one of the components I_i. Any one of the I_i consists of a 'memory', an averaging circuit, a

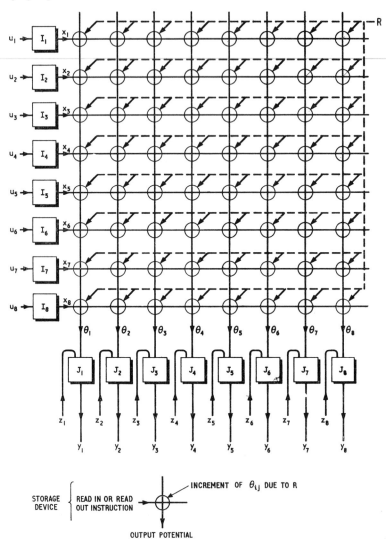

Fig. 9.3. *The plan of the machine. Each storage device retains the value of a biasing variable* θ_{ij}

current limiter and a lock circuit. The current limiters are cross coupled so that an increase in the current passing through the ith circuit inhibits the action of all the remaining circuits. If a stimulus 'search' instruction is delivered (as a positive potential) to the common cathode valve, then a decision process is instituted as a result of which the current passing through one or more of the I_i exceeds the predetermined value built into the limiter. When the limit is exceeded by the ith circuit, $x_i = 1$. The lock circuit holds this condition (irrespective of the state of the machine) until a responsive event $y_j = 1$ takes place (we shall discuss the process whereby $y_j = 1$ in a moment) and it delivers a 'response search' instruction to the response unit. Next, the event $x_i = 1$ delivers a negative, inhibitory charge to the ith memory capacitor and a small positive charge to each of

166

the remaining memory capacitors. Then, after a short delay of δt, this event cancels the stimulus search instruction so that the decision process terminates. Finally, the event $x_i = 1$ 'opens' a row of the 8×8 storage array so that a vector θ_j of values θ_{ij} is delivered as part of the input to the response unit.

The outcome of the decision process depends upon the values assumed by the variables u_i in a vector U (the external input to the I_i) and the values assumed by 8 variables μ_i (derived, as an internal input, from the memory circuits). If all of the $u_i = 0$, the action of the stimulus unit is fairly straightforward. The inhibitory cross coupling between the I_i fosters (though it does not strictly enforce) the condition that no more than one $x_i = 1$ at once. Suppose that the stimulus search instruction, cancelled by the event $x_i = 1$ is again instituted (by a mechanism we shall discuss in a moment) and that x_i is set equal to 0. The decision process now searches for and produces the least 'likely' or the most 'unusual' event.

These conditions no longer hold true if the external input is energised; for example, it is possible to make several of the u_i positive valued and to secure several x_i conjointly equal to 1. Even so, the external input, U, still acts upon an underlying search and memory process of the sort we have described. In particular, because of the memory feedback signal, the machine is prone to reject repeated and familiar inputs. Conversely, the value of u_i required to elicit the event $x_i = 1$, increases with repetition. In other words, the stimulus unit exhibits habituation (see p. 171).

Response Unit

The response unit is also shown in Fig. 9.4. This resembles the stimulus unit closely, but differs in the following two respects: (1) in addition to the external input Z (analogous to U), and the internal inputs η_i (analogous to the μ_i), the J_j averager receives an input θ_{ij}; (2) the lock circuit of a component I_i is replaced, in a component J_j, by a circuit that holds the condition $y_j = 1$, (analogous to $x_i = 1$) for an interval Δt. With these comments it will be evident that on receipt of a response search instruction (analogous to the stimulus search instruction) a decision process is set up in the response unit which leads to one or more events of the form $y_j = 1$. However, even if the variables z_j in Z are zero valued, this process is biassed by an input from the 8×8 array of Fig. 9.3.

In considering the form of the bias, notice that the feedback to the memory elements in the response unit is derived directly from the current limiting circuits through non-linear components. The time constants of these memory circuits are short compared with the time constant of the stimulus unit memories, and the feedback acts within the compass of a single decision process. The effect of a high valued input θ_j at the jth component is to drive this circuit into the state $y_j = 1$. However, if the input does not succeed in doing so, within a given interval, its action is inhibited by an increasingly negative η_j from the memory circuit output. As a result of this, the θ biassing effect is not unique, for example, the event $y_j = 1$ may occur either because θ_{ij} is higher than the other entries in the biassing vector θ_i, or because there is an ordering of the form $\theta_{il} = \theta_{im} > \theta_{ij} > \ldots$ when the tendencies to produce $y_l = 1$ and $y_m = 1$ compete and are inhibited by increasing η_l and η_m so that ultimately $y_j = 1$. There are, of course, a large number of competitive impasses that are resolved in this fashion.

The response search instruction is delivered whenever $x_i = 1$; further, the particular row of the 8×8 array presented as a biassing input to the response

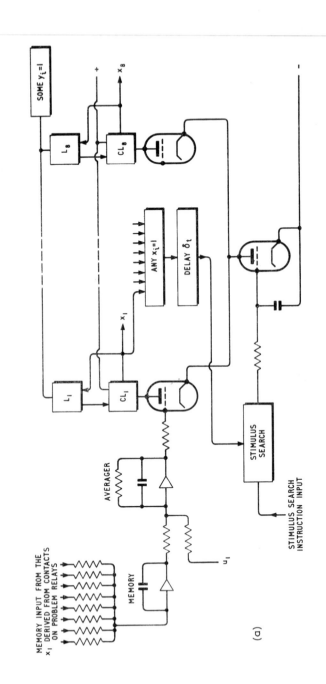

(a)

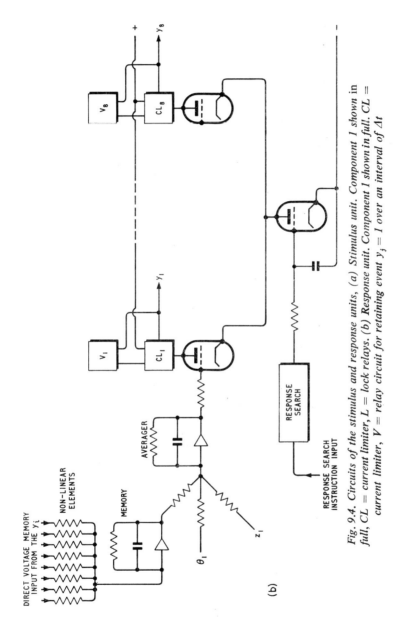

Fig. 9.4. Circuits of the stimulus and response units, (a) Stimulus unit. Component 1 shown in full, CL = current limiter, L = lock relays. (b) Response unit. Component 1 shown in full. CL = current limiter, V = relay circuit for retaining event $y_j = 1$ over an interval of Δt

unit depends upon the particular event x_i (this event 'opens' the row of storage devices and presents a vector θ_i to the response unit); hence, the array serves to couple the stimulus and the response units. To close the cycle, we note that the stimulus search instruction is delivered at the termination of any event $y_j = 1$ (that is, Δt seconds after such an event has occurred). (NOTE: If the θ_{ij} are constant valued, this coupling is such that the machine acts as a stochastic matrix multiplier. When, as below, the θ_{ij} are variables, the entries in the stochastic matrix are functions of the performance of the machine.)

Storage Mechanism

The cyclic action gives rise to sequences of events $x_i = 1$, $y_j = 1$, which overlap by Δt seconds to form conjoint events $x_i, y_j = 1,1$. The values θ_{ij} retained by the 8×8 storage device in the 8×8 array depend upon the value assumed by a variable, R, at the moment when a relevant conjoint event occurs. Thus, at trial n in a sequence, if a single event $x_i, y_j = 1,1$ occurs, the value of θ_{ij} is incremented or decremented by an amount.

$$\Delta_1\theta(n) \approx [R(n) - \theta_{ij}] \cdot \Delta t$$

Conversely, the values of all of the entries in the vector θ_i are decremented towards 0 by an amount proportional to the values of these entries and the *interval* between the event $x_i = 1$ and event $y_j = 1$ (we shall later refer to this interval as the 'anticipation latency'). The variable R (which is later interpreted as a 'reinforcement variable') can assume values in the interval -1, 0, $+1$ and a null value, ϕ. If $R(n) = \phi$ then $\Delta_1\theta(n) = 0$.

The incrementation process is more complicated if a pair of events $x_i = 1$, $x_k = 1$, occur simultaneously or if they overlap before some $y_j = 1$. Suppose, to begin with, that $x_i = 1$ and $x_k = 1$ and $y_j = 1$ at the nth trial and that $R(n) = \phi$. In this case, if $\theta_{ij} > \theta_{kj}$ then the entry θ_{kj} receives an increment $\Delta_2\theta(n) \approx c(\theta_{ij} - \theta_{kj}) \cdot \Delta t$. If $R(n)$ is not equal to ϕ then the total incrementation is complex and consists of a component $\Delta_1\theta(n)$, the 'extrinsic reinforcement' and a component $\Delta_2\theta(n)$, the 'intrinsic reinforcement'. So far as decrementation is concerned, if $x_i = 1$ and $x_k = 1$ all of the entries in θ_i and all of the entries in θ_k, including θ_{ij} and θ_{ik}, are reduced in the direction of 0 in proportion to their several values and the length of the anticipation latency. Because of this, and because of the active characteristics of the stimulus and response units, we observe that the maintenance of a pattern of θ_{ij} values entails some sort of dynamic organisation.

THE SYSTEM

Let us talk about the system anthropomorphically. On receipt of a stimulus search instruction, the stimulus unit 'expects' to receive a 'problem' (some non-zero value of X). The problem it does receive will be biassed by 'evidence', U, from its environment but even if there is no evidence, some problem will ultimately be posed (as a result of the stimulus unit decision process). This state of 'expectancy' gives rise (when the problem is posed) to a state of 'anticipation' regarding a solution to this problem. (A solution is some non-zero value of Y; it is achieved by the response unit decision process, instituted through the response search instruction by some $x_i = 1$; the solution depends, even in the absence of the external input Z, upon the θ_{ij} values in those rows of the 8×8 array that are selected by the particular problem.) The state of 'anticipation' terminates Δt after a solution is produced and its termination gives rise to a further state of problem 'expectancy'.

In all this, the θ_{ij} values play a crucial part by determining what solutions will be given to various problems. We assume that values of R represent values of some reward or desirable commodity and that the machine would like to solve problems in such a way as to maximise the average value of R. This concept is effectively built into the design, for, as a result of the process we have described, the machine 'learns' to solve problems in a manner that is compatible with maximising the average value of R (the θ_{ij} assume a pattern that leads to this result providing that specific and consistent values of R are associated with specific problem solution pairs).

MODIFICATION OF HABITUATION MECHANISM

The habituation of the machine requires further comment since it is, in some respects, unrealistic. If a stimulus is repeated, the strength of stimulus required to elicit the problem state $x_i = 1$ increases. This is more or less as it should be, provided that $x_i = 1$ does not lead to a reinforced response (a significant event). If the result of a stimulus is significant (if $x_i, y_j = 1,1$ is reinforced) then the present machine performs as it would do if the stimulus were not significant (at least, it does so with respect to the expectancy process; the anticipation latency, the interval occupied by the response unit decision process, *is* reduced). This is not altogether satisfactory because in a real organism habituation with reference to significant stimuli is suppressed or nullified. Our model works the right way round for the anticipation latency; but it is perverse so far as the expectancy latency for significant events is concerned.

The right characteristic can be secured in several ways. We produced it by modifying the memory feedback to the stimulus unit memories so that, instead of a simple inhibitory signal, this feedback became, at the nth trial and for the event $x_i, y_j = 1,1$ a quantity $1 - \theta_{ij}(n)$ where $\theta_{ij}(n)$ is the quantity delivered as the internal input to the jth component of the response unit. If the problem event induced by a stimulus is not significant, $1 - \theta_{ij}(n)$ is high (and habituation takes place as before). If the problem event is significant, then $1 - \theta_{ij}(n)$ is low valued and habituation is suppressed. This arrangement gives the machine the required characteristics, but it does so 'unfairly'. By additions of this sort, we are trying to represent in a primarily single level model the organisation of a many level, or hierarchical structure.

THE MACHINE REGARDED AS A BLACK BOX SYSTEM

Next, let us look at the machine as a black box in the sense of Ashby[9] 'learning' system. It has an input U, which we may interpret as a stimulus vector (or as a vector of evidence in respect to a hypothesised intermediary problem vector X). It has an output, Y, which we interpret as a response vector designating an hypothetical solution vector. This is only the case if all of the y_j are brought out to external connections. In many arrangements of the system, only some of the y_j are brought out and there is a great deal of difference between a solution and a response. It has an input R, which (given a correspondence between stimuli and problems and responses and solutions) acts as a reinforcement variable. It has an input Z which manifestly guides the machine in selecting its response; we can prevent the machine from making response j by holding the jth component of Z negative valued and we can force it to make response j by holding the jth component of Z positive valued; at least we can in most conditions (to be certain of doing so, we should have to delve inside the black box). Hence, Z is identified with a cueing vector.

If we adopt this identification, it is convenient to relabel a vector U, in which one component is positive and the rest are zero valued by a letter (calling such a vector 'stimulus a' $\equiv U = 1,0,0,0,0,0,0,0$, or 'stimulus b' $\equiv U = 0,1,0,0,0,0,0,0$; there are 8 of them in all).

Similarly, the response events $y_j = 1$ are named 'response A' $\equiv Y = 1,0,0,0,0,0,0,0$, or 'response B' $\equiv Y = 0,1,0,0,0,0,0,0$. We may, of course, apply more than one stimulus at once, in which case the vector U has more than one non-zero component. (Thus, the conjunction of 'stimulus a' and 'stimulus b' is the vector $U = 1,1,0,0,0,0,0,0$.) It is also possible for the machine to make more than one response at once.

At this point, it is apt to comment upon an ambiguity in the use of words like 'stimulus' and 'response'. Amongst other things, the word 'stimulus' can designate either of the following:

1. The state of the environment that is appreciable by the machine at a given trial.
2. An appreciable and separable event (the state of some part of the total environment).

If we interpret 'stimulus' according to (1), then the several components, u_i in U, are properties of the stimulus, designating appreciable attributes. We could, in this case, talk about stimulus discrimination (that the machine comes to select certain properties as important and to disregard others as unimportant). However, we could not say that a pair of stimuli occurred simultaneously or that the machine rejected one of this pair and respected the other. (We might describe this situation by saying that the machine attended to one property of the total stimulus and disregarded the other.) Conversely, if we adopt definition (2), it is entirely possible to have coincident stimuli, but stimulus discrimination effects will be suppressed and will be manifest in connection with phenomena such as habituation that are predicates of sequences of trials.

In adopting the 'stimulus a' and 'stimulus b' nomenclature, we have opted in favour of definition (2) rather than (1). It is important to realise that this decision is not forced upon us by the machine; it is made to suit the experimental context in which we intend to examine the machine's behaviour; to subserve the sort of tricks we want the machine to exhibit. The machine's behaviour could be described equally well within the framework provided by (1) or by (2). The essential point is to bear in mind the consequences of the nomenclature that has been selected.

Similar comments apply, more obviously perhaps, to 'response'. According to a definition that parallels (1), the machine, at any trial, makes a response which is a vector Y; (to be more specific, we might adjoin latency information, stating when the various components y_i of Y undergo a transition $0 \rightarrow 1$). If, on the other hand, we choose a definition akin to (2), then the machine may make several 'responses' at a given trial and specificity is achieved by saying how and when these several responses are made. The word 'response' here is slightly misleading (it would be more usual to say 'the machine's response has several parts—these parts of the total response are made in such and such a fashion'). As a result we shall take the liberty (commonly taken in the literature) of using the word 'response' to denote either the total configuration or the parts of this configuration, providing that this practice does not give rise to confusion.

SOME EXPERIMENTAL WORK INVOLVING LEARNING AND TEACHING SITUATIONS

LEARNING EXPERIMENTS

In a suitable environment, the machine is able to mimic many features of classical conditioning and instrumental conditioning. To make it play these tricks, we tacitly identify the device with a laboratory animal such as a pigeon or a rat.

A few preliminary remarks are needed. In the context of classical conditioning, a stimulus is partially causative (it is something that gives rise to, or helps give rise to, an observable response). Broadly speaking, responses would not occur without stimuli of some sort (though these may be internal stimuli or stimuli that are concealed from the observer). By way of contrast, the field of instrumental conditioning is built around the concept of an operant, that is, a response emitted by the organism autonomously. Stimuli are chiefly discriminating stimuli; events which, in Skinner's words, provide the occasion for a response but do not give rise to it. They serve to influence and bias an autonomous response process.

The distinction, in experimental psychology, between a stimulus and a discriminating stimulus is tenuous (but the philosophical orientations of these different fields are distinct enough to deserve respect). So far as the machine is concerned, the distinction between a stimulus and a discriminating stimulus is a matter of degree—some stimuli are more causative than others; there is an underlying autonomous activity; we do not explicitly invoke the hidden stimuli that produce it, but we could invent some.

THE CLASSICAL CONDITIONING PARADIGM

If a stimulus is applied (say stimulus a) and if this gives rise to the problem state $x_i = 1$, then the machine will emit one, or usually one, response (say response A). The sequence of events 'stimulus a, response A' can be interpreted as a reflex.

To prepare the machine for experiments in classical conditioning, it is first necessary to embed in it certain unconditional reflexes—by hypothesis, innate and inherently reinforcing reflexes. To do so, we use the arrangement shown in Fig. 9.5, whereby a subset r of *outcomes* or stimulus response pairs is associated with a positive reinforcement value, the remaining outcomes being associated with $R = \phi$ or, at any rate, with a low reinforcement value. After a number of trials in the conditions of Fig. 9.5, the machine adapts so that it has a number of ingrained unconditional reflexes, the members of r. We shall assume that

173

$a \to A$ is a member of *r* and will mention any other reflexes that belong to *r*, explicitly.

In its adapted condition, the machine demonstrates some of the simple features of classical conditioning. (Although we shall not develop this point, the changes in response *latency* with conditioning replicate the form of the latency changes that are observable in animal conditioning.)

Reflex Establishment

To build up a simple conditional relex we first choose an unconditional stimulus *b* which on its own elicits some unconditional response *B* (or which elicits one of several alternative responses, depending upon the conditions, but does not produce response *A*).

The conditioning procedures for simultaneous, delayed trace and 'backwards' conditioning are shown in Fig. 9.6, in terms of the way in which the conditional stimulus is related experimentally to the unconditional stimulus *a* (the stimulus that gives rise to *A* through the unconditional reflex $a \to A$). Of these, the 'backwards' procedure is ineffective (either for a real organism or for this machine). The remaining procedures in Fig. 9.6 do work. For organisms, both simultaneous and delayed conditioning are readily instrumented but delayed conditioning is more effective than simultaneous.

So far as the machine is concerned, trace conditioning is impossible. (This is because there is no mechanism for retaining the 'trace' of the conditional stimulus

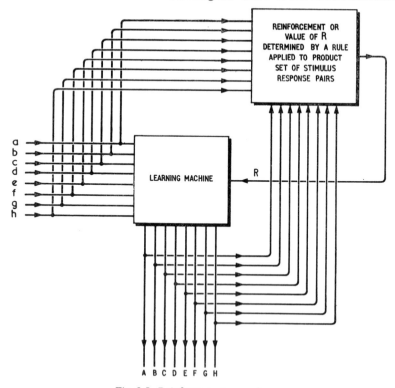

Fig. 9.5. Reinforcement procedure

which, in this procedure, is presented in the past and terminates before the unconditional stimulus. However, 'trace' conditioning is possible in certain more elaborate versions of this machine which contain loops capable of retaining a representation of the past stimulus.) Both simultaneous and delayed conditioning work well, as they do for the organism, and delayed conditioning is the more effective. Thus, if the unconditional stimulus *b* is paired (before and overlapping with) the conditional stimulus *a*, and if this pairing is repeated, the following effects may be obtained: (1) response *B* either drops out or is modified; (2) stimulus *b* comes to elicit response A (or occasionally a modified form of *A*) in the same way that $a \to A$; (3) the connection $b \to A$ is associated with a decreasing *b*, *A*, latency; (4) the connection $b \to A$ is eventually established, even in the absence of *a*. Hence, (5) $b \to A$ is a simple conditional reflex.

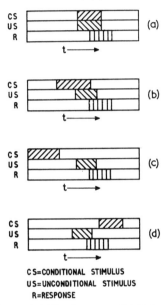

C S = CONDITIONAL STIMULUS
US = UNCONDITIONAL STIMULUS
R = RESPONSE

Fig. 9.6. Conditioning procedures: (a) Simultaneous; (b) Delayed; (c) Trace; (d) Backwards

Further, once $b \to A$ is well established, it may be used as though it were an unconditional reflex to produce another conditional reflex. Thus, if $c \to C$ is associated with $b \to A$, we can establish the reflex connection $c \to A$ and so on. Whereas the *primary* mechanism at work in establishing $b \to A$ is the 'extrinsic reinforcement' of p. 170 the *only* mechanism at work in establishing $c \to A$ is the 'intrinsic reinforcement' of p. 170.

Since each of these conditioning experiments is beset by the caveat 'or a modified form of the response' a sequence of experiments can give rise to a variety of behaviours (some of which will be modified responses that are not manifest within the conditioning experiment itself. Thus before conditioning perhaps $d \to D$; after having established $b \to A$, it may be that $d \to E$). If we also bear in mind that the experimenter is grappling with a dynamic, restless machine that does something on its own accord if he fails to stimulate it in a suitable fashion, it will be evident that the machine's behaviour has a richness comparable to that reported by Pavlov and his school in their original writings, (though its conditioned activity is more or less deterministic).

175

The chief distinctions between the behaviour of an animal and the behaviour of the machine occur at a level of complexity stressed recently by Konorski;[12] namely:

1. Only certain features of a stimulus are relevant for conditioning (the animal has an innate structure, resembling a releaser organisation, in respect to aspects of its environment that may become significant).
2. The features of the stimulus that are relevant often depend upon the form of conditional response (certain features are significant in respect to some responses and other features in respect to others).

The deficiency of our machine as a model compatible with (1) is due entirely to the chosen identification of the stimuli as unitary entities (without this constraint it will mimic an organism). To achieve a performance compatible with (2), it is necessary to introduce a hierarchical structure.

Reflex Extinction

If a conditional reflex such as $b \rightarrow A$ is elicited repeatedly in the absence of a it becomes extinguished. The b, A latency increases and ultimately b fails to produce A. The phenomenon of extinction is not a forgetting process (which may also occur due to the decay of the θ_{ij} values). Unlike forgetting, it depends upon the repetition of stimulus b.

Similarly, the phenomenon of 'spontaneous recovery' (which is often pointed out as a demonstration that extinction is not merely forgetting) can occasionally be observed with the machine. If $b \rightarrow A$ is extinguished to a high latency L_2 and if, (after a rest interval) we test $b \rightarrow A$ by applying b, then, if the rest interval is long enough, $b \rightarrow A$ will again be manifest at a lower latency L_1 where $L_2 > L_1$. The mechanism of spontaneous recovery in the machine is due to the fact that the response latency is the sum of the expectancy latency and the anticipation latency. Extinction increases each latency. After a rest interval the expectancy latency is likely to be reduced by the normal feedback to the stimulus unit memory circuits so that the total response latency is L_1 rather than L_2.

THE INSTRUMENTAL CONDITIONING PARADIGM

For experiments in instrumental conditioning, the reinforcement variable is under the experimenter's continual control and is manipulated throughout the experiment. (This is in direct contrast with classical conditioning, where reinforcement is a function of the organism's state or of an innately determined relationship between the organism and its environment.) The reinforcement may be interpreted either as primary (something like the delivery of food, that is related closely to the reduction of a basic drive) or as symbolic.

We shall consider the primary interpretation first, and in particular, the reinforcement of an operant response. As we have mentioned earlier, an operant is a response produced autonomously by an organism or the machine and the instrumental mode of conditioning is founded upon the concept of autonomous response. The organism does something (produces an operant) and is rewarded or punished for doing it. (Since our machine contains no analogue for punishment, we shall not develop the point. Technically, in the present machine it is only possible to achieve positive reinforcement or negative reinforcement of a response.) Equally, discriminating stimuli are introduced to *modify* the autonomous activity or are *provided*, by the experimenter, in response to the activity of the system. For the instrumental conditioning experiment the initial condition of the machine is a *'tabula rasa'* (apart from any residual charges that assign values to the θ_{ij}). In this condition, some response, say A, will be fortuitously rare and the experimenter selects A as the 'operant response' with which he is going to deal. In particular, he concentrates on the A response and disregards the other responses.

Interval Reinforcement

Interval reinforcement consists of assigning a positive value (say of $R = +1$) to the reinforcement variable on the first occasion that A occurs after a fixed interval from the last occurrence of A. With respect to this procedure, the machine simulates an organism such as the pigeon insofar as the rate of response A is inversely proportional to the interval chosen. The reinforced response A is, of course, gradually extinguished if the reinforcement is withheld. Extinction is reflected in the response A latency and consequently the graph of the number of response A per minute shows the short term slowing down fluctuation that is characteristic of the animal subject. The fluctuations may be reduced by using randomly chosen reinforcement intervals around a fixed mean value (in place of a fixed interval) but although this procedure leads to higher response rates, it does not lead to a greater resistance to extinction of the operant conditioning (as it does in the pigeon).

Ratio Reinforcement

In ratio reinforcement, the response A, is reinforced after a fixed number of occurrences, regardless of when they occur; the 'ratio' concerned being the ratio of unreinforced to reinforced responses. The experimental finding for animal subjects is that the *larger* the ratio, the more *rapidly* are responses emitted.

The machine parallels this behaviour within limits, and this is, at first sight, surprising. On closer inspection, however, (with an illegitimate peep inside the Black Box) the reason is fairly straightforward. With larger ratios, the response A is reinforced in connection with a greater diversity of problem events $x_i = 1$. The latency is compounded from a stimulus unit latency and a response unit latency and the mean rate of response A depends inversely upon the average latency. But the average latency is less, as the problem events in connection with which the response A has been reinforced are more diverse.

As with interval reinforcement, the behaviour shows the characteristic slowing down fluctuation which, once again, may be reduced by choosing a ratio at random (around some fixed average) in place of the fixed ratio. This procedure leads (as we might expect, in view of our glimpse of the internal mechanism) to rather high response rates.

DISCRIMINATING MODES

In the psychological laboratory, an animal may be trained according to several alternative reinforcement schedules, each of which produces a characteristic pattern of behaviour. If each reinforcement schedule is associated with a discriminating stimulus, such a sdifferent lights α and β, the appearance of a particular discriminating stimulus elicits the characteristic behaviour in the fully trained animal. The machine can be used to simulate this sort of experimental result if we choose a subset of the 'stimuli' as representative of one light and another subset of the 'stimuli' as representative of the other. Thus, light α is simulated by the vector $U = +1, +1, +1, +1, -1, -1, -1, -1$, and light β is simulated by the vector $U = -1, -1, -1, -1, +1, +1, +1, +1$. In this case, the machine is segregated functionally into a pair of subsystems α^* and β^*, one or the other of which is trained in connection with a particular stimulus. Subsequently, the appearance of α will elicit one behaviour and the appearance of β will elicit the other behaviour. So far, the machine is fairly lifelike. Unfortunately, the machine cannot react as a real organism and test the reinforcement conditions of its environment to determine how it should perform.

To simulate this 'choice' or 'test', we require a hierarchically structured machine of a sort we shall discuss later.

Let us next consider an extremely important characteristic of stimuli that act as discriminating stimuli, namely, that they become secondary reinforcers.

The paradigm experiment consists of reinforcing a response, say response A, and associating the reinforced occurrence of response A with a stimulus b which would not, on its own, elicit response A. After the conditioning is established, the response is extinguished by withholding stimulus b and allowing the organism to respond with A for trials that are not reinforced. If the reintroduction of stimulus b without any reinforcement leads to the production of response A (or to a decrease in the response A latency) then stimulus b is a secondary reinforcer (in the initial pairing process it acquired the property of acting like a reinforcement).

Obviously, if this experiment is performed with the machine it will yield a positive result. Stimulus b, having been reinforced in connection with response A, is part of a conditional reflex $b \rightarrow A$. Hence, by previous definition, stimulus b does act like a positive value of R. Further, as in the classical conditioning experiments, it is possible to build up conditional reflexes such as $c \rightarrow A$ by association with $b \rightarrow A$. Finally, because a response is not determined uniquely by the problem state evoked in the machine, it is possible to manipulate and modify the mode of response by using secondary reinforcing stimuli.

Unfortunately, in the machine as described, the secondary reinforcing stimulus will not play the crucial trick of reinforcing the emission of some response other than A, say response B. Secondary reinforcers are not generalised as they are in animal learning. It is a comparatively simple matter to modify the machine (by introducing a further mode of 'internal' reinforcement) so that 'generalisation' of this sort does take place. The modification works. But as it probably works for the wrong functional reason, we shall not dwell upon it. (To make it work for the right functional reason probably entails building a machine that can accept several sorts of reward rather than the single reward of value R.)

CHAIN RESPONSES

It is easy enough to establish chains of reflex actions. If the production of response A gives rise (in the environment of Fig. 9.7) to a stimulus b and if $b \rightarrow C$ is a conditional reflex, then the chain $A \rightarrow b \rightarrow C$ is built up. The process may be repeated up to a chain length of 8 as a maximum, for example to produce chains such as $A \rightarrow b \rightarrow C \rightarrow c \rightarrow D \rightarrow d \rightarrow E \rightarrow f \rightarrow F$. As in the case of animal conditioning, the production of chain reflexes relies upon the initial establishment of the component reflexes and a later assembly of these components into the composite reflex entity.

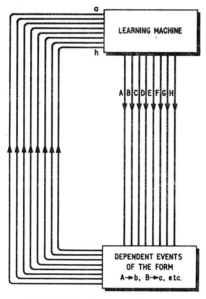

Fig. 9.7. Contingent environment

SYMBOLIC INTERPRETATION

Let us now give a symbolic interpretation to the experimental environment. Some *relationship* Ω is defined between the stimulus set and the response set (in the case we shall deal with, this is a *permutation* of the numbering of the stimuli with reference to the numbering of the responses, but a 'many to one' relationship is equally valid). Given a stimulus, the machine is required to produce the correct response (that is, the Ω related response to this stimulus). The variable, R, is identified with a knowledge of results signal that assumes the value $+1$ if the machine response is a correct response and the value 0 if it is a mistake.

Within the symbolic framework, stimuli are interpreted as events that definitely occur or do not occur; the absence of a stimulus negates an event. To embody this constraint we write '-1' in place of '0' in the stimulus vector and apply the corresponding negative potentials to the machine; thus 'stimulus a' is $U = +1, -1, -1, -1, -1, -1, -1, -1$, and 'stimulus b' is $U = -1, +1, -1, -1, -1, -1, -1, -1$. Responses designate solutions to a relational problem. 'Anticipation' becomes the characteristic of a selective process and we can talk about the response unit decision process as resolving more or less 'uncertainty' regarding an Ω related response, given the problem state engendered by a particular stimulus. (The amount of 'uncertainty' depends upon the form of the decision process at a given trial. Broadly, the greater the uncertainty, the longer the anticipation latency.)

179

The cueing variables z_j now come into the picture as constraints upon the response unit decision process. If $z_j = -1$, the machine is instructed that the decision process must not select $y_j = 1$. Generally, the assignment of negative values to some or all of the z_j for some or all of the anticipation interval at a given trial, will reduce the machine's selective uncertainty at that trial. (In conditioning terminology, this would be response differentiation.) Conversely, of course, if $z_j = +1$ the machine is instructed to select $y_j = 1$. In general, either mode of cueing is possible but in the present paper we only consider the case in which the z_j are assigned negative values.

The machine can be trained to use a skill entailing knowledge of Ω. The training procedure amounts to repeatedly presenting each stimulus, constraining the machine to make a correct response by the use of the cueing variables, and positively reinforcing the correct response when it occurs. Further, the machine will continue to perform the Ω based skill as long as the environment provides it with a sufficiently varied and rapid sequence of stimuli to replace the variety of the stimulus search process (Recall that the stimuli are associated with definite values of $u_i = \pm 1$). In particular, the machine performs adequately as a chain conditioned device where Ω is of the form $a \to A$, $b \to B$, and the environment completes the chain by consequential events of the form $A \to b$ and $B \to c$.

However, the machine *cannot* learn to sit quietly until a stimulus occurs (for an indefinite interval perhaps). The condition in which *all* stimuli are negated is contrary to the tenets of the model. Hence, it cannot be trained to 'learn Ω' in the commonsense meaning of the phrase, if Ω applies to the entire repertoire of stimuli and responses. The abhorred condition is 'all $u_1 = -1$' (so that the stimulus search process is effectively inhibited and no problems are produced). The electronic consequence of this condition is that no 'response search' instruction is delivered, so that eventually the response search process takes place autonomously, and ultimately brings all of the responses into states $y_j = 1$. The philosophical consequence is that we have disobeyed the (tacitly stated) rules of a machine that should actively search for problems and, given problems, search for their solutions.

To avoid breaking the rules whilst giving a commonsense meaning to the phrase 'the machine learns Ω', it is necessary to restrict the stimuli and responses related by Ω to a subset of the entire repertoire, for example, by saying that 'Ω relates stimuli a, b, c, d, to responses A, B, C, D; that stimuli e, f, g, h, feature as internal stimuli with $u_e = 0$, $u_f = 0$, $u_g = 0$, $u_h = 0$; and that responses E, F, G, H, are irrelevant responses'. Problems corresponding to e, f, g and h may thus occur without external stimulation, and responses E, F, G and H may be made without being counted as relevant responses. By this expedient we give the machine a field of attention on which it can concentrate even if the relevant (skill orientated) field of attention is held void by the experimenter.

Let us consider training or teaching a machine that has been partitioned in this fashion. We shall lay down some broad principles of effective teaching and will later examine their embodiment in a suitable teaching machine. Although these comments apply to a machine in which the 8×8 array is a *tabula rasa*, we are, in fact, much more interested in the case of a machine with previous experience (so that the 8×8 array contains definite entries θ_{ij}). In particular, a part of this previous experience is likely to interfere with the acquisition of the Ω skill.

180

SOME PRINCIPLES FOR THE EFFECTIVE INSTRUCTION OF SKILLS

1. The teaching procedure must retain the machine's attention. If it does not, the stimulus search process will give rise to irrelevant problems. Conversely, the rate of presentation of stimuli must not exceed the point at which the machine becomes overloaded.

It is evident that the instrumentation of this principle involves a feedback loop through which the instructor is informed whether or not the machine's attention is occupied. As a result of this information he adjusts the rate and variety of the stimulating input.

2. Correct responses must be reinforced. With a real life subject it would be sufficient to say that a certain response is correct. With the machine, we assign a positive value to R. Another feedback loop involving the machine and the instructor is required for this purpose.

3. Effective teaching should allocate more effort to problems that give rise to individual difficulties (the instructor should present the machine more often with stimuli that produce mistaken responses, so that these aspects of the skill are well rehearsed). Once again, this principle involves a feedback loop. The instructor must determine which stimuli are associated with mistaken responses, and present a controlled sequence of stimuli to the machine.

4. The instructor should co-operate with the machine by introducing cues that reduce the response selection uncertainty. This will reduce the number of mistakes and will avoid unduly long anticipation latencies.

5. There is, however, a requisite variety, in Ashby's sense,[9] built into the response search process. Hence, the response selection uncertainty must not be reduced beyond a certain point that would inhibit the response search process.

6. Again, the cueing should be minimised on the grounds that *if* the anticipation latency is cut down (by excessively rigid cueing) the machine will be unable to get rid of mistaken tendencies (or θ_{ij} entries) that interfere with the performance of the skill. This point depends, specifically, upon the form of the decrementation process. Given a wider connotation, however, we make the point that mistakes can only be rectified if the machine is allowed to exhibit its mistaken tendencies and that, in any case, the way in which a skill is learned should be adapted to the existing internal organisation of the machine.

7. To satisfy (4), (5) and (6), we introduce a delayed cueing procedure. Cues are delayed by a variable amount after the delivery of the stimulus. The delay in each cue, which may be so great that the cue never appears, is modulated as a function of the machine's activity to minimise the amount of co-operation needed to maintain learning.

More exactly, we start by delivering all the cue information with every stimulus. As the machine responds correctly, the cue information is delayed until a mistake is made. The cueing required to correct *this* mistake in respect of a *particular* stimulus is presented earlier after that stimulus, up until the mistake has been eliminated (with reference to that stimulus). Ultimately, when the machine responds correctly and with the required minimum latency to all of the stimuli, the cueing co-operation is entirely withdrawn, since all of the cues are so long delayed that none of them appear. Viewed broadly, this is a cueing strategy that selectively increases the difficulty of the task (by selectively withholding co-operation) as the machine's proficiency increases. It is evident that this strategy involves a further feedback loop.

8. The delay of a cue is a delay relative to the mean latency for a correct response, (that is, relative to the expected value of the sum of the expectation latency and the anticipation latency for a correct response) rather than an absolute delay. Hence, a final feedback loop is needed to estimate the mean latency.

Whilst these principles are *derived* from consideration of a specific machine, they are, we believe, quite generally applicable in the field of human learning and teaching. (This is *not* to suggest, of course, that our simple machine is an adequate model for human learning.) On the one hand we used these principles to design a 'teaching' machine able to effectively instruct the 'learning' machine (described below). We also used the same principles in designing a family of adaptive teaching devices that were applied to industrial and perceptual motor skills.

The efficacity of these devices has been demonstrated in various laboratory studies and in a general context. To some extent, this supports the contention that the principles determine a satisfactory teaching paradigm.[13-22]

TEACHING MACHINES

It would be quite possible for a nimble fingered, real life instructor to use these principles to teach the learning machine a relational skill. But four separate feedback loops are involved, each of them requiring a certain amount of calculation. In practice, therefore, the instructor's task would be rather difficult. Further, his difficulties are unnecessary, for the entire teaching process can be automated using a machine that engages in partially co-operative interaction with the learning machine (or, alternatively, with a real life student).

This automated system (outlined in Fig. 9.8) has been realised in the hardware of Fig. 9.2. The block outline of the teaching component is refined in Fig. 9.9; alternatively, it may be represented as a teaching algorithm.

The student's or machine's response is first compared with the Ω transform of the stimulus delivered to the student to determine its rectitude and its latency. This information is collated with reference to several parameters of the machine in Fig. 9.9 and is the basic input data to each of the four feedback loops.

1. It yields an estimate of the sum of the expectation latency and the anticipation latency from an estimate of the mean correct response latency.
2. It biases a random selection of possible stimuli so that stimuli yielding correct responses are less often selected.

182

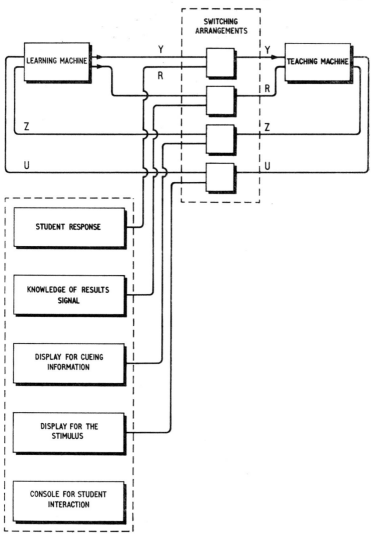

Fig. 9.8. Switching arrangements for connecting either the learning machine or a real life student into the teaching machine

3. It provides a knowledge of results signal which, in the case of the machine (rather than a human student) is returned as the value of variable R.

4. It determines the simplification of the problems posed by the selected stimuli by assigning a variable delay to the cueing information (in the case of the machine by assigning a value $z_j = -1$ to each of the cueing variables after a variable delay interval).

The last process requires further comment:

(a) The delay introduced is relative to the estimate of latency as calculated in (1) above.

(b) The delay associated with variable z_j must be computed separately for each stimulus i. Hence, the basic measures from the comparator must be averaged with reference to an array of 8×4 contingencies, 8 cueing variables combined with 4 stimuli.

There are several ways of instrumenting the requirements of (a) and (b). One of them is shown in Fig. 9.10. Here, the random selector is replaced by a stimulus search process having a basic repetition rate determined by the mean expected latency (and biassed, of course, by the inputs mentioned in (2)). The 8×4 averages of the basic performance measure are compiled in an 8×4 analogue storage array as indices θ_{ij}^* (analogous to the θ_{ij} in the learning machine), and the rows

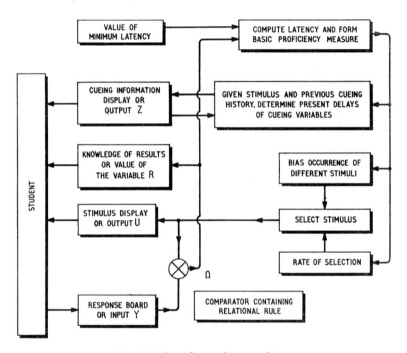

Fig. 9.9. Plan of a teaching machine

of this storage array, selected by row designating stimuli, provide a slope determining input to a set of 4 sawtooth generating circuits. These sawtooth generating circuits, which are analogous to the response circuits in the learning machine, contain voltage limiters. When the jth sawtooth voltage exceeds some predetermined value, the cueing variable z_j is set equal to -1. The sawtooth voltage is returned to 0 when the next stimulus is displayed.

The design of the learning and teaching system shown in Fig. 9.10 illustrates the concluding point of this paper—a teaching machine (in the sense of the present paradigm) is a stochastic inverse of a learning machine constrained by a rule, (such as a latency restriction and the mapping Ω) that specifies how the skill should be performed. If the phrase 'learning machine' is replaced by 'model for the learning process' this dictum is equally valid when applied to teaching machines that instruct real life subjects.

184

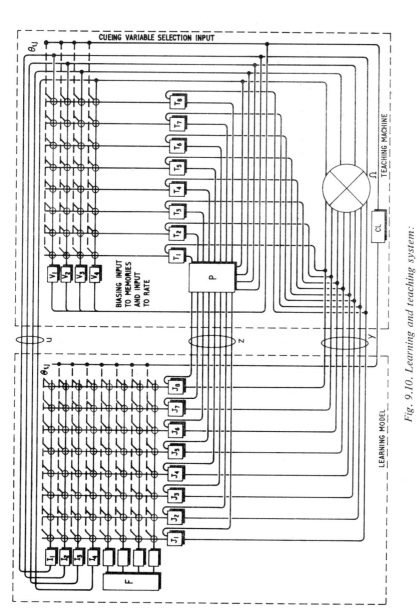

Fig. 9.10. Learning and teaching system:

F = Inputs of $u = 0$ in learning model
V = Stimulus selection generating units
T = Sawtooth cue generating units
P = Rule based on Ω determining which response should not be inhibited by the sawtooth cueing output, given a particular stimulus
CL = Compute latency and form the basic proficiency measure

REFERENCES

1. PASK, G., *An Approach to Cybernetics*, Hutchinson, London (1961).
2. BAILEY, C. E. G. and PASK, G., 'Teaching Machines,' *Contributions to U.S.S.R. Encyclopaedia on Automated Production and Industrial Electronics*, Moscow (1962).
3. PASK, G., 'Cognitive Systems' in *Proc. Symposium on Cognitive Studies and Artificial Intelligence Research*, Ed. Garvin P. Aldine Press, Chicago (1969).
4. PASK, G., 'Statistical Computation and Statistical Automata,' in *Neure Ergebnisse der Kybernetik*, Eds. Steinbuch, K. and Wagner, S. W., Oldenbourg, 69–81 (1963).
5. UTTLEY, A. M., 'Conditional Probability Computing in the Nervous System,' in *The Mechanisation of Thought Processes*, Ed. H.M.S.O. London (1959).
6. UTTLEY, A. M., 'Conditional Probability Machines and Conditional Reflexes,' in *Automata Studies*, Eds. Shannon, C. E., and Macarthay, J., Princeton University Press (1956).
7. THORPE, W. H., *Learning and Instinct in Animals*, Methuen, London (1956).
8. STEINBUCH, K. VON, 'Learning Matrices,' *Kybernetik*, **3**, 117–24 (1961).
9. ASHBY, W. R., *An Introduction to Cybernetics*, Chapman & Hall (1957).
10. HILGARD, E. R., *Theories of Learning*, Methuen, London (1958).
11. WOODWORTH, R. S. and SCHLOSBERG, H., *Experimental Psychology*, Methuen, London (1954).
12. KONORSKI, J., 'The Role of Central Factors in Differentiation,' in *Information Processing in the Central Nervous System*, I.U.S.P., Leiden (1962).
13. PASK, G., 'Electronic Keyboard Teaching Machines,' *J. natn. Ass. Educ. Commerce*, July (1958). Reprinted in *Teaching Machines and Programmed Learning, Volume 1*, Eds. Lumsdaine, A. and Glasser, R., American Association for Education 336–49 (1960).
14. PASK, G. 'Teaching Machines,' *Proc. 2nd Cong. Int. Ass. Cybernetics*, Namur, 1958, Gauthier-Villars 961–78 (1960).
15. PASK, G., and WISEMAN, D., 'Electronic Teaching Machines,' *Control Engng* (Nov., 1959).
16. PASK, G., 'The Teaching Machine as a Control Mechanism,' *Trans. Soc. Instrum. Technol.*, 72–89 (June, 1960).
17. PASK, G. and LEWIS, B. N., 'An Adaptive Automaton for Teaching Small Groups,' *Percept. Mot. Skills*, **14**, 183–88 (1962).
18. PASK, G., 'Adaptive Teaching Machines,' in *Teaching Machines*, Ed. Austwick, K., Pergamon, Oxford 79–112 (1964).
19. PASK, G., 'Teaching as a control-engineering process,' *Control* (Jan., Feb., March, April, 1965).
20. LEWIS, B. N. and PASK, G., 'The Theory and Practice of Adaptive Teaching Systems,' in *Teaching Machines and Programmed Learning, Volume 2, Data and Directions*, Ed. Glaser, R., Washington Nat. Educ. Assoc., 213–66 (1965).
21. PASK, G., 'Comments on the Organisation of Men, Machines and Concepts,' in *Education for Information Science*, Eds. Heilprin, L. B., Markusson, B. E. and Goodman, F. L., Spartan and Macmillan, Washington 133–54 (1965).
22. PASK, G. and LEWIS, B. N., 'The Adaptively Controlled Instruction of a Transformation Skill,' in *Programmed Learning*, Sweet and Maxwell 74–86 (1967).
23. PASK, G. and MALLEN, G. L., 'The Method of Adaptively Controlled Psychological Learning, Experiments,' *IFAC Symposium*, Teddington, 1965, American Instrumentation Society. Reprinted in *Theory of Self-Adaptive Control Systems*, Plenum Press, 70–-86 (1966).

Chapter 10

Models of Development

M. J. APTER, Ph.D.
Lecturer, Department of Psychology,
University College, Cardiff (U.K.)

SUMMARY

The mechanisms which an organism uses to accomplish development have long remained a mystery. Development may be interpreted as an algorithmic process of autonomous self-complexing including control features; as such it should be highly amenable to cybernetic treatment. Previous cybernetic models of development are surveyed, and other relevant cybernetic work is also mentioned. Two modelling procedures are described in more detail. The first involves the Turing machine conceptualisation of an automaton. The second, which is more general, is based on a counting process and is described using the propositional calculus. Growth, 'spatial' differentiation, 'functional' differentiation, regeneration and regulation are all simulated with this type of model. Finally, several further possible lines of research are indicated.

INTRODUCTION

While the second law of thermodynamics, the law of increasing entropy, is of the very greatest generality, it nevertheless appears to tell only part of the story of the universe as we know it. For anything like a complete picture, another general process must also be taken into account, and this is the tendency for nature to build up hierarchies of increasing complexity: elementary particles combine to form atoms, atoms to form molecules, molecules to form living cells, living cells to form multicellular organisms, and organisms to form societies. At a given level in this hierarchy, too, there is a tendency towards increasing complexity under certain conditions: thus, over the years, organisms and societies tend to become more complex.

This process of increasing complexity cannot be said to be the opposite of increasing entropy. If increasing entropy is increasing disorder, increasing complexity is not increasing order. The shape of a starfish is, intuitively, less complex than the shape of a fully grown oak tree; but it is also *more* ordered. (This topic has been discussed in more detail by Blum[1] among others.) 'Simplicity' and 'order' are almost synonymous; 'complexity' and 'disorder' are not. A satisfactory definition of 'complexity' has yet to be put forward, but it would appear to involve a vector with components of both order and disorder, or of both variety and unity.

Whatever precise definition is finally given to 'complexity', it should be consistent with the notion that organisms display an inclination towards increasing complexity. There are several senses in which this occurs: there is the *evolutionary* sense which refers to increasing complexity over generations, and there is the *developmental* sense, which applies to a particular organism during one generation. It is this latter perplexing phenomenon which is the subject of this chapter.

THE PROCESS OF DEVELOPMENT

Although formal similarities may be pointed out between the process of evolution and the process of development, these two processes would seem to differ in a fundamental respect. To use fashionable terms, evolution is essentially a *heuristic* process: there are many solutions to the problem of survival (as witnessed by the many species of organism which do, in fact, survive) and no obvious optimum solution; and a very general strategy is used of a type which was first described by Darwin and Wallace. (It can be questioned, however, whether the principle of natural selection, although necessary, is a sufficient principle to account for increasing *complexity* in evolution.[2]) Development, on the other hand, is *algorithmic*. There can only be one result of development: that is, the zygote (fertilised egg) of a given species always gives rise to an adult of that species and not to that of any other (although admittedly there will be variations of size and other features which are not crucial to the definition of a species). Also, a precise genetic pre-program would appear to be contained in the zygote.

There are several respects in which development is, in principle, very difficult to understand. It is difficult, for example, to see what kinds of algorithms could possibly achieve the ends which are achieved by developing organisms in certain aspects of their development.

First, how in principle can a complex organism develop out of instructions to only one single cell? The size of the increase in complexity which can occur should become awesomely apparent to the reader if he considers the fact that he was once, literally, no more than a single cell. Except for that increase in complexity due to learning, he has developed *autonomously* from that original cell, using no information as such from the environment (although, of course, utilising food and energy from the environment). A further limitation on this process, which makes it even more difficult to understand, is that each cell contains (it is generally accepted) the same set of instructions as every other cell. How can differentiation possibly occur when all cells are genotypically identical?

Secondly, there is the problem of how this self-complexing process is co-ordinated and controlled. For example, in organisms that are bilaterally symmetrical, development of the two sides of the body proceeds at the same pace, and the size of each organ eventually produced is proportional to the overall size of the organism. This controlling ability is demonstrated even more effectively in those organisms like the sea-urchin which can *regulate*. This means that the embryo will develop into a normally proportioned adult member of its species even if the cells are removed, added to, or rearranged. Actually, provided interference takes place early enough, a wide range of organisms can regulate, while in some simple organisms, like *Hydra*, cells can be removed even from the adult and the organism will *regenerate* the missing cells.

Putting the problems of development in this way brings out yet again the two aspects of increasing complexity and increasing diversity, matched by some form of integrated control.

In order to clarify the process of development, it is worth making some preliminary distinctions. One is between 'growth' and 'development'. As used in biology, the term 'growth' refers mainly to an increase in overall size of an organism, whereas 'development' refers mainly to the increase in complexity of the organism, with particular reference to increasing differentiation.

It is also useful to distinguish between what one might term 'functional differentiation' and 'spatial differentiation'. The former refers to the increasing number of types of cells (i.e. phenotypes) in an organism, these different cells having different functions: some cells might be cutaneous, some digestive, some nervous, and so on. 'Spatial differentiation' refers to increasingly differentiated spatial arrangements of cells. In this sense a stem with many offshoots would be spatially more differentiated than a stem with no offshoots at all. Normally, increasing differentiation of both kinds is closely related in a number of ways in a developing organism. But there are, nevertheless, these two quite different dimensions along which differentiation can be described, and it would not be logically contradictory for an organism to be highly differentiated in one respect and not in the other.

DEVELOPMENT AND CYBERNETICS

Development should obviously be considered as part of the subject matter of cybernetics, since developing systems are complex control systems depending on communication processes. The concepts and techniques developed in cybernetics should be of the greatest relevance in trying to understand this apparently mysterious process. Also, the demand of cybernetics for precise, effective models, and its preference for looking at organised systems in a holistic fashion should also be beneficial in a branch of science where these particular predilections have perhaps not, until recently, been greatly apparent.

From the cybernetic point of view the problem of understanding development may be approached by the construction of models which simulate some, or all, of the aspects of developing organisms which have just been indicated. That is, one would construct a model of a zygote, consisting essentially of a set of instructions (in whatever form they may be), including an instruction for the whole set of instructions to reproduce itself without modification, such that the emergent system differentiates functionally and spatially and can, at least in part, regulate and regenerate—or which will display any one of these properties. As with an axiom system, such instructions should be both consistent and complete. This approach is adopted later on in this chapter.

Strangely enough, this field has so far been rather overlooked by cyberneticians. The related problem of self-reproduction has, however, become one of the classic studies of automata theory and a substantial number of papers have been written on this topic from von Neumann's pioneer work[3] to recent contributions like those of Thatcher,[4] Myhill,[5] Arbib[6] and Stahl.[7,8]

189

It should be made clear, however, that the problem of self-reproduction, as it has been treated so far, is different from the problem of development. For if self-reproduction is interpreted at the level of one cell reproducing itself, then this is a process which is pre-supposed in the study of development as such. If it is interpreted at the level of one adult organism giving rise to another adult organism, then the problem of development from infancy to maturity is omitted: the gradual construction of a new automaton by another, complete automaton which happens to resemble it, is quite different from the process of development in which an incomplete automaton proceeds *to construct itself*. That is, in self-reproduction a new automaton is constructed externally by another automaton, while in development, one is faced with the more challenging problem of a completely internal process of construction. Anything less than this as a simulation of biological development would be quite unrealistic, although there is no reason, in principle, why models of self-reproduction of the type produced so far may not be considered as simulations of cellular self-reproduction. Stahl's models in particular are close simulations in this respect.

Few formal models of development have so far been proposed and those which have are varied in approach. Turing,[9] first in several fields, appears to have been the first here too, with his model showing how a regular pattern of differentiation might arise in a homogeneous, but unstable, system if that system is randomly disturbed. This model he described in terms of differential equations. A hardware model has been put forward by Goldacre,[10] who has built a system which consists of a set of identical electronic units which can be connected with each other in different patterns. He demonstrates how different patterns of impulses between these units can arise when they are connected together in different ways, and he believes that there may be an analogy between the way in which these patterns arise and the way in which morphogenetic patterns arise in a developing organism. Herdan[11] has described a simple paper and pencil model of development. The starting unit is a square, which we may imagine contains a list of instructions. Each instruction is an instruction for the square to reproduce itself on one of its sides by creating another square of equal size containing the same set of instructions. The instructions differ in that they specify (1) different surfaces for reproduction, and (2) which one of the list of instructions the newly reproduced square is to obey. (The first square obeys the first instruction on the list). Ulam[12] has shown how complicated geometrical patterns may be built up by no more than the continual application of a simple rule to an initial shape.

Stahl is now turning his attention to development as such. He and his colleagues have shown a consistent line of progression from the simulation of internal cell functioning, to the simulation of cell self-reproduction to the simulation of cell differentiation subsequent to self-reproduction. All the models are of sets of events at the biochemical level. In the cell simulation models, sets of enzymes operate on, and transform, macromolecules in a way which is consistent with current views on genetic functioning. The Turing machine terminology is adopted, the enzymes being described in terms of algorithms which act on letter strings representing the macromolecules.[13, 14] More complex cell models, involving large numbers of enzymes, are put on a computer. In the self-reproduction models, when concentrations of substances produced reach critical thresholds, and certain other defined criteria are satisfied, the cell is reproduced (by being copied elsewhere in the computer), and the concentrations split in half and distributed to the two new cells.[7] When more than one cell exists, differentiation may occur and different patterns of activities take place in different cells. So far, however, the number of cells which can be simulated at a time is limited because of the size and complexity of each cell and the limitation of computer storage facilities.[8] For these later computer models, the Turing machine mode of symbol manipulation is replaced by a list processing technique. This general line of research is exciting because the models are rigorous and effective, while at the same time keeping close to at least certain aspects of the known biochemistry of the situation.

Arbib has also turned his attention to the topic of development,[15] his interest arising, like Stahl's, out of his work on self-reproduction. His work in the latter area has been in the tradition of the von Neumann tessellation model; he differs from von Neumann in using more complicated components, which allows him to simplify the necessary programming and reduce the number of steps needed for self-reproduction to take place. A further difference is that he specifies a 'welding' operation, which allows him to attach cells to each other so that if one cell in a set of attached cells is moved, the others move concomitantly. Arbib has also shown that it is possible to simulate Turing machines with his model. By modifying his self-reproduction model he extends it in a most interesting way to the study of development—pointing out that the complexity of the components which he uses is, from the point of view of a realistic simulation of development, an advantage since development depends on highly complex units (cells). He agrees with a previous formulation by the writer[16] about the rules to be followed in the game of simulating development, disagreeing only about the extent to which information external to the developing system can be used by that system in development. His main modification to his self-reproduction model is to make each cell of the tessellation (which he regards as corresponding to a cell in the organism) contain the whole program. So far he has shown in general terms how development may be simulated using his model, rather than describing particular models and demonstrating the resulting developmental behaviour. We can, perhaps, look forward to this in future papers.

A rather different approach, since it has not involved model building as such, is that of utilising information theory in the description and discussion of developing organisms. Among others who have developed this approach are Dancoff and Quastler,[17] Raven,[18] and Elsasser.[19] Apter and Wolpert[20] have, however, criticised this approach, as has Shimbel.[21] Gatlin[22] has proposed a measure of information which, while being related to Shannon's original formulation of a measure of information,[23] is more suitable to the description of storage than to transmission systems and therefore avoids some of the criticisms which have been made. Eden's paper[24] is an exception to the general use of information theory in this area, in that he uses it to refer to some simple models of development of his in which there are a number of clearly defined developmental possibilities at each stage.

The fact must not be overlooked that less abstract models of development have also been put forward by biologists to explain the facts of development (and regulation and regeneration) in particular organisms under investigation. Examples of such models are those of Rose,[25] Brønsted,[26] Braverman,[27] Bullough,[28] Burnett[29] and Webster.[30] These models tend not to have been put in effective terms, although this does not preclude the possibility that they could be made effective. Iverson[31] has, from the cybernetic point of view, surveyed general biological theories of the control of growth and development, especially as they relate to cancer research. He points out the ubiquity of the concepts of homeostasis and feedback in these theories.

A TURING MACHINE MODEL OF DEVELOPMENT

Let us now look at a formal effective model of spatial differentiation. For this purpose, an automaton is specified whose possible outputs can include an output 'R'—a new automaton possessing instructions identical to its own. (In this way the problem of self-reproduction is by-passed, in effect, by regarding the automaton as a black box as far as self-reproduction is concerned.) If such an automaton also possesses a communication channel to each of its 'offspring', it is possible to investigate what instructions would be necessary for automata networks of different sizes and patterns to develop from an original automaton. We shall use the Turing machine conceptualisation of an automaton, the set of instructions for a given automaton being specified in terms of a Turing table showing, for given conjunctions of inputs and internal states, what in each case the output and next internal state should be. We specify that the output of one machine is the input to its offspring at the next moment. The assumption is also made that the input to the original automaton is always s_0 at each moment. (This formalisation differs slightly from that previously used by the writer.[32] For example, not assuming a continuous s_1 input to the original automaton helps to bring out the essentially autonomous nature of the process.) This means that the Turing terminology is used to describe a finite rather than an infinite automaton.

The only output which is not an input to another automaton is the output R, which is a new automaton containing identical instructions to those of its progenitor and an input communication channel from it. This takes one moment to accomplish, and the new automaton starts in state q_1.

Automata are represented diagrammatically by circles, their internal states at each moment are represented by numbers within the circles, and communication channels are represented by lines connecting the circles; the symbols being communicated are placed above these lines. For our purposes, s_0 means *no* communication. During the moment that a new automaton is being created, it is represented in the network by a circle containing the symbol R which shows that it has not yet reached state q_1. Direction of reproduction and direction of communication will always be towards the right.

A simple example will show how this works. The Turing table given in Table 10.1 would result in the development of a line three automata long.

Table 10.1. TURING TABLE RESULTING IN THE DEVELOPMENT OF A LINE THREE AUTOMATA LONG

	s_0		s_1	
q_1	R	q_2	—	q_4
q_2	s_0	q_3	s_1	q_4
q_3	s_1	q_4	—	—

The process takes place step by step, as shown in Fig. 10.1. After the sixth step, no further activity can take place because all the automata are in a terminal state. The two automata have been constructed at steps two and four.

Other simple patterns, together with the Turing tables necessary to achieve them, are illustrated in Table 10.2.

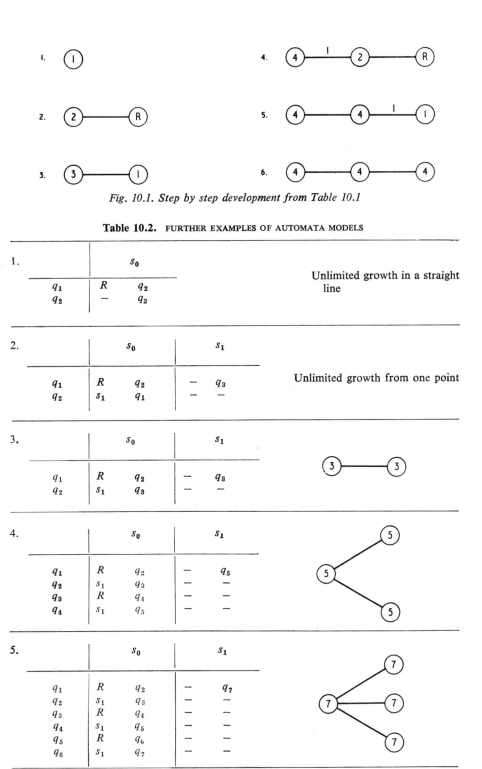

Fig. 10.1. Step by step development from Table 10.1

Table 10.2. FURTHER EXAMPLES OF AUTOMATA MODELS

1.

	s_0	
q_1	R	q_2
q_2	—	q_3

Unlimited growth in a straight line

2.

	s_0		s_1	
q_1	R	q_2	—	q_3
q_2	s_1	q_1	—	—

Unlimited growth from one point

3.

	s_0		s_1	
q_1	R	q_2	—	q_3
q_2	s_1	q_3	—	—

4.

	s_0		s_1	
q_1	R	q_2	—	q_5
q_2	s_1	q_3	—	—
q_3	R	q_4	—	—
q_4	s_1	q_5	—	—

5.

	s_0		s_1	
q_1	R	q_2	—	q_7
q_2	s_1	q_3	—	—
q_3	R	q_4	—	—
q_4	s_1	q_5	—	—
q_5	R	q_6	—	—
q_6	s_1	q_7	—	—

In the cases above, each automaton finishes in the same terminal state. It could, however, easily be arranged for the terminal states to be different for each automaton, and this could be regarded as a primitive form of functional differentiation. For example, to achieve a line of three with differentiated terminal states the table given in Table 10.3 could be used.

Table 10.3. A TURING TABLE GIVING A LINE OF THREE WITH DIFFERENTIATED TERMINAL STATES

	s_0		s_1		s_2	
q_1	R	q_2	—	—	—	q_6
q_2	s_0	q_3	s_2	q_5	—	—
q_3	s_1	q_4	—	—	—	—

The tables for the other simple patterns can be re-written in a similar way, so that in each case all automata in the final net bear a different label. More complex networks can then be built up from these module nets, each table being treated as a sub-routine which can be linked with other sub-routines by adjusting the state numbers of each sub-routine appropriately. For example, let us take the arbitrary, but more complicated net shown in Fig. 10.2.

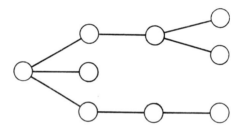

Fig. 10.2. Complex network from module nets

This net can be obtained, using the strategy mentioned, by the set of instructions given in Table 10.4, (which is presented as a list of quadruples in the conventional way).

Table 10.4. INSTRUCTIONS GIVING THE NETWORK OF FIG. 10.2

q_1	s_0	R	q_2		q_5	s_0	R	q_6
q_1	s_1	—	q_8		q_6	s_0	s_3	q_7
q_1	s_2	—	q_9		q_8	s_0	R	q_{11}
q_1	s_3	—	q_{10}		q_{10}	s_0	R	q_{20}
q_1	s_4	—	q_{13}		q_{11}	s_2	s_4	q_{12}
q_1	s_5	—	q_{18}		q_{13}	s_0	R	q_{14}
q_1	s_6	—	q_{19}		q_{14}	s_0	s_5	q_{15}
q_1	s_7	—	q_{24}		q_{15}	s_0	R	q_{16}
q_2	s_0	s_1	q_3		q_{16}	s_0	s_6	q_{17}
q_2	s_1	s_7	q_{23}		q_{20}	s_0	s_0	q_{21}
q_3	s_0	R	q_4		q_{21}	s_0	s_1	q_{22}
q_4	s_0	s_2	q_5					

The terminal states of the individual automata when development is complete are shown in Fig. 10.3.

Provided there are no limitations on the number of states or communication symbols which may be used, non-converging networks can be generated of *any degree of complexity* by this method.

This method, although rigorous, is also cumbersome. That is to say, a large number of instructions are needed to produce a comparatively small network. It is, perhaps, relevant, that the growth of a straight line, or growth from a single automaton requires few instructions for an infinite number of automata. The instructions start proliferating as a result of the growth being limited in various

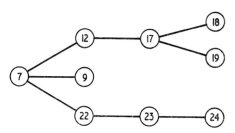

Fig. 10.3. Terminal states of individual automata

ways: thus a finite line of three automata requires more instructions than does an infinite line. Similarly, one can arrange for any net pattern to repeat itself without limitation, by putting q_1 in place of one or more of the terminal states. For example if '$q_1s_7 - q_1$' was put instead of '$q_1s_7 - q_{24}$' in the last list of instructions, the pattern would repeat itself over and over from the specified point of each net in turn. This implies that if some kind of meta-system could be arranged to count the number of times a pattern is repeated, and to stop the repetition at a certain point, then large networks based on such a pattern could be generated with a comparatively small number of instructions. Indeed, it is easy to see that in principle it should be possible to provide quite efficient instructions for complicated networks if there is an overall controlling, or meta-system, governing a set of sub-routines (each producing a module net), and calling forth each as many times as it is needed, wherever it is needed. The problem would then be to arrange for such a meta-system to emerge from the identical sets of instructions in each cell. One way in which this can be done is described in the next section.

It has been shown that if a terminal state is replaced by a q_1 in one of the sets of instructions above, then a new identical copy of the net produced by this set of instructions is achieved, the new net starting from the automaton in the particular terminal state specified. But it is possible to go further than this: it would only be necessary for the automaton in question to detach itself from its net to achieve *self-reproduction*. Thus, if in the last net

$$\text{'}q_1s_7 - q_{24}\text{'} \quad \text{was replaced by} \quad \begin{array}{l} q_1s_7 - q_{25} \\ q_{25}s_0 \, dq_1 \end{array}$$

(where 'd' stands for the automaton detaching itself from the input communication channel from its progenitor), the whole pattern would be self-reproducing. It could be arranged for this to happen from any automaton in the net with an input, but no output, channel (i.e. any automaton at the end of a line). In this

195

way, a situation is brought about in which a net gives rise to a 'seed' which in turn gives rise to a new net—a process of self-propagation which can continue over generations.

A final, and rather different point: although the Turing machine terminology has been used here, the automata that have been used have, in effect, been finite automata. It should be possible, therefore, to re-represent any of the Turing tables in the form of a network displaying the same input-output behaviour. One might be able to use, for example, a logical net of the type which has been described by George.[33] The interesting possibility then arises of a network able to create a network at a higher organisational level—a level at which the original network is but a node in the resulting network. This might bear some relevance to the tendency noted above for hierarchies of complexity to be built up in naturally occurring systems. The idea of hierarchies of networks could also be relevant (George, personal communication) to the representation of language and concepts in logical net terms.

A MODEL OF DEVELOPMENT USING THE PROPOSITIONAL CALCULUS

In this section, a modelling procedure will be presented which has a number of advantages over that used in the previous section:

1. While retaining the essentially logical features of the Turing machine model, communication between automata (cells) in the new model can be both quantitative and qualitative and the instructions depend conditionally on both quantitative and qualitative features of inputs. This is more realistic from the point of view of biological simulation and allows a greater range of developmental behaviour.

2. The result of the biological process of cell-division is that there are two identical cells in place of one. In the Turing machine model, when an automaton reproduced, the new cell was identical with it in terms of its instructions. There was a difference, however: the new automaton started automatically in state q_1, while the original automaton went to some other state specified in the instructions. This simulation difficulty is not encountered with this new modelling procedure.

3. It is possible to obtain more efficient sets of instructions because a given kind of pattern is generated with a general formula, and the net conforming to this pattern may be set at any finite size simply by substituting the appropriate quantities in the variables in the formula.

4. It is possible to represent functional as well as spatial differentiation by means of it. It could be said, of course, that the different states of the different automata in the net in the last section represented functional differentiation, but the simulation power of such a model is nevertheless severely limited as far as functional differentiation is concerned.

5. It is possible to simulate regeneration and regulation, as well as growth and differentiation.

196

MODELLING CONVENTION

A basic procedure on which this model depends is that of counting. Let us postulate that a cell (automaton), which finds itself not communicating with another cell on one side, counts 1 and passes this to the cell with which it *does* communicate. Any cell which receives a number as input automatically adds 1 to this number, passes the resulting number to the cell on its other side, and labels itself with the number which it has passed on. For the sake of convenience and conceptual simplicity it is assumed that after each moment t recounting takes place before $t+1$. So at $t+1$ the non-counting instructions which take effect (see below) do so on the basis of the new labels.

As the counting process is not in each case fully spelled out, the models are presented in a slightly less formal way than the Turing machine models. But counting is a simple algorithmic process, and the models could be made fully rigorous if necessary. The reason for not doing so here is to keep them as conceptually simple as possible.

A number of different counting operations can take place concurrently in a set of cells and each is depicted by a different letter. These can be visualised most simply as different substances whose amounts are increased by a constant amount in each cell in turn. It is assumed that each network counts in terms of substance *a* from the beginning, so that each cell in every network has an *a* label. It does not matter in which direction the network counts, and this could be determined randomly on each occasion. However, let us assume for consistency that *a* is always counted in the right hand direction, i.e. the process starts in the cell which is initially the furthest to the left.

For the development instructions which complement the counting instructions, let us use the notation of the propositional calculus, suffixed for time. Each cell then contains an instruction list described in this notation. The instruction to reproduce is represented by R as it was in the Turing machine models, and means that the cell, which is reproduced, has an identical set of instructions to its progenitor and a communication channel with it. The communication channel this time, however, is used for the process of counting and is a two-way channel.

Thus $(a = 1)_{t-1}. (b = 10)_{t-1} \equiv R_t$ means that if the substance *a* label of a cell is 1 and its substance *b* label is 10, then reproduction will take place. Any conventional mathematical symbols may be used inside the brackets.

We should visualise self-reproduction as being a process of cell division in the model. Unless otherwise specified this division takes place in such a way that the two daughter cells find themselves aligned along the axis in which the counting takes place. In other words, the angle of division is orthogonal to this axis, or row of cells.

However, cell division can also take place at an angle to the row other than right angles, so that a new axis can be set up. In this case, one daughter cell remains in the row while the other daughter cell finds itself free on one side. Whichever cell is the latter can then start a new counting process using a new letter. The letter used is specified in the relevant instruction; for example, the symbol R^c means that the daughter cell bounded on one side only counts 1 of substance *c* and hence sets up a new counting process. It is assumed that this counting proceeds as far as the end of the new axis which has been set up, but no further.

Normally it will be necessary on the first cell division to initiate a counting process in the direction opposite to the direction in which the *a* substance is counted. This is achieved by means of the instruction $(a = 1)_{t-1} \equiv R_t^b$ which in effect acts to polarise the system.

Where the symbol Σ is used, this means that the separate inputs of a given substance from other cells are added. It does *not* mean, however, that the sum is used in the self-labelling and counting process. That is, if there are three separate inputs of 1 unit of substance b the cell does not pass on $(b = 4)$, but $(b = 2)$.

The apparatus necessary to produce rows of cells of any length and to produce branches has now been set up: that is, it should be possible to generate nets of pre-determined spatial patterns. But what about functional differentiation? Let us represent different functional phenotypes using Greek letters to avoid confusion with the substances used in counting. Then, $(a = 1)_{t-1} \equiv \alpha_t$ means that if the cell counts 1 of substance a at $t-1$, then it is an α-type cell at time t. Such a functional phenotype is not permanent once adopted by a cell, but depends on the situation which gave rise to it continuing.

Let us now look at some specific models within the convention which has been adopted. Throughout, the counting process will be implicit.

SOME SIMPLE MODELS

1. Unlimited growth in a straight line from one end only is generated by the following instruction:

$$(a = 1)_{t-1} \equiv R_t$$

2. Unlimited growth in a straight line from both ends of the line simultaneously can be achieved as follows:

$$(a = 1)_{t-1} \equiv R_t^b$$
$$[(b = 1)_{t-1}] \vee [(a = 1)_{t-1} \cdot (b > 1)_{t-1}] \equiv R_t$$

Strictly, the first instruction, using the predicate calculus to supplement the propositional calculus, should have been:

$$(a = 1)_{t-1} \cdot \sim (\exists x)(bx)_{t-1} \equiv R_t^b$$

We shall, however, dispense with this kind of formality for our present purposes. In general we shall assume that the formula:

$$\cdot \sim (\exists x)(zx)_{t-1}$$

where z stands for 'an expression other than the expression already contained in that part of the formula to the left of the $\equiv$ symbol' is appended to each formula to the left of the symbol $\equiv$.

To clarify what happens, the first three stages in this process are shown in Fig. 10.4.

3. Limited growth in one direction can be represented as follows.
   Let us reproduce N cells:

$$(a = 1)_{t-1} \equiv R_t^b$$
$$(1 < b < N)_{t-1} \cdot (a = 1)_{t-1} \equiv R_t$$

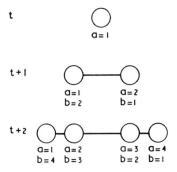

t

$a = 1$

t + 1

$a = 1$
$b = 2$

$a = 2$
$b = 1$

t + 2

$a = 1$
$b = 4$

$a = 2$
$b = 3$

$a = 3$
$b = 2$

$a = 4$
$b = 1$

Fig. 10.4. Model of unlimited growth in a straight line

An advantage over the models presented in the last section should now be apparent: a line of any finite size can be created with the same instructions, by replacing N by the length of line required. In the Turing machine model, the longer the line, the more the instructions needed.

4. Growth from one point is given by:

$$[(a = 1)_{t-1}] \lor [(a = 1)_{t-1} \cdot (\Sigma b \geqslant 1)_{t-1}] \equiv R_t^b$$

5. Limited growth from one point is given by:

$$(a = 1)_{t-1} \cdot (\Sigma b < N)_{t-1} \equiv R_t^b$$

This again is very general since N may be set at any number.

SPATIAL DIFFERENTIATION

We shall now look at some examples of spatial differentiation.

6. With the following instructions we can obtain a straight line with a side-branch:

$$(a = 1)_{t-1} \equiv R_t^b$$
$$(b = 1)_{t-1} \cdot (1 \leqslant a < 5)_{t-1} \equiv R_t$$
$$(a = 2)_{t-1} \cdot (b = 1)_{t-1} \equiv R_t^c$$
$$(c = 1)_{t-1} \cdot (a < 4)_{t-1} \equiv R_t$$

The resulting pattern using these particular instructions is shown in Fig. 10.5.

7. Another pattern is given in Fig. 10.6, which also shows the counting situation in the final state of the net.
The following instructions will achieve this:

$$(b = 1)_{t-1} \cdot (a < 5) \equiv R_t$$
$$[(a = 1)_{t-1}] \lor [(a = 5)_{t-1} \cdot (\Sigma b < 3)_{t-1}] \equiv R_t^b$$

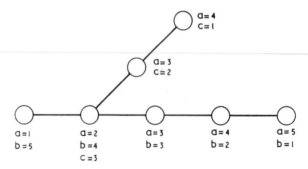

Fig. 10.5. Pattern of spatial differentiation

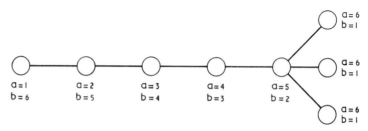

Fig. 10.6. Another pattern of spatial differentiation

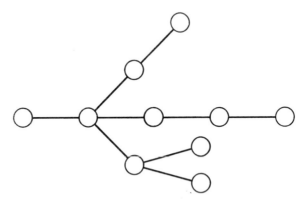

Fig. 10.7. A complex pattern

Note again how simple this is in comparison with Turing machine instructions. The line can be made as long as we like, with as many offshoot cells at the end as we like, simply by altering the appropriate figures in the formulae.

8. Let us take a slightly more complicated pattern and consider the arbitrary network of Fig. 10.7.

200

This can be achieved in a number of ways. One set of instructions to achieve it is:

$$(a = 1)_{t-1} \equiv R_t^b$$
$$[(c = 1)_{t-1}\cdot(a = 3)_{t-1}] \vee [(b = 1)_{t-1}\cdot(a < 5)_{t-1}] \equiv R_t$$
$$(b = 4)_{t-1}\cdot(a = 2)_{t-1} \equiv R_t^c$$
$$(b = 4)_{t-1}\cdot(a = 2)_{t-1}\cdot(c = 2)_{t-1} \equiv R_t^d$$
$$(d = 1)_{t-1}\cdot(a = 3)_{t-1} \equiv R_t^e$$
$$(d = 1)_{t-1}\cdot(a = 3)_{t-1}\cdot(e = 2)_{t-1} \equiv R_t^f$$

FUNCTIONAL DIFFERENTIATION

Extra instructions may be added to the models of spatial differentiation above to make them differentiate functionally as well.

9. Thus, in the case of model (7) above, the addition of the following instructions,

$$(a < 4)_{t-1} \equiv \alpha_t$$
$$(a > 4)_{t-1} \equiv \beta_t$$

results in the system becoming functionally differentiated as in Fig. 10.8.

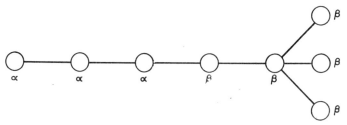

Fig. 10.8. Functional differentiation

Similarly, if we wanted the system to differentiate unevenly into three types of cell, the following instructions could be added:

$$(a < 4)_{t-1} \equiv \alpha_t$$
$$(3 < a < b)_{t-1} \equiv \beta_t$$
$$(a > 5)_{t-1} \equiv \gamma_t$$

10. In the case of model (6) above, the side-branch could be made to differentiate functionally from the rest as follows:

$$(b \geqslant 1)_{t-1}\cdot(a \geqslant 1)_{t-1} \equiv \alpha_t$$
$$(a > 2)_{t-1}\cdot(c \geqslant 1)_{t-1} \equiv \beta_t$$

THE REGULATION OF SPATIAL DIFFERENTIATION

So far, spatial differentiation has been modelled in absolute terms. But organisms (especially plants) can vary in size depending on environmental conditions, while still maintaining the same overall pattern.

201

11. Let us see if we can make the number of side-branches at a given point depend on the length of the main line. Suppose our basic instructions are:

$$(a = 1)_{t-1} \equiv R_t^b$$

$$(1 < b < N)_{t-1} \cdot (a = 1)_{t-1} \equiv R_t$$

If the following is added:

$$(b = 1)_{t-1} \cdot \left(\Sigma c < \frac{a}{2b} \right)_{t-1} \equiv R_t^c$$

a pattern is achieved rather like that in model (7) above, but in which the number of offshoots at the end of the line is proportional to the length of the line, i.e. there is one offshoot cell for every two cells in the line.

The whole process could just as easily be scaled up by arranging for one side-branch to be produced for every, say, 10^4 cells in the main stem.

12. As another example. Instead of the third instruction in model (11) above, let us put the following instruction:

$$(c < 1)_{t-1} \cdot \left(\frac{b}{a} < \frac{1}{2} \right)_{t-1} \equiv R_t^c$$

In this case the resulting system produces an offsnoot cell from every cell in one third of the main line at one end, however long this main line of cells happens to be.

So far we have looked at an organism increasing in size. But suppose that parts of the organism, or system, were removed during or after development: could instructions be given in such a way that regulation and regeneration could occur?

Consider model (11) above. As the instructions are written, if one of the offshoot cells were to be cut off, it would be regenerated automatically. Similarly, if part of the free end of the main line of cells was removed and N for the length of this line had been set at a number of cells greater than the number remaining, then the necessary cells would be regenerated; indeed, if the model was cut at any point along the main stem the two parts would regenerate the complete system. All this applies during development as well as afterwards. Of course, it is assumed that recounting continues to take place—and there is no reason why it should not, since counting is a function of the individual cells and does not depend on the system being complete.

The same considerations apply equally to model (12) too. But let us consider an earlier model, model (6), in which the instructions were described in absolute rather than relative terms of the type used in models (11) and (12). Even as written, model (6) can regenerate partially: if part of the side-branch is cut off it will regenerate, just as regeneration will occur if the cells labelled $(b = 1)$, $(b = 2)$ and $(b = 3)$ in the final pattern are removed. If the cell labelled $(a = 1)$ is cut off, however, there will be no regeneration, although a side effect will be to increase the length of the side-branch and the length of the main stem at the other end. If the side-branch is removed completely, it will not regenerate. Powers of regulation are also limited: if the first two cells produced are parted, regulation will occur and both cells will produce perfect patterns; but after this, the same limitations apply as those which apply to regeneration.

But if for instruction:

$$(a = 2)_{t-1} \cdot (b = 1)_{t-1} \equiv R_t^c$$

the following instruction was substituted:

$$[(a = 2)_{t-1} \cdot (c < 1)_{t-1} \equiv R_t^c$$

complete regulation or regeneration of the side-branch would occur if it was removed, since the only factor that prevents the cell at $(a = 2)$ from producing further branches is the presence of the branch itself. In general, here, the use of a substance c allows: (1) the second axis to develop differently from the main axis (in this case it allows it to be of a different length); and (2) the inhibition of any more branches developing from the same cell.

In this case, however, a further difficulty does arise, for if $(a = 1)$ is cut off, a new side-branch will develop from the cell which was previously at $(a = 3)$. No doubt by using further conventions and more complicated instructions, this could be overcome. What this discussion does show is that regulation for certain spatial patterns would appear to be more difficult to achieve than with others. We have also seen that a side-branch, for example, can be achieved by instructions which generate it at a given moment of development or by instructions which is principle allow it to develop at any time *after* a given moment of development, and that each results in different regeneration possibilities. It is possible that a more detailed study of this point could throw some light on the different regenerative powers and weaknesses of different organisms.

THE REGULATION OF FUNCTIONAL DIFFERENTIATION

13. Let us take a straight line of cells, and see if we can produce instructions so that, however long or short the line, whether cells are added, removed or re-assorted, the line still remains divided into two halves with α-cells on one side and β-cells on the other. Instructions for producing a straight line of cells have already been given. The following instructions, if added to these, will in fact achieve the control of phenotype pattern required:

$$\left(\frac{a}{b} < 1\right)_{t-1} \equiv \alpha_t$$

$$\left(\frac{a}{b} > 1\right)_{t-1} \equiv \beta_t$$

(For lengths having an odd number of cells, the phenotype of the central cell would have to be determined randomly.)

14. What about a line divided functionally into three equal regions? This can be achieved as follows:

$$\left(\frac{a}{b} < \frac{1}{2}\right)_{t-1} \equiv \alpha_t$$

$$\left(\frac{1}{2} < \frac{a}{b} < 2\right)_{t-1} \equiv \beta_t$$

$$\left(2 < \frac{a}{b}\right)_{t-1} \equiv \gamma_t$$

15. Similarly, for a line to divide into four equal parts, one can put:

$$\left(\frac{a}{b} < \frac{1}{3}\right)_{t-1} \equiv \alpha_t$$

$$\left(\frac{1}{3} < \frac{a}{b} < 1\right)_{t-1} \equiv \beta_t$$

$$\left(1 < \frac{a}{b} < 3\right)_{t-1} \equiv \gamma_t$$

$$\left(3 < \frac{a}{b}\right)_{t-1} \equiv \delta_t$$

Using the same principle, the line of cells could be divided into any number of equal parts, or indeed into any number of unequal parts, the proportions of the parts to each other remaining constant whatever the length of the line.

The principle used for the control of functional differentiation can, of course, be applied to more complex nets than straight lines and, as before, instructions for functional differentiation may be added to those for spatial differentiation. For the models to be realistic, however, it would be necessary to arrange for cells to de-differentiate before reproducing.

The process of counting on which the models in this section have been based may seem to be biologically a little unrealistic, although it has been shown[34] that such behaviour could be displayed by cells containing genetic units of the kind postulated by Monod and Jacob.[35] However, counting as such by individual cells may not be essential, and it is likely that the same results could be achieved, when instructions are appropriately modified, on the basis of various processes involving the continuous amplification or diminution of substances across the organism.

An advantage of the terminology which has been used is that, if required, it can be computerised easily. Consider, for example, the flow diagram for model (3) above (excluding the counting operation) shown in Fig. 10.9.

'Reproduce' in computer terms means that the whole set of instructions representing the cell (or automaton) in question should be rewritten (copied) elsewhere in the computer. Ideally, the set of instructions to be reproduced should contain the instructions which caused the reproduction to take place. The writer[36] has shown elsewhere that it is possible to write a general reproduction sub-routine which can be used when the control of the computer is passed to it from a set of instructions to rewrite that set of instructions in a new set of locations in the computer. This will work for a set of instructions of any finite size (compatible, of course, with the size of the computer storage) provided that these instructions specify themselves suitably. Such a set of instructions could in principle contain the reproduction sub-routine itself, and therefore be self-reproducing.

In this connection, the writer has suggested that a form of list-processing procedure may be useful to represent spatial relationships between different cells represented in computer terms.

The models which have been demonstrated in this section have been quite simple, although in some cases they could be made extremely large. However, it can be seen that the principles outlined could be combined to make complex networks that are differentiated both spatially and functionally, and that display various degrees of regulative and regenerative potential. It should perhaps be added that they also share a feature with the Turing machine models in the last section: it only needs one cell (automaton) to break off for the whole system to reconstruct itself anew, that is, to reproduce itself.

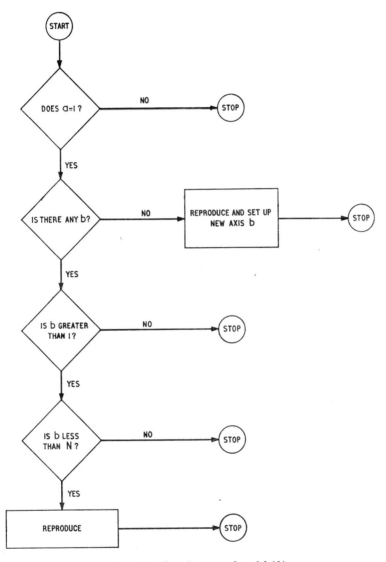

Fig. 10.9. Flow diagram of model (3)

DISCUSSION

Further lines of research suggest themselves as a continuation of the research outlined so far. For example, the models presented so far have been deterministic and not probabilistic, since the main concern at this stage has been to discover algorithms of development. However, it would be interesting to consider strategies which could be used not only to overcome external interference with development but also the internal malfunctioning of instructions. The work on reliability, of Lofgren,[37] Winograd and Cowan[38] and others, would be relevant here.

The spatial properties of the models in both previous sections have been topological. An alternative approach, which would be more geometrical in conception, would be to think in terms of a tesselation, and follow the tradition started by von Neumann. This could be done with little basic modification to the representations of instructions which have been used here. Advantages would be that patterns could be obtained with converging as well as diverging features, areas could be obtained more than one cell thick, and morphogenetic movements could be simulated. Arbib[15] has been especially concerned with this last named feature of many developing systems.

One aspect of development which cannot be simulated by either the topological or tesselation models (at least as conceived so far) is the way in which changes in shape in a tissue may be caused mechanically by expansion, contraction, and changes in the adhesive properties of individual cells.[39] Fortunately, new graphical input-output computer devices are being developed rapidly at present[40] and these may in the future prove invaluable for this purpose.

The spirit in which this chapter has been written has been well expressed by Bernal:[41]

'Life is beginning to cease to be a mystery and becoming practically a cryptogram, a puzzle, a code that can be broken, a working model that sooner or later can be made.

The aim of the chapter has been, first, to demonstrate from the point of view of automata theory that at least some features of development can be accomplished by automata. Secondly, it has attempted to feel a way towards a general formalisation for simulating development in precise and effective terms. In particular, it is hoped that formalisations such as this might help in due course by mediating between knowledge of events at the genetic level and descriptions of development by the organism as a whole. Thirdly, while the main aim has not been to suggest specific hypotheses to explain development in particular organisms, some fairly general hypotheses have inevitably been suggested in passing.

Norbert Wiener[42] has said:

'If a new scientific subject has real vitality, the centre of interest in it must and should shift in the course of years.'

Is it too much to suppose that biological development, in the next few years, might move if not to the centre of attention in cybernetics, at least a little further in from the periphery of this exciting subject?

REFERENCES

1. BLUM, H. F., 'Complexity and Organisation,' *Synthèse*, **15**, No. 1, 115 (1963).
2. WHYTE, L. L., *Internal Factors in Evolution*, Tavistoch Press, London (1965).
3. VON NEUMANN, J., *Theory of Self-reproducing Automata*, Ed. Burks, A. W., University of Illinois Press, Urbana (1966).

4. THATCHER, J. W., 'The Construction of a Self-Describing Turing Machine,' *Proc. Symp. Math. Theory Automata*, Polytechnic Press, Brooklyn, New York (1963).
5. MYHILL, J., 'The Abstract Theory of Self-reproduction,' in *Views on General Systems Theory*, Ed. Mesarovic, M. D., John Wiley, New York (1964).
6. ARBIB, M. A., 'Simple Self-reproducing Universal Automata, *Inf. Control*, **9**, 2, 177 (1966).
7. STAHL, W. R., 'A Model of Self-reproduction based on String-processing Finite Automata,' in *Natural Automata and Useful Simulations*, Proceedings of a Symposium on Fundamental Biological Models, Stanford University, June 17, 1966., Eds., Pattee, H. H., Edelsack, E. A., Callahan A. B., and Callahan, L. F., Spartan Books, Washington D.C. (1966).
8. STAHL, W. R., 'A Computer Model of Cellular Self-reproduction,' *J. Theoret. Biol.*, **14**, 187 (1967).
9. TURING, A. M., 'The Chemical Basis of Morphogenesis,' *Phil. Trans. R. Soc.*, B, **237**, 37 (1952).
10. GOLDACRE, R. J., 'Morphogenesis and Communication between Cells,' *Proc. 2nd Cong. Int. Ass. Cybernetics*, Namur, 1958, Gauthier-Villars (1960).
11. HERDAN, R., 'A Logical Model for Growth and Differentiation in Multicelled Organisms,' *Bull. Math. Biophys.*, **27**, 379 (1965).
12. ULAM, S. 'On Some Mathematical Problems Connected with Patterns of Growth of Figures,' in *Mathematical Problems in the Biological Sciences: Proceedings of Symposia in Applied Mathematics*, **14**, Ed. Bellman, R. E. American Mathematical Society, (1962).
13. STAHL, W. R. and GOHEEN, H. E., 'Molecular Algorithms,' *J. Theoret. Biol.* **5**, 2, 266 (1963).
14. STAHL, W. R., COFFIN, R. W. and GOHEEN, H. E., 'Simulation of Biological Cells by Systems Composed of String-processing Finite Automata,' in *Proc. AFIPS Spring Joint Computer Conf.*, Washington, D.C. 1964, Spartan Books, Baltimore, **25**, 89 (1964).
15. ARBIB, M. A., 'Automata Theory and Development: Part I,' *J. Theoret. Biol.* **14**, 131 (1967).
16. APTER, M. J., *Cybernetics and Development*, **29**, Pergamon, Oxford (1966).
17. DANCOFF, S. M. and QUASTLER, H., 'The Information Content and Error Rate of Living Things,' in *Information Theory in Biology*, Ed. Quastler, H., University of Illinois Press, Urbana (1953).
18. RAVEN, C. P., *Oogenesis: the Storage of Developmental Information*, Pergamon, Oxford (1961).
19. ELSASSER, W. M., *The Physical Foundation of Biology*, Pergamon, London (1958).
20. APTER, M. J. and WOLPERT, L., 'Cybernetics and Development, 1: Information Theory,' *J. Theoret. Biol.* **8**, 244 (1965).
21. SHIMBEL, A., 'Information Theory and Genetics,' *Bull. math. Biophys.*, **27**, (special issue) 177 (1965).
22. GATLIN, L. L., 'The Information Content of DNA,' *J. Theoret. Biol.* **10**, 281 (1966).
23. SHANNON, C. E. and WEAVER, W., *The Mathematical Theory of Communication*, University of Illinois Press, Urbana (1949).
24. EDEN, M., 'A Probabilistic Model for Morphogenesis,' in *Symposium on Information Theory in Biology*, Eds. Yockey, H. P., Platzman, R. L., and Quastler, H., Pergamon, London, (1958).
25. ROSE, S. M., 'A Hierarchy of Self-limiting Reactions as the Basis of Cellular Differentiation and Growth Control,' *Am. Nat.*, **86**, 337 (1952).
26. BRØNSTED, H. V., 'The Time-graded Regeneration Field in Planarians and Some of its Cyto-physiological Implications,' in *Recent Developments in Cell Physiology*, Ed., Kitching, J. A., Proceedings of the 7th Symposium of the Colston Research Society, Butterworth, London (1954).
27. BRAVERMAN, M. H., 'Regional Specificity within the Chick Brain,' *J. Morph.*, **108**, No. 3, 263 (1961).
28. BULLOUGH, W. S., 'The Control of Mitotic Activity in Adult Mammalian Tissues,' *Biol. Rev.*, **37**, 307 (1962).
29. BURNETT, A. L., 'The Maintenance of Form in Hydra,' in *Regeneration*, Ed., Rudnick, D., Ronald Press, New York (1962).
30. WEBSTER, G., 'Studies on Pattern Regulation in Hydra, III. Dynamic Aspects of Factors Controlling Hypostome Formation,' *J. Embryol. exp. Morph.*, **16**, No. 1, 123 (1966).

31. IVERSON, O. H., 'Cybernetic Aspects of the Cancer Problem,' in *Progress in Biocybernetics—Vol. 2.* Eds., Wiener, N. and Schadé, J. P., Elsevier, Amsterdam (1965).
32. APTER, M. J., Op. cit. Chapter 6.
33. GEORGE, F. H., 'Logical Networks and Behaviour', *Bull. math. Biophys.*, **18**, 337 (1956).
34. APTER, M. J., Op. cit. Chapter 7.
35. MONOD, J. and JACOB, F., 'Teleonomic Mechanisms in Cellular Metabolism, Growth and Differentiation,' in *Cold Spring Harbour Symposia on Quantitative Biology, Vol. 26: Cellular Regulatory Mechanisms*, (1961).
36. APTER, M. J., Op. cit. Chapter 5.
37. LOFGREN, L., 'Self-repair as a Computability Concept in the Theory of Automata,' Proceedings of the Symposium on Mathematical Theory of Automata, New York, April, 1962, *Microwave Research Institute Symposia Series, Vol. XII.*, Polytechnic Press, New York (1963).
38. WINOGRAD, S. and COWAN, J. D., *Reliable Computation in the Presence of Noise*, M.I.T. Press, Cambridge, Mass. (1963).
39. GUSTAFSON, T. and WOLPERT, L., 'The Forces that Shape the Embryo,' *Discovery, Lond.*, November (1961).
40. SUTHERLAND, I. E., 'Computer Inputs and Outputs,' *Scient. Am.* **215**, No. 3, 86 (1966).
41. BERNAL, J. D., *The Origin of Life*, Weidenfeld and Nicholson, London (1967).
42. WIENER, N., *Cybernetics: or Control and Communication in the Animal and the Machine*, 2nd Ed., John Wiley, New York (1961).

Chapter 11

Artificial Intelligence Control

C. T. LEONDES, Ph.D.
School of Engineering and Applied Science, University of California,
Los Angeles, California (U.S.A.)

and

J. M. MENDEL, Ph.D. (E.E.)
McDonnell Douglas Astronautics Co., Western Division, Santa Monica,
California (U.S.A.)

SUMMARY

Artificial intelligence techniques have recently been applied to the design of control systems. Two types of self-organising (learning) control systems have evolved: (1) on-line-learning control systems; and (2) off-line-learning control systems. Each of these systems possesses attributes that make it potentially attractive
for numerous applications. This chapter presents a survey of the technology
of self-organising control systems, a discussion of potential space vehicle applications for such systems, and discussions on four concepts which are basic to the
designs of learning control systems.

INTRODUCTION

Within the past few years, artificial intelligence techniques have been applied to
the design of learning control systems. Two types of such systems have been
postulated: (1) on-line-learning control systems; (2) off-line-learning control
systems. Each of these systems possesses one or more of the following attributes,
making it attractive for numerous applications: (1) the ability to maintain satisfactory performance in the face of random, unpredictable environments; (2) the
ability to prolong satisfactory performance in the face of hostile environments
which cause progressive component failure; and (3) the ability to provide sub-
optimal control of complex plants for which present analytical methods are
inadequate.

209

This chapter presents a survey of learning control systems, first covering self-organising systems in general, then discussing these particular control systems. This permits discussion of on-line- and off-line-learning control systems within a common frame of reference. Additionally, four concepts (or, loosely speaking, artificial intelligence techniques) which are basic to the design of learning control systems are discussed. These concepts are referred to as follows: (1) mappings, (2) control situations, (3) memory, and (4) sub-goals. Although these concepts are in themselves not unique to learning control systems, when combined, they are at the very heart of such systems. The relations between these concepts and *learning* and *pattern recognition* are demonstrated.

SELF-ORGANISING SYSTEMS

A *self-organising system* is one that changes its basic structure as a function of its experience and/or environment. Its general aim is to evolve toward some desired output state or mode of behaviour, in spite of some degree of ignorance of process, inputs, or controls. Because its structure changes as a function of experience, the self-organising system can be said to 'learn.' This is consistent with most definitions of learning provided that such a system improves its future performance by analysing its past performance. A complete discussion of learning as it is related to control systems has been given by Fu *et al.*[1] An elaboration on learning as it is related to artificial intelligence techniques appears in a later section entitled 'Basic Concepts,' (p. 221).

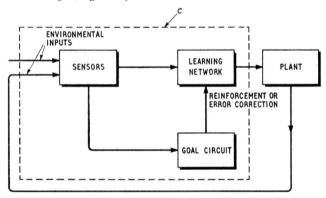

Fig. 11.1. Self-organising controller

A controller that is also a self-organising system is called a self-organising controller. Such a controller contains the following three basic sub-systems, as depicted in Fig. 11.1: (1) sensors, (2) learning network, and (3) a goal circuit. The *sensors* (rate gyros, pressure pickups, horizon scanners, etc.) observe the environment and provide descriptive data to the learning network and the goal circuit. The *learning network* is the changeable portion of the self-organising system. It may be a device which changes its structure physically or chemically; it may be a device which contains variable components (weights); or, it may just be part of an algorithm programmed for a computer. At present, only the last two types of learning networks have been applied to control systems. These learning networks are comprised of decision elements which operate on data input from the sensors and which render a desirable output response. Output data from the learning network are supplied to the system being controlled. The *goal circuit* directs the system organisation towards a specific objective and provides information on the degree of success attained by each trial in terms of the specific objective. This is usually accomplished by one of the following techniques:

1. *Reinforcement*—If present performance is an improvement upon recent past performance, the goal circuit generates a reward signal to the learning network, indicating that improvement has occurred. On the other hand, if present performance is worse than recent past performance, a punishment signal is generated, notifying the learning network of that fact. In effect, the reward signal reinforces those states of the network that contribute to improvement, while the punishment signal reverses the states that produced improper behaviour.
2. *Error Correction*—A signal is generated by the goal circuit only if present performance is worse than recent past performance. This signal reverses those states that produced improper behaviour. Improved performance is not rewarded.

In the following paragraphs, a system with a self-organising controller is referred to as a *learning control system*. There are two types of these systems: (1) on-line-learning control systems, in which the self-organising controller learns to control a system whose inputs and/or plant are incompletely specified and/or known; and (2) off-line-learning control systems (trainable controllers) in which the self-organising controller learns to control a system whose actual control law is incompletely specified.

ON-LINE-LEARNING CONTROL SYSTEMS

This section and the next present a comprehensive survey of both on-line- and off-line-learning control systems. In addition, a discussion of potential space vehicle applications for learning control systems is included because this survey was performed as part of a study for the National Aeronautics and Space Administration.

An *on-line-learning control system* is one in which the inputs and plant may not be known *a priori;* the controller is self-organising and learns to control the system properly on-line. A representative on-line-learning control system is shown in Fig. 11.2. Note the similarity between the systems in Figs. 11.1 and 11.2.

Learning occurs with the self-organising controller, C, embedded in the control system during real-time operation of the overall system. Learning that occurs when the performance history of the overall system—over a sequence of trials—indicates a trend toward improved performance[1] automatically improves the control law through the following functions:

1. Evaluation of results of control choices made by the self-organising controller for a given situation and according to a prescribed criterion.
2. Modification of the controller's memory store of parameters or its logic, so that subsequent control choices reflect the evaluation.

211

Two systems illustrate the on-line-learning philosophy. The first system, shown in Fig. 11.3 is an adaptive type. Parameters a and b are variable. Each contains two components, $a = \alpha + K_1$ and $b = \beta + K_2$; α and β represent random variations in a and b, respectively; and K_1 and K_2 represent the controls to offset the random variations in a and b, respectively. The random variations in a and b are assumed to change sufficiently often so that purely adaptive action could not optimise the system during the periods of constant α and β. The system is sub-

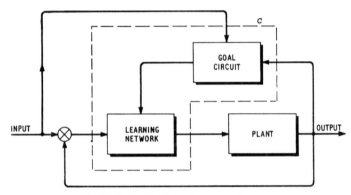

Fig. 11.2. On-line-learning control system

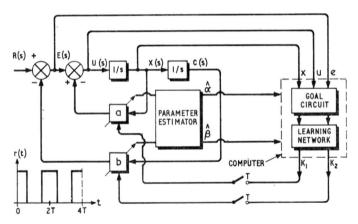

Fig. 11.3. Second-order system with a learning capability

jected to a fixed-amplitude square-wave input, $r(t)$, to facilitate the optimisation of a performance index (in the goal circuit) with respect to K_1 and K_2. The performance index, denoted *PI*, is given as:

$$PI = \int_{kT}^{(k+1)T} [\lambda_1 e^2(t) + \lambda_2 x^2(t) + \lambda_3 u^2(t)]\, dt \qquad (11.1)$$

for $k = 0, 1, 2, 3$, where λ_1, λ_2 and λ_3 are pre-specified weights. Constants α and β are constrained to remain constant over two periods of the square-wave input; and at each occurrence of an (α, β) pair, four computations of the *PI* are carried

212

out, one at each transition of the square wave. The *PI* is optimised on a computer. Specifically, after each computation of the *PI*, K_1 and K_2 are adjusted by a two-dimensional hill climbing technique. The best current values of K_1 and K_2 for a given pair (α_i, β_i), the directions of K_1 and K_2 adjustment, and the best current value of *PI* are stored in the computer memory.

The first time the system sees the pair (α_i, β_i) it reacts as a conventional adaptive-control system. When the pair (α_i, β_i) re-occurs, however, the best values of K_1 and K_2 are set from memory, and the best directions to increment K_1 and K_2 are known. Adaptation then proceeds, and better values of K_1, K_2, direction, and *PI* replace the old values for (α_i, β_i) in the memory. In this way, the system's past experience is incorporated into the machinery responsible for future control choices (K_1 and K_2). The random state variable (RSV) learning strategy discussed by Barron *et al.*[2,3] utilises a random search technique for obtaining K_1 and K_2. The system begins by making a random experimental change in K_1 and K_2. If system performance is improved as a consequence of this experiment, as determined in the goal circuit, the new values for K_1 and K_2 are retained; otherwise, the initial changes are discarded, and a new random experiment centred about the original values of K_1 and K_2 is tried. Learning proceeds in this fashion to those values of K_1 and K_2 that provide the best performance.

This first on-line-learning control system has a greater capability than a conventional adaptive system because it recognises similarly recurring control situations (combinations of α and β) and uses and improves the best previously obtained values of K_1 and K_2 for each control situation. It is convenient to view it as an adaptive control system with memory.

A second on-line-learning control system is shown in Fig. 11.4. A description of the plant is given in Eqn. 11.2 below:

$$\dot{x}_1(t) = x_2(t)$$
$$\dot{x}_2(t) = -x_2(t) + 100\, u(t) \tag{11.2}$$

In this system, the controller learns to drive the state vector from any set of initial conditions to within a distance δ of the origin in the state space in a way that approaches the optimum as defined by the system *PI*. (This was chosen to be:

$$PI = \sum_{=1}^{n} jx_1^2(jT) \tag{11.3}$$

where n is the sampling instant when the state vector arrives to within δ of the origin.) Learning occurs through a set stimulus-response relationship between elements of the state space and the control-choice space, which, in this case, contains only the elements $+1$ and -1.

The approach is first to design a controller that partitions the state space into sets called *control situations*, and then to learn the best control choice for each situation.[1-4] To be specific, the state space is partitioned into circular sets, as in Fig. 11.5. For higher-order systems, the state space would be partitioned into hyperspherical sets. This space, according to Fu *et al.*[1] '...is partitioned (into control situations) by constructing circular sets of pre-specified, fixed radius *D*. A given measurement vector (state vector) is considered a member of the set which it is closest to, providing the distance between the set vector (centre of the set) and the measurement vector is less than *D*. If this distance is greater than *D*, a new set is established, and its set vector is equal to the measurement vector. Initially there are no sets, and sets are only established in the vicinity of observed measurement vectors. Thus, memory is not wasted in establishing sets in regions where measurements never occur.'

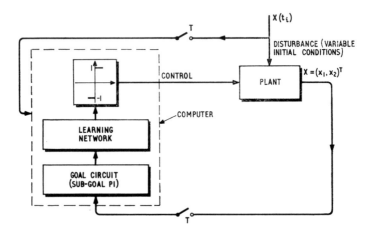

Fig. 11.4. Bang-bang learning control system

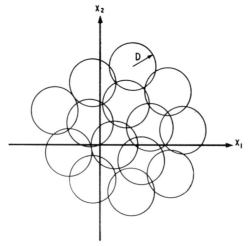

Fig. 11.5. Partitioning of state space into control situations

Each circular set (control situation) has either a $+1$ or a -1 control choice. All state vectors within the same circular region are assumed to have the same control choice. Initially, the probability of either a $+1$ or a -1 control choice is assumed to be the same. In this case, learning is by reinforcement of the probability that either $+1$ or -1 will be chosen for a given control situation. This reinforcement is based partially on the optimisation of a quadratic *sub-goal PI* every T seconds. (The control choice is fixed over each sampling interval.) In effect, the optimisation leads to either a positive or a negative reinforcement of

214

the probability that the control choice for a control situation is $+1$ or -1. Finally, as learning proceeds, the probability approaches unity for one of the control choices in each control situation.

In this case, the *PI* does not enter directly into the design of the controller (which contrasts with the preceding system) although, as stated by Fu *et al.*[1], it does enter into the choice of a proper sub-goal *PI*. Usually, the overall *PI* has an integral form over a number of sampling periods. On the other hand, the sub-goal *PI* is usually defined over each sampling period. Nevertheless, the *PI* in this case, as well as in the preceding learning control system, may be used as an indicator of learning on a *learning curve*.

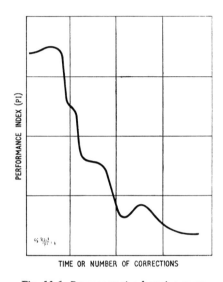

TIME OR NUMBER OF CORRECTIONS

Fig. 11.6. Representative learning curve

A learning curve is a plot of performance as a function of time (as for the system in Fig. 11.3), or the number of practice trials (as for the system in Fig. 11.4) used to measure learning. A typical learning curve for an arbitrary *PI* is shown in Fig. 11.6. Improved performance in this case is demonstrated by a reduction in the *PI* as a function of increasing values of time. One difficulty in the design of either of the preceding systems is the choice of meaningful *PI*'s and sub-goal *PI*'s. This is pointed out by Fu *et al.*[1] who note that the *PI*'s chosen should have a unique minimum that will be sought out by the system. In terms of learning curves, this means that after sufficient time or practice trials, the *PI* should remain constant. An interesting choice for an index of performance is made by Connelly *et al.*[5] and Barron *et al.*[3], who demonstrate the feasibility of using stability criteria in the goal circuit.

The object of Connelly's study was to design a bang-bang controller that maintains stable operation for the plant $K/s(s+a)$ in the face of plant changes, controller changes, and controller deterioration. A Lyapunov function, $V(\mathbf{x})$, is defined and evaluated in the goal circuit. The goal circuit then rewards those control choices for which $\dot{V}(\mathbf{x}) < 0$ and punishes those for which $\dot{V}(\mathbf{x}) > 0$. The system is similar in many respects to the system in Fig. 11.4, except that the learning network consists of statistical switches which learn under the influence of the goal circuit to provide the proper control choice. Barron claims better control when using $\ddot{V}(\mathbf{x})$ instead of $\dot{V}(\mathbf{x})$. This means that his goal circuit generates a reward signal if $\ddot{V}(\mathbf{x}) < 0$ and a punish signal if $\ddot{V}(\mathbf{x}) > 0$.

The ability of a system to improve its performance to a recurrent situation typifies the behaviour of an on-line-learning system. For example, if the system in Fig. 11.4 is subjected to the disturbance $\mathbf{x}_A(t_i)$, then $\mathbf{x}_B(t_i)$, and then $\mathbf{x}_A(t_i)$ again, it does not behave as if it had never encountered $\mathbf{x}_A(t_i)$. In short, its adaptation to $\mathbf{x}_B(t_i)$ does not destroy its previous adaptation to $\mathbf{x}_A(t_i)$.

There is a distinction between the use of the on-line-learning principle as a design tool and as a means for improving a system's performance on-line. When everything is known or is thought to be known about the plant and its environment *a priori*, on-line-learning may be used during a design as a design tool. In this case, the on-line-learning principle provides an algorithmic approach to the solution of a difficult design (optimisation) problem; that is to say, it provides an approach to the solution of problems where present analytical methods are inadequate.

On the other hand, for on-line-learning to improve a system's performance while on-line, new information must be made available to the on-line-performance assessor. This means that information not available *a priori* must be utilised by the performance assessor in making the decisions as to how or if the controls should be modified. If no new information becomes available on-line, the controller could have been designed ahead of time, and there would be no need for an on-line-learning capability. On-line-learning seems most appropriate, therefore, for systems which will be operating in partially known environments.

Space vehicle applications for the on-line-learning concept seem abundant. On-line-learning control appears most suited to unmanned applications, such as attitude control of orbiting vehicles, solar probes, and atmospheric-entry vehicles. Unmanned geophysical research and weather satellites are required to maintain attitude control with respect to earth for long durations. For greater pointing accuracies than those afforded by gravity-gradient techniques, a long life, active system is needed. This could be a system with current-carrying coils that are powered by solar energy and that interact with the earth's magnetic fields. On-line-learning could minimise energy use and attitude perturbations during seasonal changes in radiation and atmospheric external torques.

On-line-learning could also be used to provide fine-attitude control such as would be required by a laser communication satellite in Mars or earth orbit. In these applications, the overall goal would be to keep a number of state variables (attitude errors) within a region centred at the origin of the state space when the satellite is subject to random disturbances (for example, solar and atmospheric perturbation torques) and/or component deterioration, including progressive failures. A second application in which the on-line-learning concept would cope with progressive failures is a solar probe to distances of less than one-half an astronomical unit (AU). This application suggests the use of fluid control rather than electronic components and is contingent upon advances in the survivability of other sub-systems as well, particularly communications.

Finally, an application of on-line-learning for the distant future would be the logical organisation of automata to implement exploration and experimentation on other planets. On-line-learning could minimise energy use in the performance of assigned tasks.

OFF-LINE-LEARNING CONTROL SYSTEMS

An *off-line-learning control system* is one in which the inputs and plant are known *a priori*; the actual controller is incompletely specified (partially known) and is replaced by a self-organising system which learns (is trained) to control the system properly off-line.

A representative off-line-learning control system is shown in Fig. 11.7. Learning occurs with the switch S in position ①; the self-organising system, C, is shown representative problems and their solutions. For each sample, certain internal modifications to the learning network increase its proficiency. Training requires

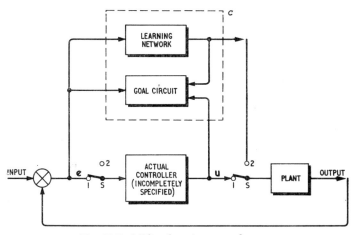

Fig. 11.7. Off-line-learning control system

no external intervention and is systematically convergent towards a learned state. At this point, internal modification of the learning network stops, and it now behaves in a conventional deterministic fashion; i.e. its responses to problems are not based upon any statistical phenomena or past history but are dependent upon its present static internal state. Its performance, therefore, will be exactly repeatable. Furthermore, if well trained, the learning network will be able to generalise problems not encountered in training and obtain solutions corresponding to the most similar problem encountered in training. The generalisation ability of the learning network allows the incompletely specified actual controller to be by-passed during the real-time control of the plant. With the switch S in position ②, however, the system shown in Fig. 11.7 behaves like a conventional non-adaptive control system: learning does not occur.

In the control-system applications of off-line-learning discussed in the literature,[6-10] the self-organising controller is of the type shown in Fig. 11.8; for clarity, e (Fig. 11.7) is assumed to be a two-dimensional vector and **u** is assumed to be a scalar.

This type of system—without the input encoder—has been described variously as a learning machine, an adaptive pattern recogniser or classifier, an adaptive majority-vote taker, an adaptive linear neuron, and an adaptive linear-threshold element (ADALINE). In the sequel, the complete system is referred to as an adaptive computer.

217

The inputs to the adaptive computer (e_1 and e_2) in Fig. 11.8 are each divided into m quanta. The v's are binary signals having the value of $+1$ or -1 (or $+1$ and 0); v_0 is a fixed threshold input set at $+1$. The set of $2m$ inputs $v_1, \ldots, v_{2m}$ is referred to as an *input pattern*.[8] The weights, w_i, are learning parameters. The learning feature of the adaptive computer is provided by the adaptor which adjusts weight values through an iterative training procedure (learning algorithm) to minimise the error between the output, u_L, of the adaptive computer and some desired output, u.

During the training process, the input patterns are selected one at a time, and a learning algorithm for updating the weights, $w_0, w_1, \ldots, w_{2m}$ is applied for each pattern. Training continues until all patterns have been classified correctly or

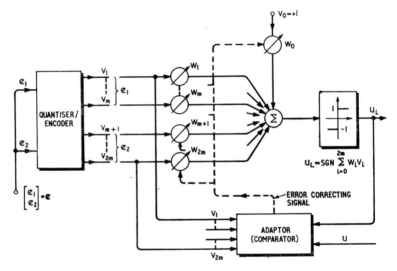

Fig. 11.8. Adaptive computer C

until the number of classification errors has been minimised. The convergence of the training process is usually depicted by plotting an index of performance, such as the number of incorrectly classified patterns divided by the total number of patterns (computed during a non-adaptive period), versus the corrections made during the adaptation period; or, the sum of the squares of the errors between the desired and actual outputs of the adaptive computer, versus the total number of input patterns adapted to by the adaptive computer. Such curves indicate the learning progress of the adaptive computer during training; however, they are meaningful only when switch S (Fig. 11.7) is in position ①. As noted previously, learning does not occur when switch S is in position ②.

Two types of learning algorithms may be distinguished: error correcting and positive reinforcement. The error correcting algorithms require a modification of the weights when a disagreement exists between u and u_L for an input pattern (Fig. 11.7); the weights are modified in a direction that tends to reduce or to eliminate classification errors. No changes are made when u and u_L are in agreement. Positive reinforcement algorithms correct for errors as described but, as opposed to error correcting algorithms, also reinforce the weights when agreement exists between u and u_L.

When a weight modification is required, the amount varies with different algorithms. The simplest, the so called increment algorithm, merely adds a fixed increment, $\pm W$, to each weight; the sign of the increment is consistent with eliminating or reducing classification error. The details of specific training algorithms are beyond the scope of this paper; excellent discussions on different training techniques appear in Zapalac,[11] Mendel and Zapalac[12] and Nilsson.[13]

An overall *PI* and sub-goal *PI* for the adaptive computer are distinguishable (see the second on-line-learning control system, discussed above). The sub-goal of the adaptive computer is correct classification of each input pattern. This sub-goal directs the updating of the weights, w_i. The overall *PI* is that the adaptive computer classifies correctly all such input patterns. The overall goal determines how often the sequence of input training patterns has to be applied to the adaptive computer before complete learning occurs.

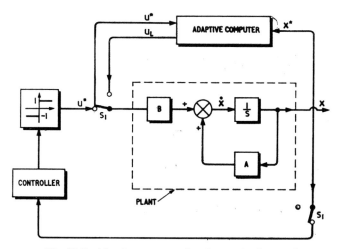

Fig. 11.9. Adaptive computer for time-optimal control

The most attractive feature of the adaptive computer is its ability to generalise input patterns not encountered in training and to obtain solutions corresponding to the most similar input patterns encountered in training. Generalisation relates to the concepts of linear separability[9] and projectability.[6] Moreover, the adaptive computer remains very reliable despite component failures (the weights, w_i) and is particularly well suited to resolve problems for which no analytical solutions can be found.

In Fig. 11.8, u_L is limited to two values, ± 1; thus, the desired output, u, must also be limited to ± 1, otherwise the adaptive computer could not learn to simulate the actual controller. The adaptive computer is especially useful, therefore, in those situations where the actual controller is of the bang-bang type; hence almost all applications of the adaptive computer in off-line-learning control systems have been limited to the time-optimal control of linear systems where the actual controller is bang-bang. These studies involved (with modifications resulting from individual treatment by each author) the following (Fig. 11.9):

1. Quantisation of the state space in the region of interest, and identification of the resulting hypercubes with linearly independent codes.

219

2. Selection of a subset I from the complete set of initial conditions $\{x_0\}$.
3. Computation of the open-loop optimal control, $u^*(t)$, and trajectory $x^*(t)$, for each element of I and for a specific plant.
4. Identification of the controls for the hypercubes through which the trajectories pass; let these hypercubes and their controls constitute the training set S.
5. Training of an off-line-learning controller by means of the set S in 4.

A significant difference in the studies reported in the literature,[7-11] is the selection of the subset I from the complete set of initial conditions, $\{x_0\}$, sufficient for complete learning. Van Nortwick[9] and Zapalac[11] train the adaptive computer on a set of input patterns from every square in the quantised state space. F. W. Smith[8] trains the adaptive computer on a set of input patterns from every hypercube in the quantised state space that borders the optimal switching surface. In this case, the optimal switching surface is known *a priori*. Both of these approaches are practical only for low-order plants. However, F. B. Smith[7] and Zapalac[10] consider high-order systems for which the exact form of the optimal switching surface, as a function of the state variables, is not known. In these systems, the adaptive computer is trained on a set of input patterns distributed uniformly in the quantised state space. For example, in the control of a third-order vehicle, an arbitrary region of the three-space is defined and quantised into 27,000 three-dimensional cubes. The adaptive computer is trained on a set of 1,000 initial conditions chosen at uniform intervals in the arbitrary region. This represents only $3 \cdot 7\%$ of the total input patterns.[10] If the training set S is sufficiently representative, then the controller obtained will provide control with desirable characteristics for a much wider class of inputs than the training set.

The most important conclusion to be drawn from the previous work is that off-line-training can achieve a practical realisation of the closed-loop (sub-) optimal-control law with a small set of open-loop optimal-control laws (subset I, above). It is termed practical for the following reasons:[10]

1. Quantisation can be coarse (for example, 20 levels per variable).
2. The size of the subset I is small (for example, 10 initial conditions).
3. The solution is relatively insensitive to changes in the vector **w**.
4. Excessive amounts of data processing time are not required.
5. Implementation of the trained controller with resistive-type networks is straightforward.

The five-step procedure discussed in this section provides a *technique for synthesising modern closed-loop controllers*. It is motivated not only by the need for closed-loop optimal controllers, but also by the close similarities between conventional and modern control system synthesis problems, when the modern problem is viewed in terms of off-line-training. Modern and conventional, in this context, refer to the state space and frequency domain (S plane) points of view, respectively. Both the modern and conventional synthesis problems can be summarised in three steps, as follows:

1. *Conventional control system synthesis problem*
   (a) Synthesise a closed-loop transfer function which satisfies given performance specifications.
   (b) Synthesise an open-loop controller transfer function using a technique such as the Truxal-Guillemin method[14] for example.

(c) Mechanise the controller transfer function using R-C circuits, active devices, etc.

2. *Modern control system synthesis problem*
   (a) Obtain open-loop optimal controls by optimising a given performance function.
   (b) Synthesise the feedback controller (trained controller) using off-line training.
   (c) Mechanise the trained controller using resistors and transistors, for example.

Observe the correspondences between the three steps in the two synthesis problems.

The full potential of off-line-learning control systems has not yet been realised. At present, the only self-organising system apparently utilised in the systems is an adaptive computer with a single, linear-threshold element. This necessarily restricts the application of this type of computer to the class of bang-bang controllers. Although this includes the important application of time-optimal control, it eliminates problems that occur frequently in space vehicle applications, such as minimum fuel control, minimum energy control, and any controller requiring multi-level outputs. Finally, all time-optimal switching surfaces are not necessarily realisable with single linear-threshold elements. The surface usually must be projectable to permit this realisation.[6, 11] By including more threshold devices in the adaptive computer, it should be possible to make them applicable to control problems other than time-optimal ones. For example, it has been shown that two linear-threshold elements can realise the three states, -1, 0, and $+1$. It is likely, therefore, that an adaptive computer containing two threshold devices would be useful in the minimum fuel problem for realising the closed-loop optimal control law, where, as is well known, the optimal control law (for linear systems) is of the on-off variety. An interesting space vehicle application is one in which the off-line-learning controller is trained to act as a back-up mode for man during a specific mission, such as re-entry. In this application, man supplies the required training samples through on-ground simulations. This can be considered analogous to optimisation theory which supplies the open-loop optimal controls (training samples) when the off-line-learning controller is used, for example, to realise closed-loop time-optimal control.

BASIC CONCEPTS

At the heart of the on-line-and off-line-learning control systems, described in the preceding sections, are four basic concepts. These concepts, which are also referred to as *artificial intelligence techniques*, are those of: (1) mapping, (2) control situations, (3) memory, and (4) sub-goals. Each of these concepts is elaborated upon in the present section.

MAPPINGS

The mapping concept permits one to view control system design problems as collections of mappings either (1) from points in a plant parameter space to respective points in a feedback gain space, or (2) from points in state space to re-

221

spective points in a control category space, or (3) from points in an augmented
state space (a state space with an additional dimension for each variable plant
parameter) to respective points in some control choice space. This allows the
control engineer to formulate his design problem in a form which is suitable for
pattern recognition interpretations. Consider the first example of an on-line-
learning control system depicted in Fig. 11.3. There, an on-line optimisation procedure is achieving mappings from points:

$$\{\alpha_i, \beta_i\}_{i=1}^I$$

in the plant parameter space to respective points:

$$\{K_{1i}, K_{2i}\}_{i=1}^I$$

in the feedback gain space. These mappings are depicted in Fig. 11.10.

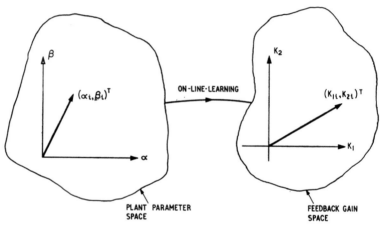

Fig. 11.10. Mapping interpretation for system in Fig. 11.3

In order to demonstrate the analogy between the mapping concept (as described above) and pattern recognition, there follows a brief review of some pattern
classification concepts.

A *pattern* is a set of n real numbers, y_1, y_2, $\ldots$, y_n; it represents a set of data
to be classified. A *pattern classifier* (Fig. 11.11) is a device which sorts patterns
into categories. The inputs to the pattern classifier (a pattern vector $\mathbf{y}$) are assumed to be applied simultaneously to the classifier. The output, r, is the classification of the pattern and may assume any one of p distinct values. It is assumed
that there is one category associated with each value of r; hence, the classifier
sorts patterns into p categories.

A geometric interpretation of pattern classification is indicated in the example
in Fig. 11.12. Two point sets are delineated; each point set represents the population of patterns to be classified for a specific category. For this example, $r = 1$
or 2; category $r = 1$ might be associated with the feedback gain vector $(K_{11},
K_{21})^T$; $r = 2$ might be associated with the feedback gain vector $(K_{12}, K_{22})^T$.
The surfaces which separate the point sets are called *decision surfaces* and are
implicitly defined in the pattern classifier by a set of functions $f_1(\mathbf{y}), f_2(\mathbf{y}), \ldots,$

222

$f_q(\mathbf{y})$, which are scalar and single-valued functions of the pattern vector, $\mathbf{y}$. It is convenient to think of these functions as effecting a *mapping* of the point sets from the pattern space into their appropriate category, r. Suppose, for example, that only two feedback gain vectors are available for the system in Fig. 11.3, $(K_{11}, K_{21})^T$ and $(K_{12}, K_{22})^T$. Loosely speaking, during on-line-learning, points in the plant parameter space (Fig. 11.10) are classified into one of the two categories, $(K_{11}, K_{21})^T$ or $(K_{12}, K_{22})^T$; hence, on-line-learning is effecting the realisation of a decision surface in the plant parameter space. This surface separates

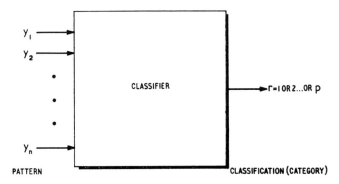

Fig. 11.11. A pattern classifier

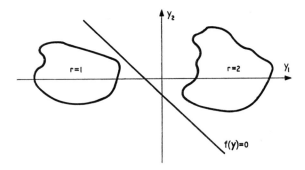

Fig. 11.12. Example of a decision surface

the points in plant parameter space which are associated with the feedback gain vector $(K_{11}, K_{21})^T$ from the points which are associated with the vector $(K_{12}, K_{22})^T$.

A second example which illustrates the mapping concept is the bang-bang system in Fig. 11.4. There, on-line-learning is achieving mappings from points in state space ($x_1 - x_2$ space) to either one or the other of two control categories, $+1$ or -1 control. As a matter of fact, the mappings for this system are achieved from *regions* in state space to respective control categories.

CONTROL SITUATIONS

Control situations are regions in either plant parameter space, state space, or augmented state space for which a single control choice (e.g. set of feedback gains, or $+1$ or -1 control) leads to *satisfactory performance* for all points contained therein. Such regions may result from a pre-gridding of the plant parameter space, state space, or augmented state space, or they may be created on-line as the need for additional control situations manifests itself. The rationale for partitioning the different spaces into control situations is the assumption that neighbouring points within a small region should have the same or similar control choices.

One might assume that control situations can be constructed quite arbitrarily. This assumption is incorrect, in the sense of the definition above, because there is usually no guarantee that all points within an arbitrary region will have a satisfactory performance associated with them. This is elaborated upon, in the context of a specific spacecraft application, by Mendel.[15]

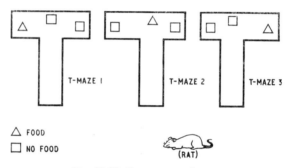

Fig. 11.13. T-maze experiment

Control situations permit localisations of an optimisation problem from the entire plant parameter space, state space, or augmented state space to regions in the respective spaces, and, in this way, are analogous to *events* in learning theory.[16] Consider, for example, a learning experiment in which a hungry rat is directed to one of a group of different T-mazes on each trial (Fig. 11.13). Each T-maze represents a different event; the purpose of the experiment is for the rat to learn which way to move in *any one* of the T-mazes to satisfy his hunger.

There are a number of different ways in which this experiment can be conducted. Assume, first, that the rat is *exposed repeatedly* to the *same* T-maze until he learns which way to move within it to satisfy his hunger. Within a T-maze, the rat is faced with a number of alternatives (e.g. turn left, turn right, straight in, etc.). Stochastic learning theory[16] tells us to assign a probability to each alternative, and that the *outcome* of each trial (e.g. hunger satisfied, still hungry) reinforces these probabilities (alternatives). As the number of trials increases, the rat learns which way to move within a T-maze to satisfy his hunger; that is to say, the probability associated with one of the possible alternatives (e.g. turning to the right, in T-maze 3) dominates the probabilities associated with the remaining alternatives. The rat has, in effect, learned the equivalent of a single control choice (in probability) for each T-maze. Exposing the rat to the same event on a number of trials is analogous, in an on-line-learning control problem (such as the system in Fig. 11.4), to continuing (more iterations) an on-line optimisation procedure associated with a specific control situation for as long as the system remains within that control situation. In a trainable controller problem, it is analogous to an error-correction rule which is used to adjust the variable weights each time the same input pattern (associated with a specific hypercube) is presented to the adaptive computer (Fig. 11.8).

Because of the described training, the rat probably will not remember what the correct alternative for T-maze 3 is after he has learned what the correct alternatives are for the other T-mazes. The overall purpose of the learning experiment is to train the rat which way to move in *any one* of the T-mazes; hence, it may be more expedient to expose him to a *sequence* of the three T-mazes (e.g. a systematic sequence such as 1132, 1132, 1132, etc.). Exposing the rat to a sequence of T-mazes(events) is analogous, in an on-line-learning control problem (such as the system in Fig. 11.4), to a passage in plant parameter space, state space, or augmented state space through a sequence of control situations (Fig. 11.5). To promote this analogy, the control system must be provided with memory of what it has learned within each control situation.

MEMORY

With the memory concept, a separate memory compartment is associated with each control situation. In the event that learning is not completed the first time a control situation is entered (first time rat enters a T-maze), pertinent information is stored in a memory compartment so that when the control situation is re-entered, learning may *continue*. Memory, therefore, is essential to the meaning of learning.

One may distinguish between two forms of memory; *short term* and *long term*. Short term memory refers to the remembering of pertinent information for as long as the system is in the same control situation. Long term memory, on the other hand, refers to the remembering of pertinent information out of the control situation. Consider, for example, the bang-bang system depicted in Fig. 11.4. As long as the system remains within a control situation, a short term memory is required to facilitate the updating of the probabilities associated with a $+1$ or -1 control choice. The long term memory remembers the last computed values for these two probabilities when the system leaves the control situation. In this way, when the control situation is re-entered, the previously learned probabilities are recalled for subsequent trials. The analogy between the short term and long term memory requirements in a control system, and the memory requirements of the rat in the learning experiment described above, is apparent.

SUB-GOALS

Often, the main goal or objective for a control system cannot be formulated precisely, or if it can be, the formulation is mathematically intractable. A quite common approach (not elaborated upon here to any great extent) is to formulate a mathematically tractable cost function (e.g. quadratic cost function) and to optimise it to obtain a control which leads to *satisfactory system performance*. Satisfactory system performance may not, however, be compatible with the measure of performance provided by the mathematical cost function. In this sense, the cost function acts as a sub-goal and need not, in general, be compatible with the overall goal, although compatibility is desirable. In addition, the overall goal may provide a measure of the system's performance over the entire time interval of interest, whereas a sub-goal may provide a measure of the system's performance over a much smaller interval of time. The use of a sub-goal in both off-line- and on-line-learning control systems is quite prevalent.

It is important to re-emphasise that the above four concepts, while in themselves not unique to learning control systems, when combined, are at the very heart of such systems.

CONCLUDING REMARKS

To combine the advantages of on-line and off-line systems, one could provide the off-line-learning control system with an on-line-learning capability. A block diagram of such a system is shown in Fig. 11.14.[17] With switches S_1 in position ①

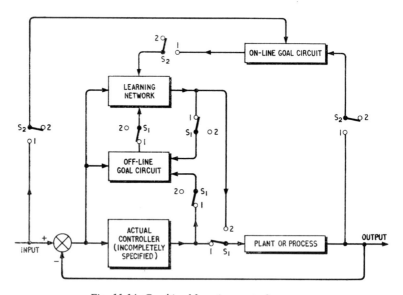

Fig. 11.14. Combined learning control system

and S_2 in position ②, the system reduces to the off-line-learning control system shown in Fig. 11.7. On the other hand, with switches S_1 in position ② and S_2 in position ① the system reduces to the on-line-learning control system shown in Fig. 11.2.

While the combined system is conditioned on all available *a priori* information about the plant and environment, as in an off-line-learning controller, its main advantage is that it would be able to reorganise if the system experienced a partially known or unknown environment, or if components deteriorated, as in an on-line-learning controller. Such a combined system is described by Mendel[15] in connection with the fine-attitude control of a laser communication satellite in Mars orbit. Nominal controls are designed with *a priori* information about variations in plant parameters and disturbance torques. On-line, the nominal controls may be updated via on-line learning to compensate for incorrect or incomplete information about actual disturbance torques. Here, on-line-learning is applied to a system operating in a partially known environment.

To demonstrate another advantage of a combined learning control system over off-line- and on-line-learning control systems, a hypothetical *PI* is assumed which is meaningful for both off-line- and on-line-learning. Fig. 11.15 presents a comparison of the three control situations: (1) training plus on-line-learning; (2) training and no on-line-learning; and (3) on-line-learning with no prior train-

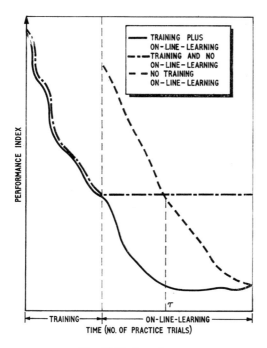

Fig. 11.15. Learning curves

ing. Learning occurs in (2) only during the training period, as is evident from the constancy of the training, and no on-line learning curve during on-line operation. Note that until time τ, the performance of (2) is better than the performance of (3). For $t > \tau$, however, (3) swiftly overtakes the performance of (2), and eventually reaches the minimum *PI*, whereas the performance of (2) remains unchanged. Also, (1) reaches the minimum *PI* sooner than (3) because when on-line-learning begins, (1) starts out with a lower *PI* than (3).

At present, the technology associated with trainable controllers is further advanced than the technology associated with on-line-learning controllers. In Mendel,[15] for example, the following ground rule was adopted for on-line-learning control systems. Ground Rule: an on-line-learning controller must be able to satisfactorily correct any degradation in performance that could have been treated satisfactorily had its cause been anticipated. Hence, on-line-learning controllers are, at present, only as good as the on-line-learning strategies. Those strategies are decided upon by the control system engineer and are, for the most part, still in the very early stages of development.

ACKNOWLEDGMENT

The work discussed in this chapter was accomplished by the Douglas Missile and Space Systems Division, partially under Company-sponsored Research and Development funds and partially under a programme sponsored by the Electronics Research Center (ERC) of the National Aeronautics and Space Administration (Contract No. NAS 12–23).

REFERENCES

1. FU, K. S., *et al.*, *Philosophy and State of the Art of Learning Control Systems*, Rep TR-EE63-7 (AF Report AFOSR 5144). Control and Information Systems Lab., School of Electrical Engineering, Purdue University, November (1963).
2. BARRON, R. L., DAVIES, J. M., SCHALKOWSKY, S. and SNYDER, R. F., *Self-Organizing Adaptive Systems for Space Vehicle Attitude Control*, Presented at the SAE-18 Committee Meeting, Miami Beach, Florida, December (1964).
3. BARRON, R. L., DAVIES, J. M., SCHALKOWSKY, S. and SNYDER, R. F., *Self-Organizing Adaptive Systems for Space Vehicle Attitude Control*, Presented at the AIAA/ION Guidance and Control Conference, Minneapolis, Minnesota, August (1965).
   (NOTE: Content of this paper is different from that of Reference 2.)
4. FU, K. S. and WALTZ, M. D., 'A Computer-Simulated Learning Control System,' *IEEE International Conference Record, Part 1*, 190–201 (1964).
5. CONNELLY, E. M., MIRABELLI, R. E. and WORTHEN, J. H., *Feasibility Studies on Use of Artrons as Logic Elements in Flight Control Systems*, FDL-TDR-64-23, Wright-Patterson AFB, Ohio, February (1964).
6. BERKOVEC, J. W. and EPLEY, D. L., *On Time-Optimal Control with Threshold Logic Units* Preprint 4. 1, WESCON, August (1964).
7. SMITH, F. B., Jr., *A Logical Net Mechanization for Time-Optimal Regulation*, NASA TN D-1678 (1962).
8. SMITH, F. W., *Contactor Control by Adaptive Pattern-Recognition Techniques*, Rep. No. 6762-1, Stanford Electronics Laboratories, Stanford University, April (1964).
9. VAN NORTWICK, K. G., *An Adaptive Computer Applied to a Second-Order Non-Linear Control System*, Boeing Report No. D2-90192-7, May (1963).
10. ZAPALAC, J. J., *Self-Organizing Control Systems, Vol. 4. Synthesis of a Time-Optimal Controller Through Off-Line Training*, Douglas Report DAC-59322, August (1966).
11. ZAPALAC, J. J., *Self-Organizing Control Systems, Vol. 1. On Adaptive Computers*, Douglas Report SM-47857, July (1965).
12. MENDEL, J. M. and ZAPALAC, J. J., *Self-Organizing Control Systems, Vol. 3. Off-Line Training of Time-Optimal, Fuel-Optimal, and Minimum-Energy Controllers*, Douglas Report SM-51975, February (1966).
13. NILSSON, N. J., *Learning Machines: Foundations of Trainable Pattern-Classifying Systems*, McGraw-Hill, New York (1965).
14. TRUXAL, J. G., *Automatic Feedback Control System Synthesis*, McGraw-Hill, New York (1955).
15. MENDEL, J. M., *Applications of Artificial Intelligence Techniques to a Spacecraft Control Problem*, NASA CR-755 (May, 1967).
16. BUSH, R. R. and MOSTELLER, F., *Stochastic Models for Learning*, John Wiley, New York (1955).
17. MENDEL, J. M., *On Applications of Biological Principles to the Design of Feedback Control Systems*, Douglas Report SM-47772, Santa Monica, California (1964).

PART 4

CYBERNETICS AND INDUSTRY

'There is more to life than increasing its speed'
Mahatma Gandhi

Chapter 12

Cybernetics and Process Control (Linear Processes)

V. STREJC, Ph.D., D.Sc., Dr.Sc. (Mech. Eng.)
Czechoslovak Academy of Sciences,
The University of Prague (Czechoslovakia)

SUMMARY

This chapter deals with Wiener's synthesis of single and multi-parameter control loops. The first part deals with the synthesis of continuously acting control loops with a semi-free configuration. The synthesis is performed by the calculus of variations with indetermined Lagrange multipliers, on the one hand, and with the direct determination of the optimum solution in the complex plane, on the other. Apart from the normal arrangement of the control loop with random input variables, the loop is solved with a limited input signal of the controlled system by compensating for random disturbances at a constant or analytically determined command signal. In multi-parameter control loops, loops with cross correlated input signals are differentiated from those with no-cross correlated input signals. The second case is solved by the factorisation of the determinants and matrices.

The second part of the paper discusses DDC in Wiener's sense. Attention is drawn especially to deviations from the synthesis of continuously acting control loops. The difference is explained between the case of the synthesis according to the continuous and discrete least square error. Special attention is paid to the problems of physical realisability and of hybrid control loops. In multi-parameter control loops with cross correlated input variables, the factorisation of determinants and that of matrices is again applied.

INTRODUCTION

In the first half of this century science provided engineers with theoretical methods for the determination and analysis of stabilised states and responses of systems exposed to the action of input signals. When the response to unit impulse was once known, it was possible to determine, at least theoretically, the response of the system to any input signal. Subsequently, it was comparatively easy to find the way to the analytical expression of the dynamic properties of systems. This possibility immediately produced efforts to influence system responses and to establish optimal control policy. The solution of these problems was made possible by synthesis methods. However, even this cannot be regarded at the last link of development. Control theory is being further elaborated and the position of today clearly shows that many problems have still to be solved. The theory of the complex variable, and the Fourier and Laplace transforms represent beyond any doubt significant contributions to the development of control theory methods. Nevertheless, many new ideas and methods had to be added to make control theory applicable to numerous practical problems encountered by engineers. The original control theory could not be used for the analysis of the random, analytically inexpressible transients of many variables, mostly disturbances, and of the many related problems of statistical nature. The theory was even less suited for considering the effect of random processes in the calculation of optimal systems. The introduction of random functions into engineering calculations was only made possible by the works of A. Kolmogoroff[1] and N. Wiener[2] on optimal filtration and on the theory of prediction, together with the works of Bode and Shannon[3] on information theory. N. Wiener showed how to determine in advance, i.e. by synthesis, the transfer function of a filter having the required properties. By using the criterion of the mean square error he showed that in linear systems the transfer function of the filter depends only on the two-dimensional correlation functions of input signals. The original works of A. Kolmogoroff[1] and of N. Wiener[2] solved the problem in the time domain. The solution in the frequency domain, most frequently used today, was first used by H. W. Bode and C. E. Shannon.[3] In the early sixties this theory already appeared in basic text books, and in the field of theoretical research attention has been concentrated on further special problems, e.g. the solution of the problem by means of polynomial equations, the analysis of the degree of sensitivity, the stipulation of the conditions of physical realisability, the solution of synthesis for hybrid control systems, the numerical solution of synthesis by means of an automatic computer, etc. In this connection it would be possible to name many authors and to list many significant results obtained.

The generalisation of the theory to multi-dimensional loops was already presented in Wiener's original work.[2] Though he used the method of determined multipliers, the method of matrix factorisation was also pointed out. N. Wiener continued working on the problems of matrix factorisation,[4] and the solution formulated for discrete processes was published jointly with P. Masani.[5, 6]

This work also was an incentive for other authors. D. C. Youla[7] derived the method of matrix factorisation for continuous processes. From the list of further authors particularly engaged in the simplification of original methods it is proper to mention R. J. Kavanagh[8] and M. C. Davis.[9]

The theory of synthesis in Wiener's sense has been, in fact, used in few cases only. This is due to obstacles of three kinds:

1. The majority of engineers engaged in practical work have not mastered the theory to date to a degree sufficient for normal practical use. Moreover, excessive simplification frequently introduced by practical workers has proved to be equally damaging to the popularisation of the application of this theory as the exaggerated abstract forms sometimes used in the mathematical formulation of the theory.

2. The analysis of initial data, i.e. the verification of the stationary character and the determination of correlation functions, or of the spectral densities of useful and disturbing signals, is not an easy matter. It requires not only prolonged measurements on real objects but also exacting measuring and calculating techniques.

3. Filters determined by the synthesis may happen to be rather complex. Their realisation must frequently be preceded by a suitable simplification.

In spite of these difficulties, Wiener's theory shows how to conceive more intimately processes proceeding in real systems; and though the synthesis of optimum control cannot be brought to full conclusion, the theory at least indicates how the optimum solution can be approached.

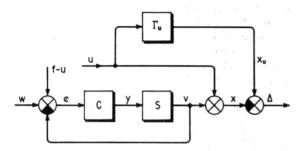

Fig. 12.1. Control loop (Wiener's synthesis)

The development of automatic computers and of numerical calculating methods makes easier the application of all methods which are excessively complex and exacting in the analytical version. A program of numerical calculation once set up can be easily used in practical operation without the necessity of the user mastering the whole theoretical apparatus required for preparing the program. It can thus be expected that automatic computers will also make easier the introduction into practice of Wiener's theory of synthesis. Such evolution will certainly be speeded up by the ever increasing dimensions and complexity of production processes connected with efforts directed towards the highest possible efficiency of production.

A block diagram representing the arrangement of a control loop for synthesis in Wiener's sense is shown in Fig. 12.1. Block S represents the continuously acting controlled system, S_u the part of the controlled system through which the influence of disturbances h is transmitted, C is the controller and Γ the ideal loop. The input signals of the loop are: useful command variables w, disturbances f (noise) acting at the same points of the loop as the command signals, and disturbances h acting on the controlled system. Disturbances h can always be recalculated into variables u acting at the output of the controlled system so that, with no adverse effect on the generalising nature of the solution and with due regard to the simplification of mathematical relationships, only variables u will be used in further calculations. The output signals of the loop are: the ideal controlled variables x_w and the real controlled variables x which in linear loops equal the sum

$$x = v + u \qquad (12.1)$$

233

At the output of the ideal and real loops the error is calculated

$$\varDelta = x_w - x \tag{12.2}$$

The error of the real loop is

$$e = w + f - x \tag{12.3}$$

Several varieties of control loop may occur in practice which can be derived from the block diagram in Fig. 12.1. Let us mention some of them:

1. The control loop is one- or multi-dimensional.
2. The controller is acting continuously or discontinuously, or a mixed (hybrid) action of controllers is applied in each control loop.
3. The useful command signals are either of a random and stationary character with zero mean value as are all input disturbances, or the command signals are determined by analytical functions, or the command signals are constant and only random disturbances are acting on the loop.
4. Random command signals are either stationarily cross correlated, or not. However, they need not be stationarily correlated with the input disturbances.
5. The real control loop has, or has not free configuration. For instance, there may be an advance determination of some poles or zeros of the transfer function of the real control loop. In control loops with discretly acting controllers the transfer function of the real c ontrol loop may have a semi-free configuration in respect of, e.g. conditions of stability,[10] conditions of physical realisability,[11] etc.
6. The input signals of the controlled system are either limited or not.

Naturally, each of the listed varieties does not require, in principle, a solution different from the others. Therefore, further chapters can be confined to the analytical solution of some selected cases. In all these cases it will be assumed that the controlled system is continuously acting, linear and having concentrated non-varying parameters. The transfer function of the system can thus be expressed as quotients of rational functions of the complex variable s. The integral square error will be used as the criterion of control quality for analytically defined command signals, while the mean square error will serve the same purpose for random variables. The control loop will thus be optimal, if the criterion of control quality attains a minimum value.

THE SYNTHESIS OF CONTINUOUSLY ACTING ONE-DIMENSIONAL CONTROL LOOPS

RANDOM COMMAND SIGNAL (SEMI-FREE CONFIGURATION OF THE LOOP TRANSFER FUNCTION, DISTURBANCE $u = 0$)

Let the transfer function of the real control loop, $K_w(s)$, have semi-free configuration in the sense that it can be written as:

$$K_w(s) = K_0(s) K_d(s) \tag{12.4}$$

where $K_d(s)$ is the part determined in advance, while $K_0(s)$ is the part to be determined. If command signal w and disturbance f are random variables cross-correlated in the sense of the definition given in the Introduction, and if disturbance $u = 0$, the error density spectrum according to Fig. 12.1 will be:

$$S_{\Delta\Delta}(s) = K_0(-s) K_d(-s) S_{w+f,\,w+f}(s) K_0(s) K_d(s)$$
$$-\Gamma(-s) S_{w,\,w+f}(s) K_0(s) K_d(s)$$
$$- K_0(-s) K_d(-s) S_{w+f,\,w}(s) \Gamma(s) + \Gamma(-s) S_{w,\,w}(s) \Gamma(s) \qquad (12.5)$$

where individual spectral densities are defined as follows:

$$S_{w+f,\,w+f}(s) = S_{ww}(s) + S_{wf}(s) + S_{fw}(s) + S_{ff}(s)$$
$$S_{w,\,w+f}(s) = S_{ww}(s) + S_{wf}(s) = S_{w+f,\,w}(-s) \qquad (12.6)$$
$$S_{w+f,\,w}(s) = S_{ww}(s) + S_{fw}(s) = S_{w,\,w+f}(-s)$$

It is known that now the mean square error is

$$\overline{\Delta^2(t)} = R_{\Delta\Delta}(0) = \frac{1}{2\pi j} \int_{-j\infty}^{+j\infty} S_{\Delta\Delta}(s)\,ds \qquad (12.7)$$

where $R_{\Delta\Delta}(0)$ is the value of the auto-correlation function $R_{\Delta\Delta}(\tau)$ of error Δ for $\tau = 0$.

Now the task is given to determine $K_0(s)$ so that mean square error $\overline{\Delta^2(t)}$ is minimum. At the same time transfer function $K_w(s)$ of the loop must be stable (all poles of transfer function $K_w(s)$ must lie inside the left half-plane (LHP) of the complex plane s) and physically realisable (the degree of the polynomial of the numerator must be lower that the degree of the polynomial of the denominator). From the stated requirements on the stability and physical realisability of the transfer function $K_w(s)$ can logically follow the limitations on the form of the function $K_d(s)$.

For the sake of brevity and clarity of mathematical relations, all functions of argument s will be written without the argument, and all functions of argument $(-s)$ will be marked with a bar. For instance $K_0 \equiv K_0(s)$, $\overline{K}_0 \equiv K_0(-s)$, etc.

Two methods of the solution of the given problem will be presented here. Both belong to methods based on the calculus of variations. The first is the method of undetermined (Lagrange) multipliers which Wiener used in his original work. Let us substitute for spectral density $S_{\Delta\Delta}$ in Eqn. 12.7 the value given by Eqn. 12.5.

Let us stipulate that

$$K_0 = K_m + \lambda K_\lambda \qquad (12.8)$$

where K_m is the assumed solution by which $\overline{\Delta^2(t)}$ attains its minimum value, and K_λ is an arbitrary function subject to the same boundary conditions as K_m ($K_\lambda(t) = 0$ for $t \leq 0$ and for $t \to \infty$). Further λ is an undetermined parameter which can be varied and used for verifying whether K_m is the desired solution. With the substitution of Eqn. 12.8 the mean square error can be expressed by

$$\overline{\Delta^2(t)} = I_a + \lambda(I_b + I_c) + \lambda^2 I_d \tag{12.9}$$

where I_a, I_b, I_c and I_d are integrals of functions of the complex variable s.
The sufficient condition for a minimum $\overline{\Delta^2(t)}$ is thus

$$\lim_{\lambda \to 0} \frac{\partial \overline{\Delta^2(t)}}{\partial \lambda} = 0 \tag{12.10}$$

According to condition (12.10) we can calculate from Eqn. 12.9 that

$$I_b + I_c = 0 \tag{12.11}$$

Since $I_c = \bar{I}_b$ it will suffice to satisfy the condition

$$I_b = 0 \tag{12.12}$$

where in the case under consideration it holds that

$$I_b = \frac{1}{2\pi j} \int\limits_{-j\infty}^{+j\infty} \left(K_m K_d \bar{K}_d S_{w+f,\, w+f} - \bar{K}_d S_{w+f,\, w} \Gamma \right) \bar{K}_\lambda \, ds \tag{12.13}$$

Condition (12.12) must thus be satisfied for any arbitrary $\bar{K}_\lambda$, provided that the latter complies with the requirements stated above. Let us prove by contradiction that condition (12.12) is also a necessary condition. It can be shown that the value of the integral I_a depends on the assumed solution K_m, while the value of the integral I_d is independent of this solution and always positive. If $I_b \neq 0$, it would always be possible to select some λ for which $\lambda^2 I_d < 2|\lambda I_b|$ and $\lambda I_b < 0$. With λ selected in this way, and K_0 given according to Eqn. 12.8, the mean square error $\overline{\Delta^2(t)}$ is smaller than with the solution of K_m and this is in disagreement with the definition of K_m. Consequently, condition (12.12) is a sufficient but also a necessary condition.

Condition (12.12) can be satisfied if the integrand of Eqn. 12.13 will be regular in the left half-plane (LHP) of the complex plane s. The case where the sum of residues of the integrand equals zero, cannot generally be complied with.

Since, according to the definition function, K_λ is regular inside the right half-plane (RHP) of the complex plane s, function $\bar{K}_\lambda$ is regular inside the LHP. To satisfy condition (12.12) it will thus suffice that

$$K_m K_d \bar{K}_d S_{w+f,\, w+f} - \bar{K}_d S_{w+f,\, w} \Gamma = \Lambda \tag{12.14}$$

where Λ is a regular function inside the LHP.

The further solution of this condition will be presented later on. Now let us discuss the second method based on the calculus of variations as published by S.S.L. Chang[12] which employs a far simpler way for obtaining the condition for the minimum value of the mean square error.

236

Let the mean square error be generally expressed by the integral

$$I = \frac{1}{2\pi j} \int\limits_{-j\infty}^{+j\infty} \sum_{m=1}^{M} \lambda_m \psi_m(s, F_i, \bar{F}_i)\, \mathrm{d}s \qquad (12.15)$$

where $i = 1, 2, \ldots, n$; λ_m are weighting coefficients and functions ψ_m and F_i fulfil the following conditions:

1. Functions F_i have all their poles inside the LHP (the imaginary axis is excluded).
2. Functions ψ_m are conjugate in the sense that for any arbitrary i, m and ω it holds that

$$\lim_{s=j\omega} \frac{\partial \psi_m}{\partial F_i} = \lim_{s=-j\omega} \frac{\partial \psi_m}{\partial \bar{F}_i}$$

    The partial derivatives, F_i and $\bar{F}_i$, are mutually independent.
3. The admissible functions of F_i comply with the condition

$$\lim_{s \to \infty} s\bar{F}_i \frac{\partial \psi_m}{\partial \bar{F}_i} = 0$$

if $\partial \psi_m / \partial \bar{F}_i$ has essential singularities for $s \to \infty$, e.g. e^{rs}, it will be sufficient that the condition is satisfied only for the negative real component of s.

For the minimum of I we can now stipulate the following theorem the proof of which will not be given here: If conditions 1, 2 and 3 are satisfied, the necessary and sufficient condition for the minimum of I is

$$\sum_{m=1}^{M} \lambda_m \frac{\partial \psi_m}{\partial \bar{F}_i} = \Lambda \qquad (12.16)$$

where Λ is a regular function inside the LHP. When the above theorem is applied to function $\psi_m = S_{\Delta\Delta}$ expressed in Eqn. 12.5 condition (12.14) is directly obtained.

Let us deal now with the next portion of the synthesis, i.e. the determination of the desired function K_m in accordance with condition (12.14). Apart from satisfying this condition, function K_m must be stable (all its poles must lie inside the LHP). Eqn 12.14 can be rewritten in the form

$$K_m A - B = \Lambda \qquad (12.17)$$

where A and B are known functions the zeros and poles of which can lie within the whole complex plane s. Eqn. 12.17 will now be arranged so that all functions with poles inside the LHP will be on one side of the equation, while functions with poles inside the RHP will be on the other. For this purpose the so called spectral factorisation will be applied to function A, i.e. the function will be replaced by the product of two functions:

$$A = \phi^+ \phi^- \qquad (12.18)$$

so that function ϕ^+ has all its zeros and poles inside the LHP, while function ϕ^- will have them inside the RHP. Eqn. 12.17 can now be rewritten in the form

$$K_m \phi^+ = \frac{B+\Lambda}{\phi^-} \tag{12.19}$$

where on the right-hand side of the equation there still remains a function, i.e. function B, the poles of which may lie inside the whole plane s. The right-hand side of Eqn. 12.19 will therefore be expanded into partial fractions some with poles α_i inside the LHP, and some with poles α_j inside the RHP, i.e.

$$\frac{B+\Lambda}{\phi^-} = \sum_i \frac{c_i}{s-\alpha_i} + \sum_j \frac{c_j}{s-\alpha_j} \tag{12.20}$$

This decomposition into fractions is normally denoted as follows:

$$\frac{B+\Lambda}{\phi^-} = \left[\frac{B+\Lambda}{\phi^-}\right]_+ + \left[\frac{B+\Lambda}{\phi^-}\right]_- \tag{12.21}$$

where all symbols have been explained in the foregoing text. By Eqn. 12.21, Eqn. 12.19 can now be rewritten into the desired form:

$$K_m \phi^+ - \left[\frac{B+\Lambda}{\phi^-}\right]_+ = \left[\frac{B+\Lambda}{\phi^-}\right]_- \tag{12.22}$$

containing on the left-hand side only those functions with poles in the LHP, and on the right-hand side only those functions with poles inside the RHP. A function fulfilling the condition of Eqn. 12.22 is a constant.

Since $[\Lambda/\phi^-]_+ = 0$, the second term on the left-hand side of Eqn. 12.22 can be written as $[B/\phi^-]_+$. Both terms, i.e. $K_m \phi^+$ and $[B/\phi^-]_+$ are of the order of $1/s$ for $s \to \infty$, and thus the constant satisfying Eqn. 12.22 is equal to zero. In an explicit form the desired solution is

$$K_m = \frac{1}{\phi^+} \left[\frac{B}{\phi^-}\right]_+ \tag{12.23}$$

The variation discussed here is thus a slightly modified alternative of the original ingenious solution by Wiener. Obviously, we do not determine here directly the optimum transfer function of controller C (see block diagram in Fig. 12.1); we only determine the optimum transfer function of the selectable portion of the transfer function of the closed control loop. That is to say, we optimise the weighting function of a closed control loop. Function K_m determined according to Eqn. 12.23 is stable. According to Eqn. 12.4 the resultant transfer function of the closed control loop is

$$K_w = K_m K_d^s \tag{12.24}$$

and thus also K_d being determined in advance must be a stable function in order that K_w is a stable function, too. Nevertheless, the resultant solution may be phy-

238

sically not realisable (the degree of the numerator of transfer function K_w is not lower than the degree of the denominator of K_w). In such a case the function K_d determined in advance must be suitably changed. According to Fig. 12.1 the transfer function of the real control loop is

$$K_w = (1+SC)^{-1}SC \tag{12.25}$$

where S and C are the transfer functions of the controlled system and the controller respectively. If S and the optimum K_w are known, it is possible to determine the optimum transfer function of the controller

$$C = S^{-1}K_w(1-K_w)^{-1} \tag{12.26}$$

LIMITED INPUT SIGNAL OF THE CONTROLLED SYSTEM

The described method of synthesis does not change, if the input signal y of the controlled system is limited according to the following conditions:

$$\left. \begin{aligned} \min I_1 = \overline{\mit\Delta^2(t)} \\ I_2 \leq M \end{aligned} \right\} \tag{12.27}$$

where M is the given limiting value and

$$I_2 = \overline{y^2(t)} = \frac{1}{2\pi j} \int_{-j\infty}^{+j\infty} S_{yy}\, ds \tag{12.28}$$

According to Fig. 12.1 it holds that

$$y = C(w+f-x) = C(1-K_w)(w+f) \tag{12.29}$$

By using Eqn. 12.26 it holds that

$$y = \frac{K_w}{S}(w+f) \tag{12.30}$$

and the spectral density

$$S_{yy} = \frac{K_w \overline{K_w}}{S\overline{S}} S_{w+f,\, w+f} \tag{12.31}$$

The problem is solved by finding the minimum of the linear combination

$$I = I_1 + kI_2 \tag{12.32}$$

for various selected values of weighting constant k. In this way $K_w(k)$ dependent on k is determined, and $I_1(k)$ and $I_2(k)$ can be calculated. From the diagram in Fig. 12.2 it is now possible to determine the optimal k according to the given limitation M.

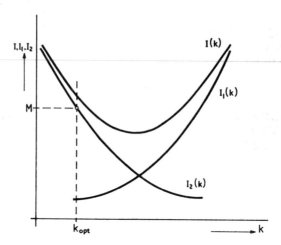

Fig. 12.2. Determination of optimal k (limited input signal)

COMPENSATION OF THE DISTURBANCE ENTERING THE CONTROLLED SYSTEM; THE COMMAND SIGNAL IS CONSTANT

Let us consider now the case where the controlled system is exposed to the action of disturbance h according to Fig. 12.1. If this disturbance is recalculated into signal u acting at the output of the controlled system, the block diagram of the control loop can be formally changed into the arrangement shown in Fig. 12.3. This arrangement will permit an easy comparison with results obtained in other cases solved. Assuming that the transfer function of the real control loop has free configuration, the controlled variable is

$$x = K_w R + u \tag{12.33}$$

where $R = w + f - u$, and the spectral density of error Δ is

$$S_{\Delta\Delta} = \Gamma S_{ww}\Gamma - \Gamma S_{wr}K_w - \Gamma S_{wu} - \bar{K}_w S_{rw}\Gamma$$
$$- S_{uw}\Gamma + \bar{K}_w S_{rr}K_w + \bar{K}_w S_{ru} + S_{ur}K_w + S_{uu} \tag{12.34}$$

where

$$\left. \begin{aligned} S_{rr} &= S_{ww} + S_{ff} + S_{uu} + S_{wf} + S_{fw} - S_{wu} - S_{uw} - S_{fu} - S_{uf} \\ S_{ru} &= S_{ww} + S_{wf} - S_{wu} = \bar{S}_{ur} \end{aligned} \right\} \tag{12.35}$$

As long as u and f are random variables in the defined sense (see Introduction), the solution is found by the same procedure as in the example discussed in pp. 234–39. According to Eqn. 12.16 the condition for minimum $\overline{\Delta^2(t)}$ is

$$K_w S_{rr} - (\Gamma S_{rw} - S_{ru}) = \Delta \tag{12.36}$$

which can be solved in the same way as Eqn. 12.17.

In the case $w = \text{const.} = 0$ and $f = 0$ it is necessary to achieve the optimal filtration of disturbance u. For such case the arrangement of the control loop

240

according to Fig. 12.3 is incorrect. It is necessary to determine the ideal filter Γ for the filtration of random disturbance u, and to arrange the control loop according to Fig. 12.4. Eqn. 12.33 now becomes

$$x = (1 - K_w)u \tag{12.37}$$

and the spectral density of error Δ is

$$S_{\Delta\Delta} = (1 - \bar{K}_w)S_{uu}(1 - K_w) - (1 - \bar{K}_w)S_{uu}\Gamma_u - \bar{\Gamma}_u S_{uu}(1 - K_w) + \bar{\Gamma}_u S_{uu}\Gamma \tag{12.38}$$

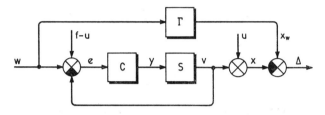

Fig. 12.3. *Control loop (disturbance when command signnl is constant)*

According to Eqn. 12.16 it follows that

$$K_w S_{uu} - S_{uu}(1 - \Gamma_u) = \Delta \tag{12.39}$$

for $\Gamma_u = $ const. the solution is obviously trivial, physically unrealisable, $K_w = $ const.

If, however, the transfer function of the real control loop has a semi-free configuration according to Eqn. 12.4, Eqn. 12.39 will acquire the form

$$K_0 \bar{K}_d K_d S_{uu} - \bar{K}_d S_{uu}(1 - \Gamma_u) = \Delta \tag{12.40}$$

and this equation need not yield a trivial solution even for $\Gamma_u = 0$.

THE COMMAND SIGNAL IS ANALYTICALLY DETERMINED

The arrangement of the control loop according to Fig. 12.4 is also suitable for cases where the command signal is analytically determined, of non-zero value, and where noise $f \neq 0$. Owing to the fact that the loop contains a single filter (con-

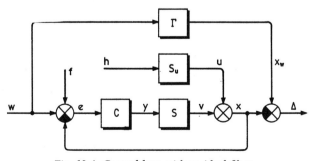

Fig. 12.4. *Control loop with an ideal filter*

troller C) which has the task of ensuring the most accurate following of variable w by variable x, and simultaneously the best possible filtration of disturbances u and f, a problem of this type can be solved only by compromise. The solution will be the more efficient the larger the difference between the frequency spectrum of useful signal w and that of disturbances u and f. The frequency spectrum of signal w frequently lies in the region of very low frequencies, while the frequency spectrum of signals u and f is normally wide and contains components of relatively high frequencies. In this case the problem can be formulated so that a system is sought with a minimum bandwith of permeability corresponding to the command signal w.

The problem is solved by finding the minimum of the linear combination

$$I = I_1 + kI_2 = \frac{1}{2\pi j} \int_{-j\infty}^{+j\infty} (S_{\varDelta\varDelta} + kS_e)\, ds \tag{12.41}$$

where

$$S_{\varDelta\varDelta} = (1-\bar{K}_w)S_{uu}(1-K_w) - \bar{\varGamma}_u S_{uu}(1-K_w)$$
$$- (1-\bar{K}_w)S_{uu}\varGamma_u + \bar{\varGamma}_u S_{uu}\varGamma_u + \bar{K}_w S_{ff}K_w \tag{12.42}$$

$$S_e = (1-\bar{K}_w)\bar{w}w(1-K_w) \tag{12.43}$$

In Eqn. 12.41

$$I_1 = \frac{1}{2\pi j} \int_{-j\infty}^{+j\infty} S_{\varDelta\varDelta}\, ds = \overline{\varDelta^2(t)} \tag{12.44}$$

is the mean square error due only to the action of disturbances, while

$$I_2 = \frac{1}{2\pi j} \int_{-j\infty}^{+j\infty} S_e\, ds = \int_0^\infty e^2(t)\, dt \tag{12.45}$$

is the integral of the square control error the value of which is not affected by disturbances.

Weighting constant k can be suitably selected by using functions $I_1(k)$ and $I_2(k)$ calculated from Eqns. 12.44 and 12.45 respectively and an optimal $K_w(k)$. As far as it is possible to state a limitation for I_1 or I_2 the optimal value of k, k_{opt}, can be determined similarly to the problem on p. 239.

It is worthwhile to mention that in cases where disturbance u (or h) is measurable, signal u can be fed to the input of a further filter C_u the output of which is added to the output of filter C. The transfer function of filter C_u can be devised in such a way that the influence of the disturbance on the controlled variable is fully compensated regardless of any statistical properties of the disturbance. For the loop shown in Fig. 12.1 the transfer function of filter C_u is determined from the condition

$$C_u S - S_u = 0 \tag{12.46}$$

If in this case the filter C_u is physically realisable, transfer function C can be determined in the sense of Wiener's synthesis (see pp. 234–39).

THE SYNTHESIS OF CONTINUOUSLY ACTING, MULTI-DIMENSIONAL CONTROL LOOPS

THE INPUT VARIABLES OF THE LOOP ARE NOT CROSS-CORRELATED

The method of synthesis for different variants of one-dimensional control loops described on pp. 234–42 can easily be generalised for multi-dimensional control loops. Instead of individual variables and functions, mutual relationships will be expressed by the pertinent vectors of the variables and by matrices of functions. The procedure will be demonstrated in a simple case of a multi-dimensional control loop with not cross-correlated input variables. Further let it be assumed that the transfer functions of real control loops have free configuration and that the vectors of disturbances, h or u, are zeros (Fig. 12.1).

For a ν-dimensional control loop the mean square errors can be expressed by the relationship

$$\Delta(t)\,\Delta^T(t) = R_{\Delta\Delta}(0) \tag{12.47}$$

where $\Delta^T(t)$ is the transposed, i.e. the row vector of errors $\Delta(t)$ and $R_{\Delta\Delta}(\tau)$ is the matrix of the correlation functions of the vector of error $\Delta(t)$. Now, the control loop is optimal in Wiener's sense, if the sum of the diagonal elements of matrix $R_{\Delta\Delta}(0)$, i.e. the trace of the matrix, attains its minimum value. It also holds that

$$\min I = \min \operatorname{tr} R_{\Delta\Delta}(0) = \min \operatorname{tr} \frac{1}{2\pi j} \int_{-j\infty}^{+j\infty} S_{\Delta\Delta}\, ds \tag{12.48}$$

where $S_{\Delta\Delta}$ is the matrix of the spectral densities of the vector of error $\Delta(t)$, and to denotes trace of the matrix. In the case under discussion it holds that

$$S_{\Delta\Delta} = \bar{K}_w S_{w+f,\,w+f} K_w^T - \bar{K}_w S_{w+f,\,w} \Gamma^T - \bar{\Gamma} S_{w,\,w+f} K_w^T + \Gamma S_{ww} \Gamma^T \tag{12.49}$$

where T always denotes matrices transposed towards the original ones. According to Eqn. 12.16 the condition can be determined for I:

$$S_{w+f,\,w+f} K_w^T - S_{w+f,\,w} \Gamma^T = \Delta^T \tag{12.50}$$

When the input variables of the control loop are not cross correlated, the matrices of spectral densities

$$\left.\begin{aligned} S_{w+f,\,w+f} &= S_{ww} + S_{ff} = {}^1S \\ S_{w+f,\,w} &= S_{ww} \quad\;\; = {}^2S \end{aligned}\right\} \tag{12.51}$$

are diagonal matrices so that synthesis of a ν-dimensional control loop decomposes into the solution of ν^2 Wiener–Hopf equations. According to Eqn. 12.50 for individual loops ($i, j = 1, 2, \ldots, \nu$) it holds that

$$K_{wij}{}^1S_{jj} - \Gamma_{ij}{}^2S_{jj} = \Delta_{ij} \tag{12.52}$$

i.e. the same equations as Eqn. 12.17 the solution of which is already known.

THE INPUT VARIABLES OF THE LOOP ARE CROSS-CORRELATED. THE FACTORISATION OF DETERMINANTS

The synthesis of a ν-dimensional loop with cross correlated input variables is more difficult and the solution does not directly follow from what has been discussed in the foregoing sections.

Considering the control loop discussed in the previous section but with cross correlated input variables, condition (12.50) changes in the sense that the matrices of spectral densities are not diagonal anymore. By using the denotation of Eqn. 12.51, Eqn. 12.50 can be rewritten in the form of

$$^1SK_w^T = {}^2S\Gamma^T + \Lambda^T \tag{12.53}$$

from which follow ν independent equations

$$^1SK_{wi} = {}^2S\Gamma_i + \Lambda_i \tag{12.54}$$

for $i = 1, 2, \ldots, \nu$. By expanding Eqn. 12.54 on the left with a matrix inverse to ^1S, i.e. with matrix

$$^1S^{-1} = \frac{1}{^1\Delta_S}{}^1\sigma = \frac{1}{^1\Delta_S^+ {}^1\Delta_S^-}{}^1\sigma \tag{12.55}$$

where $^1\Delta_S$ is the determinant of matrix ^1S, divided into the product of functions $^1\Delta_S^+$ and $^1\Delta_S^-$ according to the principles of spectral factorisation (see Eqn. 12.18), and by applying the procedure described on pp. 234–39, it is possible to determine

$$K_{wi} = \frac{1}{^1\Delta_S^+}\left[\frac{^1\sigma\,{}^2S\Gamma_i}{^1\Delta_S^-} + \frac{^1\sigma\Lambda_i}{^1\Delta_S^-}\right]_+ \tag{12.56}$$

This expression corresponds to the solution 12.23. For the elements of matrix K_{wi} it holds that

$$K_{wij} = \frac{1}{^1\Delta_S^+}\left[\frac{1}{^1\Delta_S^-}\sum_{j_1=1}^{\nu}{}^1\sigma_{j_1 j}\sum_{j_2=1}^{\nu}{}^2S_{j_1 j_2}\Gamma_{ij_2} + \frac{1}{^1\Delta_S^-}\sum_{j_1=1}^{\nu}{}^1\sigma_{j_1 j}\Lambda_{ij_1}\right]_+ \tag{12.57}$$

for $i, j = 1, 2, \ldots, \nu$.

The first term in the brackets of Eqn. 12.57 can be divided into partial fractions and all fractions having poles inside the LHP added together, since all functions in the first term are known. In the second term it holds that

$$\left[\frac{1}{^1\Delta_S^-}\sum_{j_1=1}^{\nu}{}^1\sigma_{j_1 j}\Lambda_{ij_1}\right]_+ = \sum_k \frac{c_{kij}}{s - s_k} \tag{12.58}$$

where s_k are poles of functions $\sigma_{j_1 j}$ inside the LHP. However, constants c_{kij} cannot be determined when dividing the term into fractions, since on the left-hand side of Eqn. 12.58 the functions Λ_{ij_1} are unknown. Constants c_{kij} are determined in such a way that transfer functions $K_{wij}(j=1, 2, \ldots, \nu)$ calculated according to Eqn. 12.57 are substituted into one of Eqns. 12.54. All functions of this equation are expanded into partial fractions and all partial fractions with poles inside the RHP are excluded. For selected i and j_1, it follows that

$$\left[\sum_{j=1}^{\nu} {}^1S_{j_1 j} K_{wij}\right]_+ = \left[\sum_{j=1}^{\nu} {}^2S_{j_1 j} \Gamma_{ij}\right]_+ \tag{12.59}$$

From the condition that partial fractions on both sides of Eqn. 12.59 must also have identical coefficients in the numerator, it is possible to determine the desired coefficients of c_{kij}. Eqn. 12.59 determines thus a system of linear algebraic equations the unknown quantities of which are the coefficients c_{kij}. If any one of the poles s_k does not appear on the right-hand side of Eqn. 12.59, the corresponding coefficient c_{kij} on the left-hand side of Eqn. 12.59 is necessarily equal to zero.

Eqns. 12.56 and 12.57 represent the explicit expression of the desired transfer function K_{wij}, $i, j = 1, 2, \ldots, \nu$, with cross-correlated input signals.

MATRIX FACTORISATION

As stated in the introduction, N. Wiener used matrix factorisation for the solution of the synthesis of a multi-dimensional control loop with cross-correlated input variables. Let us outline here the principal ideas of this approach to the solution of the given problem. As far as matrix factorisation is concerned, the reader is best referred to original works[5-8] and particularly that of Davis.[9]

The factorisation of matrix S of the functions of complex variable s is understood as the decomposition

$$S = S^- S^+ \quad \text{or} \quad S = S^+ S^- \tag{12.60}$$

where matrix S^- and its inverse matrix $(S^-)^{-1}$ are regular inside some region of the complex plane s (e.g. inside the LHP), while matrix S^+ and its inverse matrix $(S^+)^{-1}$ are regular outside this region (e.g. inside RHP).

If we know how to make decomposition 12.60, the solution of Eqn. 12.53 can be mathematically formulated rather simply. It is found that

$$^1S^{-1}S^+ K_w^T = {}^2S\Gamma^T + \Lambda^T \tag{12.61}$$

By using the same procedure as on pp. 234–39 for a one-dimensional control loop, the solution is obtained

$$K_w^T = ({}^1S^+)^{-1}[({}^1S^-)^{-1} {}^2S\Gamma^T]_+ \tag{12.62}$$

where the term $[({}^1S^-)^{-1}\Lambda^T] = 0$ for the same reasons as those given for the term $[\Lambda/\phi^-]_+^+$ in the solution 12.23.

From the foregoing it is obvious that by using matrix factorisation a formally unified mathematical procedure is applicable to the solution of one and multi-dimensional control loops even in the case of cross correlated input variables of the multi-dimensional control loop. Nevertheless, it should be stated that matrix factorisation is a rather difficult and laborious task, and that the synthesis method described in on pp. 239–45 seems to be better suited for practical applications.

THE DDC SYNTHESIS OF ONE-DIMENSIONAL CONTROL LOOPS

THE LEAST MEAN SQUARE ERROR OF A CONTINUOUS OUTPUT VARIABLE

In control loops where the computer acts as a controller the continuous input variables of the computer are sampled and converted into digital values. Continuous variables are mostly sampled in equidistant time instants, i.e. with a constant sampling period T. The output of the computer, i.e. the actuating variables, is also discontinuous. These variables are represented by numbers issued by the computer in the same period T in which the input variables of the computer are

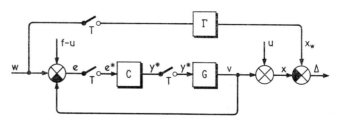

Fig. 12.5. Block diagram of DDC (Wiener's synthesis)

sampled. These numbers are converted into an analogue signal to which a certain time scale for the duration of one sampling interval is allocated in the so-called forming member. For the duration of interval T the actuating variable is most frequently held at a constant value proportional to the number supplied by the computer at the beginning of interval T. In such cases the forming member is called the holding member. The output signal of the holding member acts then on the servomotor of the controlling member at the input of the controlled system.

The holding member together with the controlled system are the continuously acting part of the control loop, while the automatic computer is the discontinuously, i.e. discretely, acting part of the control loop.

The block diagram of DDC for synthesis in Wiener's sense is shown in Fig. 12.5. This diagram already includes the modifications incorporated in the arrangement for continuously acting control loops as shown in Fig. 12.3. In Fig. 12.5 discrete variables are marked by an asterisk, continuous ones are without asterisk. The contacts shown before and after the computer represent a symbolic division between the discrete and the continuously acting part of the control loop. It is shown that both contacts have the same closing period T. It is also assumed that the contacts have a synchronous operation, with no delay in the computer.

The transfer function of the continuously acting part of the control loop is

$$G(s) = H(s)S(s) \qquad (12.63)$$

where $H(s)$ is the transfer function of the forming member, while $S(s)$ is the transfer function of the controlled system. The transfer function of the holding mem-

246

ber is

$$H(s) = k\frac{1-e^{-sT}}{s} \tag{12.64}$$

where k is the gain factor.

Owing to the discrete action of the computer the function transforms in the complex plane are expressed by means of the discrete Laplace transform or by the Z transform. The complex variable of the Z transform is $z = \exp sT$ where $sT = q$ is the dimensionless complex variable of the continuous Laplace transform. The discrete transforms of discrete functions are the functions of argument z, e.g. $F(z)$, while the discrete transforms of continuous functions are the functions of two arguments z and ε, i.e. $F(z, \varepsilon)$. Here ε denotes shifting which follows from

$$\frac{t}{T} = \frac{nT+\Delta t}{T} = n+\varepsilon \tag{12.65}$$

where t is the continuous independent variable of time, and $n = 0, 1, 2, \ldots$ is the discrete independent variable of time. According to Eqn. 12.65 it obviously holds that $\Delta t\varepsilon \langle 0, T\rangle$ and $\varepsilon\varepsilon \langle 0, 1\rangle$. Owing to these facts all previously stated results for continuously acting control loops are modified even if the method of synthesis remains essentially without change. Therefore, it will suffice to point out only the deviations in the solution without necessarily repeating all variants discussed in a pp. 234–45. For the sake of clarity and brevity the argument z in the Z-transform will be omitted as in the L-transform, while argument ε will be kept in the discrete transforms of continuous functions. The functions of argument z^{-1} will be marked with a bar. For instance,

$$F(z) = F, \quad F(z, \varepsilon) = F(\varepsilon), \quad F(z^{-1}) = \bar{F}, \quad F(z^{-1}, \varepsilon) = \bar{F}(\varepsilon), \text{ etc.}$$

The transfer function of a one-dimensional control loop according to Fig. 12.5 is

$$K_w(\varepsilon) = G(\varepsilon)C(1+GC)^{-1} \tag{12.66}$$

Since the digital correcting member C can influence only that part of transfer function $K_w(\varepsilon)$ which is independent of ε, it is possible to express $K_w(\varepsilon)$ by the relation

$$K_w(\varepsilon) = G(\varepsilon)D \tag{12.67}$$

Now, the task is to the determine function D so that the mean square error $\overline{\Delta^2(t)}$ should attain its minimum. At the same time, transfer function $K_w(\varepsilon)$, whose semi-free configuration is given by function $G(\varepsilon)$, must be stable.

The mean square error is

$$\overline{\Delta^2(t)} = \lim_{N\to\infty}\frac{1}{2N+1}\sum_{n=-N}^{+N}\int_0^1 \Delta^2(n, \varepsilon)\,d\varepsilon = \int_0^1 R_{\Delta\Delta}(0, \varepsilon)\,d\varepsilon = \frac{1}{2\pi j}\int_{\Gamma_0}\int_0^1 S_{\Delta\Delta}(\varepsilon)\frac{dz}{z}\,d\varepsilon \tag{12.68}$$

where Γ_0 denotes the integration path along the unit circle whose centre lies in the origin of complex plane z.

For comparing the results obtained, let us discuss the synthesis of a control loop identical with that discussed in pp. 234–239, i.e. a loop with a random command variable and with disturbance $u = 0$.

As in Eqn. 12.5 spectral density $S_{\varDelta\varDelta}(\varepsilon)$ is determined by

$$S_{\varDelta\varDelta}(\varepsilon) = \bar{G}(\varepsilon)\bar{D}S_{w+f,\,w+f}DG(\varepsilon) - \Gamma(\varepsilon)S_{w,\,w+f}DG(\varepsilon)$$
$$-\bar{G}(\varepsilon)\bar{D}S_{w+f,\,w}\Gamma(\varepsilon) + \Gamma(\varepsilon)S_{ww}\Gamma(\varepsilon) \tag{12.69}$$

The condition for minimum $\overline{\varDelta^2(t)}$ can again be calculated by using undetermined multipliers and by writing, similarly as in Eqn. 12.8

$$D = D_m + \lambda D_\lambda \tag{12.70}$$

or it is possible to apply the discrete version of condition in Eqn. 12.16.
If $\overline{\varDelta^2(t)}$ is generally expressed by the integral

$$I = \frac{1}{2\pi j} \int_{\Gamma_0} \int_0^1 \sum_{m=1}^M \lambda_m \Psi_m[z_1 F_i(\varepsilon)\bar{F}_i(\varepsilon)]\frac{dz}{z}\, d\varepsilon \tag{12.71}$$

$i = 1, 2, \ldots, n$, where λ_m are the weighting coefficients, and functions Ψ_m and $F_i(\varepsilon)$ fulfil the condition related to Eqn. 12.16 but modified for complex plane z, the necessary and sufficient condition for minimum I will be that

$$z^{-1}\int_0^1 \sum_{m=1}^M \lambda_m \frac{\partial \Psi_m(\varepsilon)}{\partial \bar{F}_i(\varepsilon)}\, d\varepsilon = \varLambda \tag{12.72}$$

In the case under consideration $\Psi_m(\varepsilon) = S_{\varDelta\varDelta}(\varepsilon)$, and $\bar{F}_i(\varepsilon) = \bar{D}$. According to Eqns. 12.72 and 12.69 we can calculate

$$z^{-1}\int_0^1 [\bar{G}(\varepsilon)S_{w+f,\,w+f}DG(\varepsilon) - \bar{G}(\varepsilon)S_{w+f,\,w}\Gamma(\varepsilon)]\, d\varepsilon \tag{12.73}$$

With definitions

$$\left.\begin{aligned} A &= S_{w+f,\,w+f}\int_0^1 \bar{G}(\varepsilon)G(\varepsilon)\, d\varepsilon \\ B &= S_{w+f,\,w}\int_0^1 \bar{G}(\varepsilon)\Gamma(\varepsilon)\, d\varepsilon \end{aligned}\right\} \tag{12.74}$$

the condition of minimum $\overline{\varDelta^2(t)}$ can be expressed by the equation

$$z^{-1}(DA - B) = \varLambda \tag{12.75}$$

which is the discrete version of Eqn. 12.17. By a similar procedure as used in Eqns. 12.17 and 12.23 we arrive at the explicit solution

$$D = \frac{z}{\phi^+}\left[\frac{B}{z\phi^-}\right]_+ \tag{12.76}$$

where $\phi^+ \phi^- = A$. In this case, however, the imaginary axis, the LHP, and the RHP of plane s have been respectively replaced by the unit circle, the inner, and outer region of the unit circle in plane z.

Once D is known, the determination of the transfer functions of correcting member C is quite easy, if we consider the definition of function D as it follows from Eqns. 12.66 and 12.67.

THE LEAST MEAN SQUARE ERROR OF THE DISCRETE OUTPUT VARIABLE

It should be noted that the solution given in previous section is accurate in the sense of the formulation of the problem but rather laborious, since the function $G(\varepsilon)$ can be very complicated in concrete cases and, moreover, it is necessary to integrate with respect to ε.

Frequently it will suffice to perform the synthesis in such a way that integration with respect to ε is omitted, and function D is determined from the condition of a minimum mean square error of the discrete variable $\varDelta(n)$. This means that the solution is made for $\varepsilon = 0$. This, however, is a criterion different from that used in the previous section. If the same consideration was applied as that used for the introduction of function D into Eqn. 12.67, it would follow that $K_n = D$ and the real control loop would have free configuration. This could be an advantage, however, for in such a case the stability for $\varepsilon \neq 0$ would not be generally ensured. It is known (see, e.g. [10]) that a stable solution is obtained with

$$K_w = B^- D \qquad (12.77)$$

where B^- is the product of the unstable root factors of the numerator in the transfer function G of the continuously acting part of the control loop, i.e. of factors the roots of which lie outside the unit circle Γ_0 of plane z.

Transfer function K_w has thus again a semi-free configuration, in this case given by the stability conditions for $\varepsilon \neq 0$. However, function B^- is simpler than function $G(\varepsilon)$ in Eqn. 12.67, and the whole solution is easier.

SECURING PHYSICAL REALISABILITY

The optimal transfer function of a closed control loop determined in Wiener's sense by relations given on pp. 246–49 can be physically unrealisable in the sense that the impulse response curve, i.e. the original function $K_w(n, \varepsilon)$ of the transfer function $K_w(\varepsilon)$ has for $n = 0$ and $\varepsilon = 0$ the value of $K_w(0, 0) \neq 0$ which physically cannot be fulfilled in control loops with a controlled system of the first or higher order.

The requirement of physical realisability, however, can be secured by the factor $z^{-\varrho}$ which determines in advance the transfer function of the closed control loop. By using the factor $z^{-\varrho}$, Eqn. 12.67, for example, acquires the form

$$K_w(\varepsilon) = G(\varepsilon) z^{-\varrho} D \qquad (12.78)$$

and Eqn. 12.77 the form

$$K_w = B^- z^{-\varrho} D \qquad (12.79)$$

Exponent ϱ can be unequivocally determined in advance (see [11]) so that the determination of the optimal $K_w(\varepsilon)$ or K_w is identical with the previously described procedure.

HYBRID CONTROL LOOPS

If the automatic computer fails during the DDC, it is normally necessary to stop operation in order to prevent losses in production or damage to the plant. Operation need not be stopped in the case of computer failure, if a hybrid arrangement of control is devised at least for the most important control loops. Under normal conditions the control loops contain then a digital correcting member

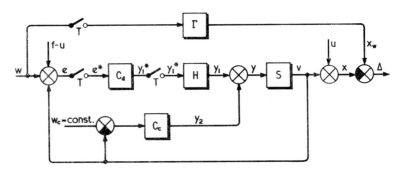

Fig. 12.6. Hybrid control loops

and a continuously acting controller connected in parallel or in series. If computer failure occurs, emergency operation is provided by the continuously acting controller only. The main emphasis is laid on the simplicity and reliability of this member, while the quality of emergency control may still be at the limit of admissibility. Under normal conditions high quality of control is achieved by the automatic computer.

The parallel arrangement of both controllers is shown in Fig. 12.6 where C_d is the digital correcting member (automatic computer) and C_c is the continuously acting controller. In this arrangement the transfer function of the real control loop is

$$K_w(\varepsilon) = N(\varepsilon)D \tag{12.80}$$

where

$$D = C_d(1+NC_d)^{-1} \tag{12.81}$$

$$N(s) = [1+S(s)C_s(s)]^{-1}H(s)S(s) \tag{12.82}$$

The synthesis method is used for determining the optimal function D. Transfer function $K_w(\varepsilon)$ has semi-free configuration given by function $N(\varepsilon)$.

In a simplified solution discussed on p. 249, Eqn. 12.80 changes into form 12.77 where B^- is now the product of the unstable root factors of the numerator of function N.

The series arrangement of the control loop with discretely and continuously acting controllers connected in series is shown in Fig. 12.7. The transfer function of the continuously acting control loop is here

$$M(s) = [1+S(s)C_c(s)]^{-1}S(s)C_c(s) \tag{12.83}$$

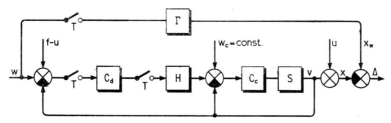

Fig. 12.7. Control loops with continuous and discrete controllers

and the transfer function of the whole control loop is

$$K_w(\varepsilon) = M(\varepsilon)C_d(1+MC_d)^{-1} \tag{12.84}$$

$$K_w(\varepsilon) = M(\varepsilon)D \tag{12.85}$$

It is obvious that this variant of the arrangement of the control loop also be solved by the formerly described procedure. In the simplified solution given on pp. 249–50 the term B^- in Eqn. 12.77 is now equal to the product of the unstable root factors of the numerator of function M.

The possibilities of the application of hybrid control loops are discussed here only very briefly. More details can be found in the references.[10]

THE SYNTHESIS OF DDC OF MULTI-DIMENSIONAL CONTROL LOOPS

FACTORISATION OF DETERMINANTS

In multi-dimensional control loops the discussion will be confined to loops with cross-correlated input variables, since this variant requires the statement of some new facts not occurring in problems hitherto discussed. On the other hand, we may limit the discussion to the case where the vector of disturbance $u = 0$, since all previously stated notions are applicable to the case $u \neq 0$.

As for continuously acting multi-dimensional control loops, the desired result is the minimum of the sum of mean square errors, i.e. the minimum of the sum

$$I = \sum_{i=1}^{v} \overline{\Delta_{ii}^2(t)} = \int_0^1 \sum_{i=1}^{v} \Delta_{ii}^2(n, \varepsilon)\, d\varepsilon = \mathrm{tr} \int_0^1 \overline{\Delta(n, \varepsilon) \cdot \Delta^T(n, \varepsilon)}\, d\varepsilon$$

$$= \mathrm{tr} \int_0^1 R_{\Delta\Delta}(0, \varepsilon)\, d\varepsilon = \mathrm{tr} \int_{\Gamma_0}^1 \int_0^1 S_{\Delta\Delta}(\varepsilon)\frac{dz}{z}\, d\varepsilon \tag{12.86}$$

where tr denotes the trace of the matrices quoted. Similarly to $S_{\Delta\Delta}(\varepsilon)$ in Eqn. 12.69 the matrix $S_{\Delta\Delta}(\varepsilon)$ of spectral densities can be expressed by the relation

$$S_{\Delta\Delta}(\varepsilon) = \overline{G}(\varepsilon)\overline{D}S_{w+f,\,w+f}D^T G^T(\varepsilon) - \overline{\Gamma}(\varepsilon)S_{w,\,w+f}D^T G^T(\varepsilon)$$

$$- \overline{G}(\varepsilon)\overline{D}S_{w+f,\,w}\Gamma^T(\varepsilon) + \overline{\Gamma}(\varepsilon)S_{ww}\Gamma^T(\varepsilon) \tag{12.87}$$

251

where T again denotes matrices transposed to the original ones. Condition 12.72 leads to the equation

$$\operatorname{tr} z^{-1} \int_0^1 \left[\overline{G}(\varepsilon) S_{w+f,\, w+f} D^T G^T(\varepsilon) - \overline{G}(\varepsilon) S_{w+f,\, w} \Gamma^T(\varepsilon) \right] d\varepsilon = \Lambda^T \qquad (12.88)$$

Contrary to Eqn. 12.73 integration with respect to ε cannot be performed yet, since in Eqn. 12.88 the known matrices of argument ε are still separated by unknown matrices. However, it can be proved that the trace of the product of matrices does not change, if the sequence of matrices in the product is cyclically interchanged. Expression 12.88 can thus be arranged in the form

$$\operatorname{tr} z^{-1} \left[S_{w+f,\, w+f} D^T \int_0^1 G^T(\varepsilon) \overline{G}(\varepsilon) \, d\varepsilon - S_{w+f,\, w} \int_0^1 \Gamma^T(\varepsilon) \overline{G}(\varepsilon) \, d\varepsilon \right] = \Lambda^T \quad (12.89)$$

By using the definitions

$$\left. \begin{aligned} {}^1S &= S_{w+f,\, w+f} \\ {}^2S &= S_{w+f,\, w} \\ A &= \int_0^1 G^T(\varepsilon) \overline{G}(\varepsilon) \, d\varepsilon \\ B^T &= \int_0^1 \Gamma^T(\varepsilon) \overline{G}(\varepsilon) \, d\varepsilon \end{aligned} \right\} \qquad (12.90)$$

Eqn. 12.89 can be rewritten in the form

$$\frac{1}{z} {}^1S D^T A = \frac{1}{z} {}^2S B^T + \Lambda^T \qquad (12.91)$$

Let us extend Eqn. 12.91 on the left by the matrix inverse to matrix ${}^1S$, i.e. by the matrix

$$ {}^1S^{-1} = \frac{1}{{}^1\Delta_S} {}^1\sigma = \frac{1}{{}^1\Delta_S^+\, {}^1\Delta_S^-} {}^1\sigma \qquad (12.92)$$

and on the right by the matrix inverse to A, i.e. by the matrix

$$A^{-1} = \frac{1}{\Delta_A} \alpha = \frac{1}{\Delta_A^+\, \Delta_A^-} \alpha \qquad (12.93)$$

where ${}^1\Delta_S$ and Δ_A are determinants of matrices ${}^1S$ and A respectively which will be divided according to the principles of spectral factorisation (see Eqn. 12.18) into products ${}^1\Delta_S^+\, {}^1\Delta_S^-$ and $\Delta_A^+\, \Delta_A^-$ respectively. If we define further

$$\left. \begin{aligned} \Delta^+ &= {}^1\Delta_S^+\, \Delta_A^+ \\ \Delta^- &= {}^1\Delta_S^-\, \Delta_A^- \end{aligned} \right\} \qquad (12.94)$$

Eqn. 12.91 can be arranged in the form

$$\frac{1}{z} \varDelta^+ D^T = \frac{{}^1\sigma\,{}^2SB^T\alpha}{z\varDelta^-} + \frac{{}^1\sigma\varLambda^T\alpha}{z\varDelta^-} \qquad (12.95)$$

from which follow v independent equations

$$\frac{1}{z} \varDelta^+ D_i = \frac{{}^1\sigma\,{}^2SB^T\alpha_i}{Z\varDelta^-} + \frac{{}^1\sigma\varLambda^T\alpha_i}{\varDelta^-} \qquad (12.96)$$

for $i = 1, 2, \ldots, v$. By the procedure already known we arrive at the expression

$$D_i = \frac{z}{\varDelta^+}\left[\frac{{}^1\sigma\,{}^2SB^T\alpha_i}{z\varDelta^-} + \frac{{}^1\sigma\varLambda^T\alpha_i}{\varDelta^-}\right]_+ \qquad (12.97)$$

Individual elements of matrix D_i can be expressed in the following way:

$$D_{ij} = \frac{z}{\varDelta^+}\left[\frac{1}{z\varDelta^-} \sum_{j_1=1}^{v} {}^1\sigma_{j_1 j} \sum_{j_2=1}^{v} {}^2S_{j_1 j_2} \sum_{j_3=1}^{v} B_{j_3 j_2}\, \alpha_{ij_3}\right.$$
$$\left. + \frac{1}{\varDelta^-} \sum_{j_1=1}^{v} {}^1\sigma_{j_1 j} \sum_{j_2=1}^{v} \varLambda_{j_2 j_1}\, \alpha_{ij_2}\right]_+ \qquad (12.98)$$

for $i, j = 1, 2, \ldots, v$.

Eqn. 12.98 represents the discrete version of Eqn. 12.97 so that the conclusion of the solution is similar as on pp. 244–45. Owing to the fact that the second term in the brackets of Eqn. 12.98 contains the unknown functions $\varLambda_{j_2 j_1}$ having no poles inside the stable zone of plane z, this member can be rewritten in the form

$$\left[\frac{1}{\varDelta^-} \sum_{j_1=1}^{v} {}^1\sigma_{j_1 j} \sum_{j_2=1}^{v} \varLambda_{j_2 j_1}\, \alpha_{ij_2}\right]_+ = \sum_{k} \frac{c_{kij}}{z - z_k} \qquad (12.99)$$

where z_k are the poles of functions ${}^1\sigma_{j_1 j}$ and α_{ij_2} lying inside the stable zone of plane z. The still unknown coefficients c_{kij} in Eqn. 12.99 will be determined after substituting functions D_{ij} $(i, j = 1, 2, \ldots, v)$ calculated according to Eqn. 12.98 into one of the Eqns. 12.91. All functions of this equation are expanded into partial fractions, and those partial fractions are excluded with poles which lie outside the stable zone of plane z. For any selected j_1 and j_2 we obtain

$$\left[\frac{1}{z} \sum_{j=1}^{v} {}^1S_{j_1 j} \sum_{i=1}^{v} D_{ij}\, A_{ij_2}\right]_+ = \left[\frac{1}{z} \sum_{j=1}^{v} {}^2S_{j_1 j}\, B_{j_2 j}\right]_+ \qquad (12.100)$$

The unknown coefficients C_{kij} are determined from the condition that partial fractions with identical poles on both sides of Eqns. 12.100 must also have identical coefficients in the numerators. In this way we obtain a system of linear algebraic equations for the coefficients c_{kij}.

MATRIX FACTORISATION

The synthesis of a multi-dimensional control loop with cross-correlated input variables differs, as regards matrix factorisation, from the procedure stated in the previous section from Eqn. 12.91 onwards.

In the sense of the definition on matrix factorisation given by Eqn. 12.60 let us divide matrices ^1S and A in Eqn. 12.91 as follows

$$\left.\begin{aligned} ^1S &= \phi^-\phi^+ \\ A &= \psi^+\psi^- \end{aligned}\right\} \tag{12.101}$$

After substituting the factorised matrices according to Eqn. 12.101 into Eqn. 12.91 we obtain

$$\frac{1}{z}\phi^-\phi^+D^T\psi^+\psi^- = \frac{1}{z}\,{}^2SB^T + \varDelta^T \tag{12.102}$$

By steps already described the final solution is obtained as

$$D^T = z(\phi^+)^{-1}\left[\frac{1}{z}(\phi^-)^{-1}\,{}^2SB^T(\psi^-)^{-1}\right]_+ (\psi^+)^{-1} \tag{12.103}$$

As far as the laboriousness of matrix factorisation is concerned the same note applies as stated in the conclusion on p. 245. The factorisations of matrices of discrete and continuous functions differ as do the methods of synthesis of discrete and continuously acting control loops differ in details. The method of the practical factorisation of discrete functions is discussed in reference 13.

REFERENCES

1. KOLMOGOROFF, A., 'Interpolation und Extrapolation von Stationaren Zufalligen Folgen, *Bull. Acad. Sci.*, ser. math., **4**, 3 (1941).
2. WIENER, N., *The Extrapolation, Interpolation and Smoothing of Stationary Time Series*, John Wiley, New York (1949).
3. BODE, H. W. and SHANNON, C. E., 'A Simplified Derivation of Linear Least Square Smoothing and Prediction Theory,' *Proc. Instn. Radio Engrs.*, **38**, No. 4, 417 (1950).
4. WIENER, N. and MASANI, P., 'The Prediction Theory of Multi-variable Stochastic Processes—1: The Regularity Condition,' *Acta math.*, **98**, 111 (1957).
5. WIENER, N., 'On Factorisation of Matrices, Comment' *Math. Helv.*, **29**, 97 (1955).
6. WIENER, N. and MASANI, P., 'The Prediction Theory of Multi-variable Stochastic Processes—2: The Linear Predictor,' *Acta Math.* **99**, 93 (1958).
7. YOULA, D. C., 'On the Factorisation of Rational Matrices,' *IRE Trans.*, IT 7, No. 3, 172 (1961).
8. KAVANAGH, R. J., 'A Note on Optimum Linear Multi-variable Filters,' *Proc. Brit. Inst. Elec. Engrs.*, **108**, pt.C, 412 (1961).
9. DAVIS, M. C., 'Factoring the Spectral Matrix,' *IEEE Trans.*, AC-8, No. 4, 296 (1963).
10. STREJC V., *et al.*, *Syntéza regulačnich obvodu s číslicovým počítačem (The Synthesis of Control Loops with Digital Computers)*, Czechoslovak Academy of Sciences, Praha (1965).
11. STREJC V., 'The Physical Realisability of an Optimal Parameter, Discrete, Linear Control System Determined in Wiener's Sense,' *Congress IFAC*, paper 8B, London (1966).
12. CHANG, S. S. L., *Synthesis of Optimum Control Systems*, McGraw-Hill, New York (1961).
13. HALOUSKOVÁ A., *Syntéza mnohaparametrových Lineárnich diskrétních regulačních obvodů podle kvadratických kriterií (The Synthesis of Multi-parameter, Linear, Discrete Control Loops According to Quadratic Criteria)*, Dissertation work, Institute of Information Theory and Automation of the ČSAV, Praha (1965).

Chapter 13

Cybernetics and Industrial Processes

D. B. FOSTER Ph.D., M.Sc., F.I.E.E., C. Eng., M.I. Chem. E., F.I. Mech. E.

Consultant in Automation, Surrey (U.K.)

SUMMARY

The author interprets cybernetics as applied to the industrial field in terms of industrial automation, which he equates to 'automatically controlled processes'. The view is taken that all engineering is designed essentially for wave functions, and that this applies equally to an industrial process and to its control system. The essence of designing automatically controlled systems is to be able to identify the process waveform and to set up a corresponding and probably electronic system of equivalent waveforms.

The processes of industry are divides into four, *shaping, assembly, chemical* and *data,* all being concerned in waveform patterns on different scales of physical size. Two theories of automation are developed, the first being a general theory covering all forms of automaticity such as machines and mechanical systems. The second aspect is the special theory which is applicable to processes which would go wrong automatically if left to themselves. The chapter discusses the various interfering forces which can cause wrong process function; the three main correction techniques for automatic control are described as (1) *feedback systems,* (2) *feedforward systems,* (3) *command program systems.*

INTRODUCTION

When I first met Norbert Wiener in 1960 in Moscow, I asked him why he had invented the term 'cybernetics' and just what did he intend it to mean. His answer was: 'Cybernetics is a compound Greek word meaning the art of the steersman and I think we have to look upon it just like that. It is concerned with the direction and control of processes—any sort of process whether psychological or physical'.

Thus, as applied to the industrial world, cybernetics is concerned with the control of industrial processes and we tend to replace the word cybernetics by the word automation. This chapter will deal essentially with the fundamentals of industrial automation. First, let us define automation:

Automation = automatically controlled process   (Definition 13.1)

THE GENERAL THEORY OF AUTOMATION

AUTOMATION AS A BROAD TERM

Our definition of automation as automatically controlled process is clearly a very wide and general definition and wide terms can easily degenerate into being meaningless. It is thus necessary to elaborate on the meaning of the term and to describe some principal aspects or sub-divisions, all of which will be compatible with the general description already given.

THE ASPECTS OF AUTOMATION — FUNCTION AND PROCESS

The various constructions of engineering all embody that common essential thing known as function. Function is 'what something is intended to do'. Thus, the function of a watch is to tell the time and the function of a kettle is to boil water. The actual operation of the watch or the boiling kettle is process. Process and function are not the same thing, since function is created by conscious design whilst process is actually what happens in practice.

Thus, one can design a motor car engine to drive a motor car along a road, but the design will probably lead to three practical processes: (1) the engine will perform to the correct function, this is *the designed functional process* or *useful function;* (2) the engine will begin to wear out, but this was not intended in the design; (3) The engine may have a fault of materials or construction and may suddenly fail, but this also was not intended in the design.

Any practical process created by engineers is governed by two factors: the *intended function* designed into the system, and the non-intended *interfering functions* which are implicit in the laws of nature. Such interfering functions come from many sources but particularly from the actual properties of materials, from environmental conditions and from design mistakes. The job of a good engineer is not only to design useful function into a process, but also to anticipate the likely pattern of the interfering functions of nature and to take avoiding action. Much of the practical technology of advanced automation is concerned with techniques of implementing correction systems to deal with likely natural interference with useful function.

THE ASPECTS OF AUTOMATION — ENGINEERING AS DESIGN FOR WAVE FUNCTION

Automation calls on the techniques of process engineering and of control engineering—but to the engineer, these two disciplines are much the same thing and the real difference is related to their different useful final functions. Intrinsically, however, they are both simply engineering and both require the common attitude of the engineer as to basic analysis of the problem to be solved, properties of materials, considerations as to reliability and safety, and so forth.

But the really interesting point would be if we could find a common way of looking at design for process and design for control: are there common specific engineering principles involved other than the rather general factors given in the last paragraph? In practice, there are, and it may be best first to give the answer and then to explain it:

All engineering design is design for wave function   (Definition 13.2)

The reason for introducing this generalisation is that the more sophisticated forms of automation are all concerned with controlling mechanical and chemical wave functions by means of electronic wave functions.

A wave function is not something esoteric—it is simply the pattern made by something which moves. It can be represented equally by the lamp being waved by a railway guard, or by the track made by a motor car travelling between London and Manchester. Nor is the wave function a mathematical concept requiring equations. It is simply the shape of the path traced out in time by something doing something and in our case that something is what we have been calling engineering function.

Let us now consider practical engineering examples to see how this is always so:

1. *A watch*

   The useful function of a watch is to tell the time by the movement of its hands and it has a functional waveform. To understand these waveforms, imagine that you are looking at the watch in the dark, that there are little lamps attached to the ends of the hour and minute hands, and that the whole watch is moving from left to right to correspond to the passage of time during your observation. This traces out two wave functions corresponding to the hour hand and to the minute hand.

2. *A plastics press*

   The ram of the press comes down, slowly forms the article under pressure and then returns; the corresponding waveform of motion is expressed by a lamp on the ram viewed in the dark.

The essence of the matter is that all functions and all processes require that something is varying with time. If we plot that something against time, we can see the essential functional waveform. The two examples chosen above have essentially been engineering processes of a very tangible nature, but we can now consider almost pure control functions and see that the same basic waveform concept is applicable as in the following examples:

1. *An electric light switch*

   If we take an electric lamp with a voltmeter on the lamp side and observe what happened to the voltmeter during the day and night we create a *two-state* waveform in time.

2. *A motor car speedometer*

   This is a control functional device which operates via human observation

257

and if we assume that a car driver observes speed limits and traffic signals then it has a positional waveform with time.

We can thus see that both basic processes such as watches and plastic presses, and also control devices such as electric switches and speedometers, have as their most fundamental feature and nature a functional waveform in time. The only process, indeed if it can be called that, which does not have a functional waveform is something which does nothing in time and of this there are no known examples. One might query whether a mountain is not such a static thing, but a mountain is simply a process on a very long time scale. But a spaceman watching a mountain would see it rotate daily, so that a mountain to him is a twenty-four hour clock. Moreover, even mountains have a limited life of a few million years so that they also have a rise and fall wavetime on a rather extended time axis.

The whole of science is based on 'Pointer readings', pointer readings of displacement, velocity, temperature, pressure, chemical composition and many more; if these pointer readings are attached to a time charting device such as an automatic chart recorder, then the functional waveform involved is seen clearly.

The art of good engineering design is to be able to recognise the functional waveform inherent in what you are trying to do. The art of good automation design is to know the waveform of the basic process and to design control waveforms to keep the basic process waveforms where you want them to be.

THE ASPECTS OF AUTOMATION — PROCESS PATTERN

The basic assumption in automation is that something useful is happening without human intervention, and this is related to the *principle of automaticity*. The word *auto* comes from the Greek word *autos* meaning *self*. Thus the word *automaticity* refers to self-control or self-acting and—as applied to mechanical systems—it means that such a system can be left to look after itself. Given this principle, the next thing to know is how to achieve it.

From the previous section, it is clear that all processes, including the useful processes of engineering, relate to something happening in time. We must now be concerned with looking a little deeper into what we mean by process and with the inherent variations in that process.

All processes are concerned with inflicting some sort of pattern on to some sort of material. There are no exceptions to this: it applies to the process of plastics moulding in which a plastics press and mould inflict a pattern of shape into a plastics material, and it applies equally well to a punched tape fed to a computer which inflicts a pattern of binary digits into the registers, memories and other parts of the computer. Thus, all process is concerned with inflicting patterns on raw materials. There are four basic patterns:

1. *Assembly processes*, where the pattern inflicted is the relationship of item to item, for example, between a nut and a bolt
2. *Shaping processes*, where the pattern inflicted is that of a geometrical shape
3. *Chemical processes*, where the pattern inflicted is that of molecular shape (the same is true of nuclear processes concerned with atomic shape)
4. *Data processes*, where the pattern inflicted is the relationship of some electricity to some other electricity.

Processes are all concerned with pattern forming and the above four divisions are simply divisions as of size scale, starting at the top with the relationship between gross items: to the pattern of the item itself; to the pattern of molecules or atoms and lastly to patterns in the particles of electricity. We need not differentiate between any of these four processes, since there is in essence only a size difference, but there is another fundamental aspect of great importance. We have arrived at the point of view that *process is a variation in time of the pattern in a material* and it will be clear that there are two main factors in this situation which will affect what happens in time. The first of these factors is the material itself and the second factor is the process equipment, which is trying to do something to that material.

But *time* comes into the situation in a very vital manner and we can define an equation to take account of this:

Material pattern = raw material + process equipment pattern + time pattern

(Definition 13.3)

This means that although we may have a set of equipment in a factory (process equipment pattern) and an in-feed of raw materials, just what will happen to that raw material will depend critically on how much time is allowed. Thus, the relationship of time as between the material to be worked on and the processes to be performed is vital, and at this point we are faced by a major choice as to which of two directions to take. The two directions are:

1. Shall we establish a fixed process pattern which does not change with time, but where the required variation of material pattern is secured by moving the material through this fixed process pattern—this is called 'the continuous process'.
2. Shall we have the material stationary and vary the process pattern in time—this is called the 'batch process'.

Let us illustrate the choice by a well established example from the pottery industry. There are two methods of firing the goods to change clay into pottery. The first method is to provide a tunnel kiln which at its input end is quite cool heats up progressively into the middle of the tunnel, but at the outlet shades off to cool again; a continuously moving conveyor takes the goods through the kiln. The kiln itself thus has a static process pattern and the process variation required to inflict a new pattern of properties on the raw material is achieved by taking the raw material through this static process pattern, thereby 'scanning' the process pattern by material motion. This is the continuous process.

Alternatively, the material can be introduced into a batch furnace which first heats up, maintains its heat at the top temperature for a given time and then cools off, allowing the material to be removed. This is the batch process.

THE ASPECTS OF AUTOMATION — INHERENT AUTOMATICITY

If the above alternatives are examined from the aspect of automaticity, it will be seen that the first method of the continuous process is inherently automatic —once the tunnel kiln has settled down to a required temperature pattern distributed along its length, then all that is, necessary is to feed a continuous conveyor with raw materials, which will emerge treated correctly. This gives another definition:

> Inherent automaticity occurs in all continuous processes where a material is moved progressively through a fixed process pattern   (Definition 13.4)

Continuous processes are available in both chemical and manufacturing industries; in the latter, they take the form of progressive production lines usually round a continuously moving conveyor belt, with a small increment of useful manufacturing function being added at each successive stage. Since continuous processes are inherently automatic, this provides reason why pioneering work towards automation was carried out in the chemicals, oil refining and motor car industries.

Inherent automaticity is available wherever a process lends itself basically to the principle of material motion continuity. The foregoing example of continuous process is one such sector but another is the continuous cyclic process. Continuous cyclic processes are those in which the material motion and the process motion both have movement in time, but are co-ordinated together on a rhythmic cyclic basis in a sort of 'process waltz'.

Probably the best example of this is the motor car internal combustion engine, in which the well known four-stroke cycle system of material combustion and of mechanics involves both a cyclic motion of the material involved, petrol and air, and of the mechanics of crankshaft, pistons and valves. Each cycle of combustion is a complete miniature process pattern in itself but the end of a cycle is the signal for an identical new cycle to commence. Continuity, in this case is, established by rhythm and momentum and the only problem is how to start the system in the first place—the answer being by means of the electric starter motor.

This principle of cyclic continuity is the basis of almost all known machines and applies outstandingly to all rotating combustion engines including jet and turbine engines, machine tools such as lathes and milling machines, textile spinning machines and looms. Cyclic machines thus have inherent automaticity, in that they continue performing unless a deliberate effort is made to stop them. All are based on the principle of the wheel since it is the wheel which embodies the principle of simple continuous cyclic motion. We can now identify, as in Table 13.1, the different processes which lead to inherent automaticity or non-automaticity.

Table 13.1. PROCESSES LEADING TO INHERENT AUTOMATICITY OR NON-AUTOMATICITY

Process Type	Element of Continuity	Automaticity
Continuous	Material motion	Inherent
Cyclic Continuous	Material and process motion Co-ordinated rhythm	Inherent
Batch	Process motion	Non-inherent

From Table 13.1, it can clearly be seen that the vital factor in securing inherent automaticity is material motion rather than process motion and since inherent automaticity is the key to the easy accomplishment of automation, we are now in a position to define Rule 1 of the automation engineer:

The first rule of the automation engineer is preferably to devise a system in which the material in the process system moves either continuously or rhythmically
(Definition 13.5)

THE ASPECTS OF AUTOMATION — INHERENT ANTI-AUTOMATICITY

So far we have dealt with factors which inherently favour automaticity, i.e., processes arranged to deal with continuously moving or cyclicly moving raw materials. We next have to consider the sorts of factors which are inherently adverse to automaticity and thus make automation problems more difficult to overcome.

We touched on a line of thought relating to this earlier when we were considering the relationship of design for useful function to what happens in an actual process—the laws of nature have their own part to play which shall not be denied and, if designing a motor car engine to run smoothly, the laws of nature will also ensure that such an engine will wear out and be subject to breakdown. All these possibilities are called natural interference functions.

The simplest logical approach to the subject of anti-automaticity may be defined as:

Anti-automaticity is those factors in a process which will ensure that things will go wrong automatically unless special corrective precautions are taken
(Definition 13.6)

Anti-automaticity is, therefore, automatic negative automaticity. If you are driving a motor car along a road and suddenly freeze your driving attitudes regarding the position of the accelerator and steering wheel and close your eyes, then you may be automatically assured of an accident. In the field of industrial and commercial processes there are many which are similarly 'accident prone' and dealing with these by automation techniques is both fascinating and difficult and is also, perhaps, the very core of modern automation technology.

THE GENERAL THEORY OF AUTOMATION

From the foregoing review, we arrive at the conclusion that the processes of industry contain two factors, one of which is favourable to easy automation and one of which is unfavourable to easy automation but which possibly might yield to sophisticated technology. The art of automation is concerned with doing things automatically whether the means be easy or difficult, and we can now define a general theory of automation.

The general theory of automation covers comprehensively all aspects of the automatic control of processes. The total field is divided into two sectors:

1. Continuous flow and cyclic processes which contain within themselves a principle of *inherent automaticity* in the sense that if nothing varies, then the processes will go on working automatically and satisfactorily indefinitely.

2. Non-cyclic batch processes or those processes sensitive to interference function and which contain within themselves a principle of *inherent anti-automaticity* in the sense that if left to themselves the process will go wrong automatically. (Definition 13.7)

THE SPECIAL THEORY OF AUTOMATION

The special theory of automation is concerned with the principles involved in counteracting anti-automaticity so that interfering functions can be brought under control. It is related to making automatic provision for 'corrective precautions'. In a factory, it is very easy to see the anti-automaticity principle at work since the machines in the factory mainly represent the principle of cyclic automaticity and the workers and supervisors are there primarily to correct the anti-automaticity which would ensure that things went wrong automatically.

We can define the special theory as follows:

The special theory of automation is concerned mainly with the theory and design of systems having appreciable natural anti-automaticity in their basic materials, processes or environment, with the object of automatically detecting and nullifying such anti-automaticity. The techniques involved are called corrective automation (Definition 13.8)

THE PRINCIPAL GROUPS OF INTERFERENCE FUNCTIONS

In any process, as well as the intended or designed process pattern there are always a great number of interfering forces or factors at play which have the effect of modifying the designed process pattern so that the finished product may not be quite what it was intended to be. These interfering forces are always unhelpful. The principal interfering factors are:

1. *Raw materials* which may be off specification as to the proportion of ingredients or impurities. Thus the sand going into a ceramic factory may contain a wrong proportion of aluminium silicate, or dried fruit going into a cake factory may contain stones.
2. *Climatic variations* which can affect adversely the operation of a process. For example, the quality of printing in a newspaper factory will be affected by the flow characteristics of ink being sensitive to both temperature and humidity conditions.
3. *Energy input variations*—all processes require an input of energy sustain them. The energy may be in the form of steam, electricity, gas heat, etc. A process may work satisfactorily if supplied with a gas of 500 Btu/ft^3 but may produce variable results if the gas changes to 470 Btu/ft^3.
4. *Wear and tear*—a process may be set to give a good product but will invariably drift off performance due to wear and tear of machines and tools. The quality of metal pressed parts, for example, changes constantly due to die wear.
5. *Human errors and omissions*—The scope for these is unlimited and may include anything, from shutting down a power station by pressing the wrong button, to spoiling a batch of biscuits by forgetting to add the sugar.

262

6. *Cumulative muddle by neglect*—all process situations deteriorate if neglected. It is the universal law that all systems tend towards chaos unless countered by conscious ordering forces. Even if you lock your house up and go away for a month's holiday, it will not be quite the same when you get back: dust, spiders' webs, a burst pipe, a blown-off tile or even burglars will have effected changes to increase the chaos at the expense of order. An extreme example of this is when a strike occurs in a postal sorting office.

7. *Inefficiency by neglect.* ('Under-utilisation')—the effect of neglect is twofold. On the one hand, it tends to physical chaos as in the preceding paragraph, whilst on the other hand it means that things are going more slowly than they need. In all industrial undertakings 'time costs money and time is against you', and it is necessary to plan and program constantly and to exert pressure to get effective corresponding action. The interfering functions responsible for this are generally of a psychological nature, but are mainly the natural distaste of all human beings for that thing known as 'work'.

The preceding seven groups are the main classification of how things 'go automatically wrong'. It is the field of special automation to deal with them.

BLIND ROBOTS AND CONSCIOUS ROBOTS

The general theory of automation covers all aspects of doing things automatically-whether the principle of inherent automaticity or the principle of inherent anti, automaticity is dominant. In this chapter we see how the special theory of automation is concerned particularly with securing automaticity in the very teeth of opposition by the principle of anti-automaticity. The marvels of mechanisation exploiting the principle of inherent automaticity are all based on the wheel and on the power of the wheel to secure either continuous flow or cyclic batch flow; we physically recognise such systems in the machines and mechanised systems of industry, all of which depend on 'something going round'. Such systems based on inherent automaticity depend on sustained motion and momentum and are blind robots in that the more they go on doing the same thing, the better will be the result. The less the intelligence and the fewer the questions that such a blind robot asks itself, the better the product.

If we turn now to the corrective automation of the special theory, which is concerned with opposing the inherent anti-automaticity of certain groups of processes, we find the opposite state of affairs. Eternal vigilance and corrective action based on such vigilance is the essence of this type of automation. The principle of the mechanical wheel is the last thing to use for realising conscious robots—the means adapted will almost certainly make use of the mercurial adaptability of electricity in general and of electrons in particular.

Conscious robots?

The reader may wonder if by using the term 'conscious robot' the author is either letting his imagination run away with him or, alternatively, is using the phrase as a convenient anthropomorphic analogue. When one considers, however, that robots have been designed to land on the Moon and send pictures back automatically, or a computer can be devised which will translate a Russian book into

English, then for all practical purposes such robots have the behavioural properties which, until recently, we should have reserved exclusively for conscious human beings.

AUTOMATION TECHNIQUE — THE OVERALL AUTOMATION SYSTEM

The seven main categories of 'interfering functions' given earlier require the special theory of automation to correct them and we shall next consider the broad form of technique and hardware which is likely to be involved:

1. *Automatic measurement and recognition*
   Coming from the process concerned, with its material movements, energy supplies and mechanical and chemical processes, we shall require 'process signals' to tell us what is going on.
2. *Command signals*
   Every system requires a plan and a program, even though this is in general terms such as 'make 10,000 pairs of nylon stockings today' or 'make 50 tons of polyethylene next week'. There must be some command signals covering the overall operation of the process, but these instructions need not state exactly how the process is to be operated in order to achieve them.
3. *The central electronic brain*
   This is the nerve centre of the operation having two sorts of incoming signals, signals coming up from the process as in (1) above and general command programms coming from management as in (2) above. In addition, it has the main function of deciding how and when to control the process to make these two requirements compatible and finally it has to issue the necessary corresponding control instructions.
4. *Actuation*
   The instructions from the central electronic brain must be converted to actual operations—electric motors must start and stop, valves must open and close and so forth. This is the realm of 'automation actuation'.

We shall next examine what is involved in achieving the above four main groups of function.

AUTOMATION TECHNIQUE — MEASUREMENT AND RECOGNITION

The first aim of the automation engineer is to simulate properties of eternal vigilance, to create automatic eyes, ears and other senses, and even senses which have no human correspondence, such as ultrasonic ears which can detect sounds beyond the human range.

The apparatus required for this comes under four types:

1. *A sensing device*
   This is nearly always some special material immersed or associated with the physical or chemical phenomenon that is being measured or recognised; the material changes its properties with variations of the factor being measured. Mercury, for instance expands with temperature and is a temperature sensor. A bi-metal strip bends with temperature and is also a temperature

sensor. A piece of wire stuck to a steel rod changes its resistance with the expansion of the steel rod and is thus a displacement sensor ('strain gauge'). Cadmium sulphide changes its resistance with the intensity of light shining on it (a 'photocell').

2. *Transducing means*
Transducing is different from sensing and is concerned with converting the change in the sensor into a form of useful output signal for automatic display or other use. The output signal is nearly always required to be an electrical current, but many sensing devices will not produce electrical currents directly. Thus, if we use mercury in a thermometer as a temperature sensor, we have to induce the mercury to make a number of electrical contacts as it passes up the fine capillary tube, so that we can convert the mercury movement into an electrical current change. In many cases the sensing device and transducing means are one and the same, so that if an electrical thermocouple is used to detect temperature change, a distinct transducer arrangement is not needed since the transduction is inherent in the sensor. The trend is towards trying to find and use sensors having a direct electrical output.

3. *Standard reference signals for measurement*
So far, we have a signal in electrical form but this is not 'measurement' or 'recognition'. To convert the signal to a measurement we need to *scale* it in some way and this is done by comparing the electrical signal to one or a set of standard electrical signals. For example, if we wish to measure whether a process is operating at 85° F and we use a thermocouple which would produce a current of 10 mV at this temperature, we also set up a separate reference signal of 10 mV and take both the thermocouple signal and the reference signal to a comparator—an electrical device which indicates when two signals are equal. As the temperature rises, the voltage output of the thermocouple increases until it equals the reference voltage and the comparator gives out an 'equals' signal which may be used for alarms or process control purposes.

4. *Comparators for measurement and recognition*
There are several types of comparator used for the recognition of signals. The three main types are:

(a) *Single level*
This is as described in (3) above, in which the sensed signal is compared with a single reference signal as to whether the sensed signal is 'equal', 'above' or 'below' the referent or target signal.

(b) *Multi-level*
Here, a progressive group of reference voltages is set up and the comparator indicates in which range the sensed voltage is. In the simplest form there are two such reference voltages, one of which defines the upper permissible level, the second of which defines the lower permissible level; the resulting comparator will indicate one of three things: 'within permitted range', 'above permitted range' and 'below permitted range'.

(c) *Continuously variable*
In some processes the correct level of a signal may vary with factors other than the measured variable, so that the reference level must be continuously adjustable to suit. This is done by a comparator having a sliding reference point which is set by these other variables.

Sensing devices for physical process measurement

When vigilance of a physical process is required the most common measuring requirements relate to temperature, liquid flow, pressure, force, position, displacement and velocity. To realise these dimensions the most common sensing devices are:

1. *The thermocouple*, for the measurement of temperature, since such a device gives out an electrical voltage correspondingly.
2. *The strain gauge*, for the measurement of pressures and forces. The strain gauge consists of a wire network attached to a mechanical bar or such, so that distortion of the bar due to pressure or force causes corresponding electrical change of resistance in the wire network.
3. The *limit switch*, for positional detection. A rod attached to a moving mechanism causes the switch to operate at a certain pre-determined position.
4. *The photocell* and light beam for positional detection by obscuration of the beam by interposition of a mechanical shutter attached to a mechanism.

Given such sensing devices, a great number of derived measuring systems can be made: for example, the strain-gauge pressure detector can be placed across an orifice in a liquid flow line to measure flow rates; the photocell can be arranged on a dial of a weight detecting meter to count the number of units of weight as the pointer revolves. (The more specific and detailed applications of physical sensing devices are dealt with later.)

Sensing devices for chemical process measurement

When vigilance of a chemical process is required, the most common automatic sensing methods relate to the change in the optical properties of chemicals with composition changes. These changes may refer to colour, light absorption and scattering, light polarisation, light spectrum or detailed colour analysis. These methods are particularly useful since, ultimately, the signal can fall into a photocell which has a corresponding electrical output. As well as optical changes, wavelength changes or magnitudes of other radiations may be used such as infra-red, ultraviolet and nuclear radiations but the principle in nearly all of these is to make the chemical composition change a radiation intensity or pattern and have the form detectable by a photocell or similar radition sensitive sensing device.

AUTOMATION TECHNIQUE — COMMAND SIGNALS

By a command, we imply an instruction which shall be obeyed, and in automation systems this operates in two ways or levels:

1. *General overall commands* which we referred to earlier in the sense that only general requirements are stated such as 'make 10,000 pairs of nylon stockings today'. Such a command has to assume that the central electronic brain has all the know-how to put such a general command into detailed effect.
2. *Command programmes* which also include the necessary detailed instructions to give effect to the main implications of the command.

There is thus a great deal of difference as between general overall commands and command programmes.

General overall commands can only be inserted into a central electronic brain or computer provided that the computer has been designed to deal with them—for example, when it receives a general overall command to 'make 10,000 pairs of nylon stockings' it automatically breaks this down into sub-commands as to:

1. Known management distribution as to stockings sizes so that, per thousand stockings made, it knows that these will consist of:

   200 pairs of size 9
   600 pairs of size 10
   200 pairs of size 11

2. The electronic brain restates the command as:

   2,000 pairs of size 9
   6,000 pairs of size 10
   2,000 pairs of size 11

3. After the above analysis, it then knows enough to order up the corresponding material quantities and to give effect to the process instructions.

AUTOMATION TECHNIQUE — THE CENTRAL ELECTRONIC BRAIN

The central electronic brain is the apparatus which digests all incoming information, calculates its relevance both as to significance and operations required to give effect to the implications, and then issues instructions to control the process accordingly.

In practice a central electronic brain can vary from a couple of transistors and a few resistors effecting a simple comparator circuit, to a full blooded analogue or digital computer costing hundreds of thousands of pounds. In principle all control electronic brains have to perform some or all of the following functions:

1. Scale incoming signals as to magnitudes so that one incoming signal of, say, 1000 V can be compared and taken into account with another signal of, say, 1 mV. Thus it may well divide the former by 1,000 and multiply the latter by 1,000 so that they are on a compatible scale.
2. Change the characteristic curve of incoming signals to make them suitable for further manipulation. If, for example, a computer is measuring a flow rate by means of a pressure difference and the corresponding law is: *Flow = square root of pressure difference*, then it must first perform a square rooting operation on the incoming pressure signal.
3. Have in its memory the mathematical relationship between all process variables so that it can, as it were, say to itself: 'If that pressure is 120 lb/in² then that temperature ought to be 730°C'.
4. Know how to give effect to the implications of its mathematical information (mathematical model), so that if we take the example of (3) above it knows how to set the temperature to 730°C.

The actual form of the central electronic brain differs greatly with the application requirement.

267

AUTOMATION TECHNIQUE — ACTUATION

Finally, we have to consider how the various instructions are made effective in the process itself. Since all processes involve materials and energy, the means of control will essentially be material control devices and energy control devices. Such devices almost always make use of a wheel or a level since, in principle, the same devices are capable of hand operation. They are of two kinds:

1. *On-off devices* which only have two states. These devices include electrical switches, relays, solenoids, two position chemical valve actuators, etc. The actuation prime means will invariably be electrical, although it may be used to ensure mechanical, electrical, pneumatic or hydraulic power operating systems.
2. *Proportional devices* in which an energy or material controlling means can be set at some intermediate level, as between two extreme high and low limits. For this purpose, rather special positioning sensing devices are used whose target point is determined by the control system; appropriate electrical, pneumatic, hydraulic or mechanical power moves the device up to this setting. The positioners often contain servo-motors which will move until the difference between a target position signal and a signal corresponding to the actual position at the moment has been compared until it is zero.

THE THREE MAIN FORMS OF AUTOMATION SYSTEM

Automation systems vary primarily in the nature of the relationship between the incoming signals and the outgoing instructions, and in accordance with the following:

1. *Feedback systems*, in which the signals from the process are taken from the output of the process.
2. *Feedforward systems*, in which the signals from the process are taken from the input to the process.
3. *Command programmed systems*, in which basically no signals are received from the process, and the command program is a set of instructions.

CORRECTIVE PROCESS CONTROL USING FEEDBACK TECHNIQUE

One major group of automation techniques uses the feedback principle observation of what is coming out of a process, for example, as regards product quality, is fed back up-stream to determine process changes required to keep or adjust the process to its optimum condition, for example, keeping water hot at a temperature of 80°C. The output of the process, the water temperature, is measured by some device such as a thermocouple and the electrical output of the thermocouple is compared with a standard reference voltage which corresponds to the thermocouple output voltage at 80°C. If the temperature goes above this reference voltage, then a signal is sent out to cut off the source of heat such as a gas burner, whilst if the temperature is below 80°C, then the gas burner is permitted to operate.

Devices using this feedback system are often called 'thermostats', 'pressure stats', etc., when applied to thermal or pressure processes. More complicated systems involve adjustment of the process proportional to how far the measured factor is away from its target. Perhaps the most common example of feedback control is the ordinary ball-cock valve used on cisterns as a 'level stat' to keep the water level in the cistern at a constant height.

CORRECTIVE PROCESS CONTROL USING FEEDFORWARD TECHNIQUE

We have seen that the feedback principle operates by vigilance at the output of a process to send information back to keep the process in the optimum state. An alternative, and quite different approach, is to monitor the input to a process for input variations, and then set the process down-stream so that it is likely to be able to cater for such variations.

A typical example is in cement manufacture, where the quality of cement and the settings of the cement making process are very sensitive to the particular natural minerals being delivered to the process. With such a process it is wise first to carry out a chemical analysis on the input materials as to alkali content, etc., and then to set the process to suit the particular materials being processed from that batch of raw materials. Another example of feedforward control would be where a process required a total moisture content of, say, 10% made up of the moisture content in the input materials plus added water. Using feedforward control, one would measure continuously the moisture content of the input materials and then add sufficient water to bring the total up to 10%.

In general, feedforward control is the best method for automating processes which contain a degree of randomness as to the quantity and quality of input materials, where the feedback process would operate too late to be able to make any corrections.

AUTOMATIC COMMAND PROGRAMMING

There are some processes and process systems where each element of the process may be fundamentally stable and well behaved, but where the process itself is capable of carrying out many different instructions, i.e. it is a multi-function process. A typical example is a manufacturing machine such as a lathe, or a milling machine where the same machine could make many thousands of different kinds of parts according to the settings and instructions of the machine. To automate such a system, one requires command programming devices such as punched cards or tapes, which carry the complicated instructions involved and will cause the machine to operate accordingly. This is in fact, allied to the feedforward system of control, but the input requirements are being varied, not the input materials. An ordinary multi-product vending machine is a good example of command programming, in that by pressing one particular button, you receive the particular product requested. Indeed, the most complicated automatic warehouses of today are simply complex varieties of such a system.

CONCLUSIONS

The practical applications of cybernetics to industry is called automation, and there are two main branches of automation, both of which fall under a single general theory of 'doing things automatically'. But the facility for doing things automatically depends very much on whether the process is one based on the principle of the wheel, that is, is *inherently automatic*. There are, however, many processes which contain within themselves a principle of anti-automaticity in that they will always go wrong automatically. This is the field of the special theory of automation, involving the three techniques of variable programming, feedback control or feedforward control.

Chapter 14

Cybernetics and Ergonomics

D. A. BELL, Ph.D., M.A., B.Sc., F.I.E.E., F. Inst. P.
Department of Electronic Engineering, The University of Hull (U.K.)

SUMMARY

Ergonomics is the study of man's ability to perform tasks in various kinds of environment, the environment including the means by which he receives instructions and the means by which he controls machines. Starting with the performance of man as a source of physical effort directed towards specified ends, one proceeds to the concepts of the man-machine interface and of man as a device having an ascertainable transfer function for inclusion in a closed-loop control system. The field of study becomes progressively more cybernetic as one moves from muscular effort to the processing and transmission of information in a man-machine system.

WHAT IS ERGONOMICS

One can fall back on Norbert Wiener's definition of cybernetics as 'control and communication in the animal and the machine', but there is no authoritative definition of *ergonomics*. One is tempted to turn to etymology, but this could lead to its erroneous interpretation as 'work study'. It is safer to take one's pick from current usage, but even this is not easy, since the *Ergonomics Abstracts* issued by the Warren Springs Laboratory of the U.K. Ministry of Technology cover a diversity of topics including accident investigations, the simulation of the human mind, reduction in machine noise, artificial limbs and the design of experiments. What thread unifies all these topics? A good working definition appears in the prospectus of the Loughborough University of Technology: 'Ergonomics is the study of the capabilities and limitations of human performance at all kinds of mental and physical work tasks carried out in different physical environments'. The qualification of different *physical* environments is important because it excludes by implication the psychological factors which have a profound effect on working efficiency but fall within the provinces of industrial psychology and

271

management studies. (It might be remembered, however, that Wiener did have interests in the latter fields, as shown in his book[1] *The Human Use of Human Beings*.)

A working definition tends to be restrictive, and one therefore seeks a more imaginative approach capable of portraying the living spirit of the subject and in particular its relationship with cybernetics. The study of cybernetics arose from man's success in using mechanical devices to extend his bodily capabilities for communication, data-processing and automatic control; and ergonomics is concerned with the scientific organisation both of man's bodily capabilities and the mechanical aids which he uses for the performance of specific tasks. Ergonomics thus relates to a particular aspect of part of the subject matter of cybernetics, namely the work-effectiveness of control systems in animals and in combinations of animals (usually human) and machines. The interface between man and machine is a major concern of ergonomics, and since the tendency is for information, rather than energy, to be transmitted across the interface, this aspect of ergonomics is very close to cybernetics. One can say that the topics studied in ergonomics become more cybernetic as one progresses from the energy output of a man (and its optimum organisation) through skilled tasks to the man-machine interface type of problem.

MAN AS A SOURCE OF POWER

Regarding the human being just as a source of mechanical power, the champion athlete can work at $1\frac{1}{2}$ hp for a few seconds, or $\frac{1}{2}$ hp for a period of up to an hour or two, or $\frac{1}{5}$ hp all day. This suggests that each boat in the Oxford and Cambridge boat race is propelled by roughly 4 hp: it would be interesting to have the actual figure from drag measurements and see how efficient a machine the boat is for obtaining mechanical energy from men. Coming down from the athlete to the average human being, it is often reckoned that when walking in mountainous country any fit person should be able to gain height at a rate of 1000 ft/h or 300 m/h. Taking the walker's weight as 72 kg and the value of G as approximately 10 m/s², this rate of rise requires an energy expenditure of 720×300 N.m/h which is equivalent to 60 W. The output that is ultimately measurable as a change in potential energy is, therefore, a little under one tenth of a horsepower, though the total muscular output must be appreciably greater. If a man works at this rate for six hours the total work recorded will be $6 \times 720 \times 300 = 1.296 \times 10^6$ J or 0.36 kWh, or 310 of the kilogramme-calories used by dieticians to measure the energy value of food. It is often reckoned that a 'heavy' worker needs 1,000 to 1,500 more calories per day than a sedentary worker (3,500 to 4,000 calories against 2,500); and a conversion efficiency between additional food and useful output of 20% or more is very creditable.

As an industrial example, a study was made of man as a materials-handling machine, for example, unloading bricks for house-building.[2] The conclusion was that a man could shift 200 tons a day through a horizontal distance of one metre, or 50 tons a day through one metre vertically; and that the food corresponding to the amount of energy which he uses in the job would cost more than the same amount of energy delivered from a mechanical source. (Fifty tons lifted through 1 metre represents approximately 5×10^5 joules or roughly one seventh of a kilowatt-hour.) This suggests that in unloading bricks from a truck to an ordered stack one should use a mechanical conveyor so that a man has only to shift the bricks through a short horizontal distance from the truck to the conveyor and another man shifts them from the conveyor to the stack. One then has, in theory, a capacity for handling four times as many bricks per man as by throwing them over the side of the truck and lifting them on to the pile, for the capital and running cost of the conveyor. Whether one could in fact persuade a man to work under industrial conditions for a whole day at peak efficiency on transferring bricks to an adjacent conveyor is very doubtful. By 'under industrial conditions' we mean that the job is to be done repeatedly for a modest financial reward and with no other motivation such as research interest in the results achieved; the provision of additional motivation, if it is possible, is an application of industrial psychology rather than ergonomics. In the absence of special motivation, such a task would surely be an example of the inhuman use of human beings.

The human labour in unloading can be eliminated entirely by using a tipping truck and spewing out the bricks in a random pile, but this has several disadvantages: (1) the bricks may be damaged as they fall; (2) the random pile will occupy a much larger ground area (this consideration is decisive in loading the bricks into the truck in an ordered way); (3) removal of the bricks for subsequent use is easier from an ordered stack than from a random pile. The need for the use of human beings in this task, therefore, arises from the desire to retain order, implying the use of information about the position of the bricks already stacked and the position and orientation of the bricks which are being added to the stack.

So far we have been discussing activities in which physical exertion is a major factor; but can one become literally 'hot under the collar' through working at tasks which require dexterity or mental concentration rather than physical exertion? In the industrial use (human or otherwise) of human beings it is important to know whether an individual is working hard, particularly when setting rates of payment for piece-work, and it would be very valuable to have some objective measure of effort to replace the work-study man's 'guess based on experience'. All physically measurable effort must be derived from the oxidation of foodstuffs in the body, so Ayoub and Manuel[3] tried measuring the amount of air breathed in as a function of the working pace. The work load was such as to allow the attainment of a steady metabolic rate, and the volume of air taken into the lungs was normalised for individual differences in physique by expressing it as litres per minute per square metre of body surface area (BSA). (The latter was estimated from the formula:

$$\text{BSA} = W^{0.425} \times H^{0.0725} \times 71.84 \text{ m}^2$$

where W = body weight in pounds and H = height in inches.) Two tasks were used in the investigation, namely (1) filling a pinboard with 30 pins in 0.41 minute and (2) dealing 52 cards into the four corners of a 12-inch square in 0.5 minute. The times allowed were norms which had been established by previous investigators; timing was controlled by pacing the tasks with a metronome, allowing the pace to be set at 80%, 100% or 110% of the norm. The overall average for 108 subjects, divided between men and women and three age groups, showed a nearly linear change between about 4.5 and 5.1 litres of air per minute per square metre of body area for variation of pace between 80% and 100%, though individual variations were not consistent. (In particular, women engaged on the card-dealing task showed a *reduction* of air intake when the pace was increased from 100% to 110%.)

The application of cybernetics to industrial plant and machinery sometimes seems to drive human work to one of two extremes. On the one hand, are the designers and managers, engineers and systems analysts, whose contribution is intellectual. On the other hand, having replaced craft skill by the precision of machine tools and machine-minding by computer controls, one is left with machine-feeding, which is a task requiring very little skill. Yet the amount of information acquisition by the human senses, and data processing by the nervous system and brain, is so great that a robot with equal powers would be prohibitively expensive. The human being is neither powerful nor precise nor untiring, but he (or she) is versatile. The human central nervous system is said to contain of the order of 10^{10} neurons. Even if the use of integrated circuits allowed us to make gates and flip-flops for the odd cent each, it would still cost a billion dollars to replicate the elements of a human nervous system; and we should still have the problem of simulating all the properties of the synapses in providing refractory periods, threshold and facilitation. It is, therefore, difficult to replace the human being by a robot, though there are now some 'versatile' handling devices which are capable of going through a fairly elaborate cycle of operations provided the cycle is strictly repetitive. Examples are the *Versatran* (trade name of the American Machine and Foundry Co. in U.S.A. and Hawker-Siddeley in U.K.) and *Unimate* (Consolidated Controls Corp. in U.S.A. and Guest, Keen, Nettlefold in U.K.) If we are to continue to use the human being for energetic tasks we need ergonomics to maximise the efficiency of his utilisation.

MAN AS A CONTROLLER

Maximum utilisation of the human being requires maximisation of the rate of work together with minimisation of the number of errors. An example of a man-machine interface in which the machine provides all the power, and the man controls the machine as a result of information which he obtains independently of the machine, is the crane; and one of the most economically important applications of the crane is the manouvering of steel billets and ingots. The operator of a crane should have a seat, which is physiologically satisfactory to minimise fatigue and which is so placed that he rarely needs to leave the support provided by his seat in order to see the load which he is manoeuvering; but the seat should allow him some change of position both to avoid muscular fatigue and to vary the pressure areas on the flesh from time to time so as to permit proper blood circulation. He should also have all controls within reach, and where there is a usual sequence of use of the controls, they should be so disposed that the hand moves naturally from one to the next.[4] A more familiar example of the need to choose a sequence of control positions is in the control lever for an automobile with automatic transmission; assuming that the driver will usually go forward into a parking space and reverse out when leaving, the sequence shown in Fig. 14.1 gives the easiest procedure. The transmission is shifted from 'Park' to 'Reverse' to get out of the parking place, and then through 'Neutral' to 'Drive' to drive away. It is logical to place neutral between forward and reverse, so as to be readily accessible from either; but low-hold should also be readily accessible from forward drive, and therefore must appear at the end of the sequence.

It was mentioned above that the objective of ergonomic design is to minimise mistakes as well as maximise output. Mistakes in automobile driving often lead to 'accidents' with damage to property, injury to persons and loss of life, so that the minimisation of such mistakes is important. For many years automobiles

were designed purely as machines with emphasis either on mechanical performance (speed, acceleration, braking power, road-holding, shock-absorbing
capability of the suspension) or on minimum cost of production for a given specification. Braking power was easily recognised as a contribution to safety, but so
obvious a factor as visibility was not given priority for a long time. Much more
attention is now being given to safety and true comfort. The aim should be to
construct the driving seat to the same specification as was suggested for the crane-
driver's seat, namely, that it will fit correctly 90% of the people who will have to
use it, and accommodate the rest. In the writer's experience small cars often fail
to meet the specification because the seats are too low, a condition which is imposed by lack of head-room. The result is that the long-legged driver must either

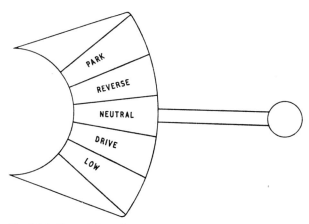

Fig. 14.1. Control lever for automatic transmission (automobile)

set the seat very far back, so that he can stretch his legs straight forward, or sit
on his haunches with his knees up. Another common fault is that the spring on
the accelerator pedal is not powerful enough to support the weight of the driver's
foot, so that for anything less than full throttle he has to keep his ankle muscles
permanently tensed.

One of the most serious contributory causes to accidents is skidding, and it is
technically possible to incorporate in the braking system a device (manufactured
under the trade name 'Maxaret') which prevents the wheels from locking, however violently the driver applies the brakes. This device modifies the interface
between man and machine in the sense of reducing the skill required of the man
by increasing the cybernetic (i.e. feedback and information-handling) complexity
of the machine.

This device is used widely on aircraft brakes, but the cost of an aircraft is so
much higher than that of a popular car that the additional cost of automatic
braking control is trivial on the aircraft. Quite apart from cost, some 'sporting'
drivers might object that by making a car skid-proof one eliminated some of the
driver's exercise of skill and the possibility of using a deliberately induced skid to
effect a rapid change of direction in certain circumstances. One is reminded of a
nineteenth-century French writer's[†] description of the pastimes of the aristocracy
as semi-difficult pursuits, such as managing high-spirited horses and enjoying

† Flaubert in *Madame Bovary.*

275

the company of loose women—in the modern idiom 'fast cars and fast women'; and if either be too docile, half the fun is lost. Most drivers, however, would welcome an anti-skid device just as they have accepted synchro-mesh gear boxes (how many know what a clutch-stop was for?) and are increasingly accepting automatic transmission.

What could be done if price were not a consideration is discussed by Dr. Stephen Black in his book *Man and his Motor Car*.[5]

THE TRANSFER FUNCTION OF THE HUMAN OPERATOR

Using the terminology of process control, one may ask whether a man should be associated with a three-term controller and if so, what are the best ratios of proportional, integral and derivative action. Automobile brakes constitute a 100% proportional system, since the retardation is related (more or less linearly) to the pressure applied to the brake pedal. This is the natural result of direct mechanical/hydraulic operation, and is retained when power-aided (servo) braking is used. The pneumatic brake on a railway train, on the other hand, has an integral mode of operation: a given setting of the driver's valve corresponds to a constant rate of change of pneumatic pressure and the force on the brake block is therefore proportional to the integral of the valve opening with respect to time. With sufficient practice the human operator can become skilled at bringing a vehicle to rest at a desired point with either of these systems. The fact is that in this task the human being is achieving a desired *distance* by varying (negative) *acceleration* so that there is a double integration between action and effect when there is direct control of braking and a triple integration when the control operates on rate of change of acceleration. One would expect the latter mode to be more difficult to operate.

The 'tracking' or 'pursuit' task rose to prominence in gun-aiming problems of the second world war,[6] though by now the behaviour of the human operator in this military task has probably ceased to be important owing to the use of automatic tracking devices. But it has remained an interesting problem, since it allows the behaviour of the human operator to be observed in a situation in which both input and output can be defined quantitatively and one is therefore tempted to seek the transfer function of the human operator, regarding him merely as a 'black box'. In the usual method of investigation a visible marker (pen of a chart recorder[7] or spot on a cathode-ray tube[8]) is subjected to disturbances of a kind chosen by the investigator, and the operator has to perform one of two tasks with the aid of some kind of manual control:

1. In 'following pursuit' the operator endeavours to make a second marker move so as to remain in coincidence with the one controlled by the investigator.
2. In 'compensatory pursuit' the operator endeavours to counter the movement of the marker so as to keep it stationary in spite of the signals injected by the investigator.

Warren *et al.*[8] (who found that following pursuit was easier than compensatory) posed four questions:

1. Is the human operator linear, and if so, under what conditions?

2. Has 'reaction time' any meaning in a seemingly continuous task?
3. What part of the human response is random?
4. Is the human operator continuous or intermittent or sometimes one and sometimes the other?

The general schematic for a compensatory task, as in control of a process plant, is sketched in Fig. 14.2. The plant is subjected to an external disturbance N and the error ε is shown on an indicator which is observed by the human eye. We know that there is a certain amount of image-processing between the retina of the eye and the brain; some complicated information-processing within the brain;

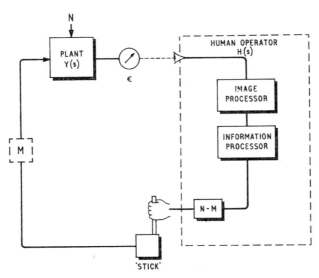

Fig. 14.2. *Compensatory task (control of a process plant). The human operator is regarded as a 'black box' with overall transfer function H(s) between visual input signals and hand movement. The optical image is processed to a considerable extent in the visual cortex; the information contained in the processed visual image is interpreted in other parts of the brain; and the output of this information processing operates via the neuromuscular system to produce movement of the hand*

and some delay, noise etc. in the neuromuscular control N–M between the brain and the movement of the limb. The hand typically moves a lever or 'stick'; and the movements of this provide input to the plant. The plant is assumed to be representable by a transfer function $Y(s)$ and the first question is whether the whole of the human physiological complex between eye and hand can be represented by another function $H(s)$.

Henderson[7] investigated only compensatory pursuit, the task of the operator being to annual the random deflection of the pointer on a recording meter by movement of a handle which controlled the velocity of the pointer; and he used the auto- and cross-correlation functions of error and handle movement to deduce an equivalent transfer function of the human operator in the form:

$$\frac{\dot{H}}{E}(p) = \frac{K(1+pT_1)\exp(-pT_0)}{p^2+2\alpha p+\omega_0^2} \tag{14.1}$$

where $\dot{H}$ = velocity of handle movement
E = magnitude of error
K = gain constant of operator
T_0 = delay between input and output of operator
T_1 = constant relating handle speed to rate of change of error
α, ω_0 = damping, natural frequency of operator.

In one particular experiment the values of the constants were

$$K = 0.27, \qquad T_0 = 0.17 \text{ s}, \qquad T_1 = 4.5, \; \alpha/\omega_0 = 0.75 \quad \text{and} \quad \omega_0 = 15.5 \text{ rad/s}.$$

The form which is now more generally adopted[9] is:

$$H(s) = \frac{K_h e^{-\tau s}(T_L s + 1)}{(T_I s + 1)(T_N s + 1)} \tag{14.2}$$

The term $e^{-\tau s}$ is interpreted as a delay (similar to a reaction time) of between 0.15 and 0.2 s; $1/(T_N s + 1)$ represents the lag in the neuromuscular system; and $(T_L s + 1)/(T_I s + 1)$ is an equaliser, which varies according to circumstances and is the term through which human adaptability operates. In addition, the human operator is a source of noise which is not correlated with the input. This implies answers to all the four questions set out above, except that the conditions under which such a linear formula are valid are: (1) that the signals are statistically stationary and plant function is constant; and (2) that the time interval is sufficiently short that the operator's function is not influenced by learning, fatigue or boredom. (McRuer *et al.*[10] verified the constancy over periods from 2.7 to 12.15 min.) All investigators have found, as might be expected, that learning produces a great improvement in the performance of a tracking task, e.g. a ten-fold reduction in mean square error. The remarkable thing is that the human operator adjusts his response so that in combination with the plant response one has a loop response, which in the neighbourhood of the cross-over frequency approximates to a slope of 6 dB per octave:

$$H(s)\,Y(s) = \frac{\omega_e \, e^{-\tau s}}{s} \tag{14.3}$$

This process of adaption may involve as much as 30 dB change in the gain of the human operator; but his bandwidth cannot exceed one or two Hz. The operator is able to learn a number of different response modes to suit different plant functions, and if the plant is suddenly switched from one mode to another (in one experiment of Elkind and Miller[9] the plant function was switched from $+8/s^2$ to $-16/s^2$, i.e. a reversal of sign of response to a given control movement as well as a doubling of gain) the operator can adjust his transfer function in a few seconds. The experiment on which these conclusions are based employed an approximation to low frequency random noise with a Gaussian distribution. If one uses a simple repetitive signal, such as a sinusoid, the operator relies on prediction of the approaching signal; and the error tends to zero on a continuous sinusoid.[11]

In Fig. 14.2, there is also shown—in dotted lines—a modifying unit M in series with the feedback via the human operator. It would be natural to suppose that one could profitably insert here some network to compensate some of the deficiencies of the human operator; but equation (14.3) says that the brain will introduce into the transfer function $H(s)$ whatever correcting factor may be required to optimise the whole loop. This is why there is so little difference between the performance of the automobile driver using proportional control of brakes and the train driver using a control which has an integrating action, or between equation (14.2) relating general input and output quantities of the human operator and equation (14.1) relating derivative of output position to derivative of error position signal. However, if for any reason a low-pass filter or integrator is to be incorporated in the loop it should be at position M immediately following the human operator so that (1) it does not delay the error signal to which the operator responds and (2) it reduces the random noise at relatively high frequency which is generated by the operator. If the response of the plant is very sluggish, owing to the cascading of several lags, the operator will find difficulty in maintaining close control. The converse of putting an integrator

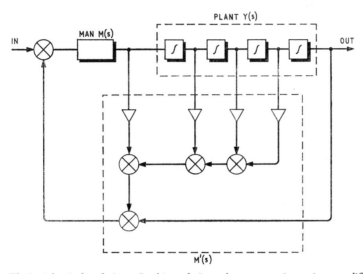

Fig. 14.3. The 'quickening' technique. In this technique the man receives, via a modifier $M'(s)$, a signal which includes derivatives of the output quantity that he has to control

after the human operator is to put a differentiating network in front of him. A technique known as 'quickening' consists of feeding back various derivatives of the output, and if access to intermediate stages of the plant is possible it is preferable to take feedback signals from ahead of their integrations rather than differentiate the fully integrated signal. A scheme proposed by Birmingham and Taylor[12] is shown in Fig. 14.3, and calls for two warnings: first, the behaviour of a multi-feedback system may become dis-organised if any part of the system saturates, and second, the characteristic of the loop will be disturbed if the relative gains of the amplifiers vary. Fortunately, the adaptability of the human operator will go far towards compensating any changes in other parts of the loop.

THE COMMUNICATION RATE OF HUMAN CHANNELS

We have seen that the neuromuscular system $N–M$ in Fig. 14.2 can be approximated by a single lag and that the information processing part of the brain may be approximated by a delay (reaction time) plus a compensating network which is infinitely variable and by learning can be brought close to the shape which will optimise the whole loop. It remains to investigate the performance of the sense organs and their associated channels, for example, the eye and the visual cortex, by which the brain acquires the information which it processes.

It is first necessary to distinguish between steady communication rate and the amount of information which can be absorbed in one flash, since there appears to be a certain amount of buffer storage which can be filled more rapidly than the following parts of the nervous system can handle information. Moreover, the only immediate way to test whether a man has received information is to see whether he acts in accordance with it. His action is limited by the slowest of (a) the information channels, (b) the part of the brain which converts incoming stimuli to instructions to respond, and (c) the physical mechanisms by which the responses are displayed. There is a good deal of evidence, which has been reviewed by Quastler[13] to show that in a single task the maximum rate at which information can flow through this composite channel is of the order of 25 bits/s. The single task in question may be reading aloud a random series of words; sight-reading and playing on the piano a random sequence of notes; or typing a random sequence of characters. Quastler also reports that Licklider used a matrix of squares of which one in each row was blacked out: the task was to record the position of the blacked out square in each row, and the highest information rate observed in this task was 15 bits/s. But Licklider also set up a double task by printing a word across each row and asking the subject to read the word as well as locate the blacked out square. This yielded a maximum rate of 35 bits/s, and it was for this reason that the statement above was qualified by the words 'in a single task'. As an example which may have involved buffer storage, W. S. McCulloch reported[14] the case of a soldier who could take in 100 semaphore signals in a time of 10 seconds and then, given freedom from distraction, could slowly produce the corresponding letters.

An important question in man-machine relations is the amount of time which a man must spend on reading an instrument dial. There is evidence[15] that this time is given by a formula of the type:

$$T = a + b \log n$$

where n is the number of distinguishable readings which the instrument might display. This shows the time as a threshold plus an amount proportional to information content. The threshold a is of the order of one sixth of a second, and the proportional term corresponds to about 5 to 7 bits/s.

A critical example of the acquisition and processing of information by a human operator is the landing of an aircraft by the pilot. It may be that by the time supersonic aircraft are in general use (if that ever happens) automatic landing will be general because the human operator cannot be trusted to cope with the amount of information and accuracy of decision required in the available time. (This would be a change from the view point now prevalent that electronic apparatus has not the reliability to be trusted with such a task.) In the meantime, while the pilot is retained in control for the sake of his reliability and adaptability, there are proposals to integrate much of the essential information (aircraft altitude and position relative to runway) and present it to the pilot in the form in which he can most easily assimilate it. It is claimed that if a pilot has to look away from the windscreen on to the instrument panel the adaptation involved may result in his needing as long as three seconds to obtain instrument information. Therefore in the 'Head-up Display' (or HUD) an image at infinity of the necessary instrument information is projected optically into the pilot's line of sight through the windscreen, by means of a semi-transparent mirror as shown in Fig. 14.4. The 'artificial horizon' line is made to coincide with the real horizon as seen by the pilot, and a diagrammatic representation of the runway is synthesised from instrument information and presented to the pilot in coincidence with his direct view of the real runway. This is achieved by a computer into which is fed information about the distance of the aircraft from the runway, its height and its altitude; and the view presented to the pilot is as sketched in Fig. 14.5. The dot in the centre of the 'flight-path and speed' image is the projec-

Fig. 14.4. Cockpit of a trainer used for HUD flight-simulation tests, showing the semi-reflecting glass between pilot and windshield, on which the guidance image is displayed. (After Snodgrass[16])

tion of the velocity vector of the aircraft, i.e. it is superimposed on the point at which the aircraft would arrive if its direction were unchanged. The short bar at the left of the 'wing' is a velocity marker which moves up or down if the aircraft speed differs in either sense from the correct approach speed. The use of this 'flight director' for combining the information from a number of instruments gives the pilot a simplified display in which he has only to secure the coincidence of various pairs of marks, instead of keeping several variables correct in terms of the numerical readings of a corresponding number of separate instruments. On the other hand it has been pointed out[17] that the brightness of the display will have to be adjustable over a wide range to match external lighting conditions; and there is also the question whether such a display might hold the pilot's attention to the detriment of the scanning of all the other instruments, an action which helps to maintain general vigilance. Moreover, the display is not a repeat of the individual instrument dials but is an indication of aircraft attitude and position which has been deduced from the instrument readings by a computer which organises the CRT pattern. It does not eliminate any error inherent in an instrument (e.g. time lag) and it will be liable to the suspicion (probably unjustified) that a breakdown in the electronics might without warning deprive the pilot of information at a critical moment when there would not be time for him to transfer his attention to the individual instruments. Such flight-director systems were used originally for weapon-aiming in military aircraft. By selection of different combinations of variables to be fed into the computer it is possible to present the pilot with a display appropriate to any one of several flying conditions such as take-off, navigation, landing, terrain following or weapon aiming.

At the present time much attention is being given to the computerisation of air-traffic control, because the traffic density will soon be so great that the flow of information will be greater than could be handled accurately by unaided human operators. It is interesting to note that a study of the information transfer between a single aircraft and an airfield controller has been estimated as a total of 51 bits, made up of 22 bits from pilot to controller and 29 bits from controller to pilot.[18] The investigators at that time reported that traffic density made no difference to this information transfer between *a single aircraft* and the controller. But increased congestion and speed has brought the problem that the controller

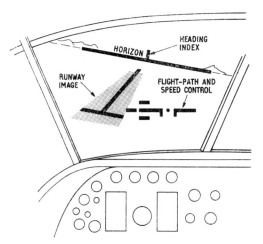

Fig. 14.5. As seen by the pilot, the guidance elements are superimposed on the direct view of the terrain. (In practice, the display would also include an altitude indication). (After Snodgrass[16])

must maintain up to date information about a large number of aircraft; and the limited instruction which he gives to an individual pilot represents decisions which the pilot could not have made for himself without extensive information about all other aircraft in the neighbourhood. Once again the air-traffic control computer is serving as a synthesiser to present the human operator with fairly simple decisions to make on the basis of very complex data.

CONCLUSION

From the examples outlined in this chapter, it would appear that ergonomics is compounded of physiology, neurology and psychology; and the questions that arise are, first whether it is a subject for study in its own right, and secondly how it is related to cybernetics. Taking the narrowest view, one might say that all physical sciences are developments of mathematics and physics, but nobody would doubt that zoology, for example, is a substantial subject in its own right although it uses physics, chemistry and mathematics. Ergonomics is one of the modern subjects (like operational research) which stands at a higher level in the hierarchy of the organisation of knowledge and can be called a *systems* study; its field was defined at the beginning of the chapter. Yet it appears to fall largely within Wiener's definition of cybernetics as the science of control and communication in the animal and the machine. It is true that the basic investigation of energy output of a man does not involve cybernetics; but we were very soon involved in a study of the moving of bricks where the justification for the employment of a man was that he could readily acquire and use the *information* needed to build an orderly stack, and this is certainly a cybernetic concept. All the work on the man-machine interface is within the definition of cybernetics and is an essential part of the 'second industrial revolution'. Like its predecessor the mechanisation revolution, the cybernetic revolution has two main objectives: these are to produce wealth with less human labour than before, and to design man-machine combinations capable of carrying out tasks which could not be performed by man with the aid of the less sophisticated machines of the pre-cybernetic era. Ergonomics has a large contribution to make to both of these developments.

REFERENCES

1. WIENER, N., *The Human Use of Human Beings*, Houghton Mifflin, Boston (1950).
2. MÜLLER, E. A., VETTER, K. and BLUMEL, E., *Ergonomics*, 1, 222, May (1958).
3. AYOUB, M. M. and MANUEL, R. R., 'A Physiological Performance Rating for Repetitive Type Sedentary Work,' *J. ind. Engng.*, 17, 366, July (1966).
4. SELL, R. G., 'The Ergonomic Aspects of the Design of Cranes,' *J. Iron Steel Inst.*, 190, 171, October (1958).
5. BLACK, S., *Man and his Motor Car*, Secker and Warburg, London (1966).
6. TUSTIN, A., 'The Nature of the Operator's Response in Manual Control and its Implications for Controller Design,' *J. Instn elect. Engrs IIA*, 94, 190 (1947).
7. HENDERSON, J. G., 'The Transfer Function of a Human Operator,' *Ergonomics*, 2, No. 3, 274 (1959).
8. WARREN, C. E., FITTS, P. M. and CLARK, J. R., 'An Electronic Apparatus for the Study of the Human Operator in a 1-Dimensional Closed-loop Continuous Pursuit Task,' *Trans. Am. Inst. elect. Engrs II*, 71, 19, January (1952).
9. ELKIND, J. I. and MILLER, D. C., 'On the Process of Adaptation by the Human Controller,' paper 30A given at the *3rd IFAC Congress*, London (1966).
10. MCRUER, D. T., GRAHAM, D., KRENDEL, E. S. and REISENER, W. C., 'System Performance and Operator Stationarity in Manual Control Systems,' paper 30B given at the *3rd IFAC Congress*, London (1966).
11. MAYNE, R., 'Some Engineering Aspects of the Mechanism of Body Control,' *Electl. Engng*, New York, 70, 207, March (1951).
12. BIRMINGHAM, H. P. and TAYLOR, F. V., 'A Design Philosophy for Man-Machine Control Systems,' *Proc. Inst. Radio Engrs*, 42, 1748, December (1954).
13. *Information Theory in Psychology*, Ed. Quastler, H., The Free Press, Illinois (1955).
14. MCCULLOCH, W. S., in *Information Theory, Third London Symposium*, Ed. Cherry, C., Butterworth, London, 371 (1956).
15. BRICKER, P. D., 'Information Measurement and Reaction Time: a Review,' in *Information Theory in Psychology*, Ed. Quastler, H., The Free Press, Illinois (1955).
16. SNODGRASS, R. P., 'Head-up Display—a New Form of Avionics,' *Sperry Engng Rev.*, 10, Fall (1964).
17. KIRKLAND, D. S., 'Electronic Flight Displays—an Airline Pilot's Viewpoint,' *Systems and Communs*, 3, 15, February (1967).
18. FRITZ, L. and GRIER, G. W., 'Pragmatic Communication,' in *Information Theory in Psychology*, Ed. Quastler, H., The Free Press, Illinois (1955).

Chapter 15

Information Storage and Retrieval
(Extending Human Memory and Recall)

NOAH S. PRYWES, M.Sc., Ph.D.
The Moore School of Electrical Engineering,
University of Pennsylvania (U.S.A.)

SUMMARY

Through modern computers, human memory and recall can be extended to vast amounts of information. Man will be able to recall information from large repositories in a manner similar to recalling information from his own memory. The organisation of the information, which is the main topic of this chapter, is central to realising this objective. The chapter reviews basic organisational principles in discussing content analysis, co-ordinate indexing and classification systems. The measuring and evaluation of retrieval effectiveness is discussed in connection with experiments concerned with measurements of recall and precision ratios. The case is then stated for automatic indexing of documents, for large uncontrolled vocabularies with highly specific index terms, for interactive man-machine mode in storage and retrieval, for retrieval through associations and natural hierarchies in the information and most importantly, for automatic classification systems.

INTRODUCTION

Through modern computers, human memory and recall can be extended to vast amounts of information confined normally to the shelves of a library or the drawers of filing cabinets. When this becomes common practice, a human will be able to recall information from large repositories through a terminal in a manner similar to recalling information from his own memory. This, coupled with the capabilities of computers for very fast computation, is bound to have a profound impact on human problem solving and make people effectively much more knowledgeable and prolific.

284

How can this capability for extended human memory be provided? The operation of modern computers has a number of aspects:

1. *On-line* aspects, where an individual can communicate with a central computer through a remote keyboard, visual or audio terminal.
2. *Real time* aspects, where the terminal is monitored continuously by a central computer which makes changes, deletes, analyses content, and retrieves information at speeds matching human thought.
3. *Mass-memory* aspects, by which the computer has a storage capacity of billions of characters with fractional-second access to any information.

The term *information system* has been used to describe a network of computers with related information banks and consoles, all interconnected by communication lines by means of which a user, through a related terminal, provides new information or receives output on demand. Thus the memory of a human problem solver can be augmented with vast amounts of information which, if well organised, can be stored selectively or recalled at speeds matching human thought. That the information be 'well' organised means here that it includes representations of connections which are directly usable for associations, ranking, or inferences among the respective information chunks.

This chapter is devoted to the needs and methods of organisation of information, which is a central issue in information storage and retrieval. Its scope excludes the many other problems inherent in information systems such as user languages, mechanisation of the management of computer resources to assure continuous monitoring of consoles and immediate response, protection of privacy of the information stored within the system, etc.[1-4]

REVIEW OF INFORMATION STORAGE AND RETRIEVAL

An information storage and retrieval system is a 'word-monger.' Text is received, classified, entered in directories, catalogued, and stored away for later retrieval. Words in a retrieval query are 'traded' frequently for many more words which are found to match the query in some algorithmic way. This may be contrasted with another type of system which may be termed a 'concept processor,' in which text would be received and processed to derive the concepts associated with it. The concepts would then be classified and stored away for later retrieval. Concepts in a retrieval query would then be 'traded' for more explicit or profound concepts in the storage. Even though work on concept formation has been conducted since the time of the ancient Greek logicians, and recently received great impetus, we still do not have any evidence of how the 'concept processor' can ever be realised. The approach selected in this chapter was to outline a methodology that is within the state of the art. The 'word-monger' type of system is considered by the writer to be feasible and realisable.

A purely utilitarian approach is advocated here, without considering what is a 'true' organisation of the information. Instead, the sole question should always be *how effective* is the system for retrieval?

The lack of direct concern with the concepts, things, and people behind the words is not important, for to conceive anything is to represent it in symbolic form, which in this context means representation in words. On the other hand, there is the additional problem that things conceived differently are almost sure to be named differently. The system must provide facilities to overcome this problem and the use or choice of words must be un-restricted and regarded as an essential matter of convenience in communications. The alternative zeal in standardising terms has proved over-restrictive.

The methods and procedures employed in information storage and retrieval for centuries,[5] indexing, classification or content analysis, have proved of lasting value and serve as a foundation for the newer systems. These are described to illustrate the principles of organisation of the information. The reader should, however, keep in mind that the computer methods to implement the desired organisation have gone through a very important change because of the development of automated repositories of information that allow direct access to any information. The organisation of information in early automated information storage and retrieval systems is very much influenced by the use of the sequential access magnetic tape storage media which required time consuming serial scan, word by word, of the entire information. It was essential, therefore, that once a scan was performed, it included as extensive a search as possible. This led to systems that were orientated toward systematic text search and content analysis according to extensive categories. Such searches resulted frequently in bulky retrieval output on various alternatives, that an investigator might only potentially want to explore.

With the newer devices (magnetic discs or magnetic strips) direct access to any single portion of the collection is possible for storage or recall without scanning the entire collection. The human can then provide (through a related terminal) associations that are interpreted by the system to identify, retrieve, or change the corresponding information. Furthermore, in an interactive back and forth conversation between the human and a computer, various associations and inferences may be utilised to browse through the information and focus on what is needed for the problem in which the human is engaged.

THE HIERARCHICAL BREAKDOWN OF THE INFORMATION

The description given below of the various components of the *information banks* will facilitate subsequent discussion of the organisation of the information.

An information bank includes a collection of document representations. Each document is an integral entity in the collection. It may be further broken down as shown in Fig. 15.1. The examination and analysis of a document usually proceeds in order, starting from the top of Fig. 15.1. Generally, as one proceeds downwards, greater depth and often greater volume of information is provided. On examination of the information in each box, a decision may be made as to whether the particular document is relevant to a query; and accordingly, examination of other items on the document may be undertaken to acquire greater depth of informations, or, if the information is found not relevant, further inspection of the document may be abandoned altogether. As a greater depth of information is obtained, however, the volume may increase with access to the lower items on the list, which are required less frequently. The more voluminous text parts, therefore, may be stored in slower access, larger capacity storage media.

The upper four boxes in Fig. 15.1 are said to contain *association terms*. These are the words or terms by which a human may identify either one or a whole class of documents, such as title, author, subject, etc. Various relationships among documents may be presented by the association terms. These relationships may include: having an association term in common (such as subject heading or citing the same reference), sequence of events (such as date of publication) and various subordinated, related, or superior ranking (such as documents on the more generic subject, as compared with documents on the more specific sub-subjects).

The lower portion of the document shown in Fig. 15.1 is mostly in text form and may require more complex content analysis, including references to thesauri and syntactic or semantic analysis.

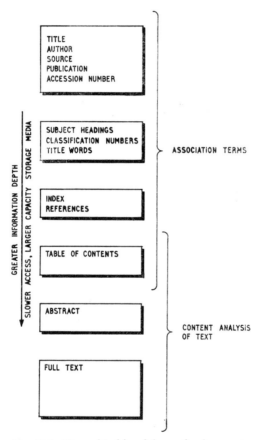

Fig. 15.1. Hierarchical breakdown of a document

The document collection forms only one part of the information banks shown in Fig. 15.2. The other parts contain directories of the document collections, directories of directories, etc., providing a stratified classification system. These directories may be considered to be information about information. The directories may be generated *a posteriori* from the documents themselves. Namely, the association terms (such as terms shown in Fig. 15.1) may be extracted automatically from each document as it enters the collection.[6] The aggregate of the various types of association terms then constitutes an all-inclusive directory or concordance of the association terms.

The terms in the directory may be ordered, for instance, alphabetically or numerically, thereby constituting an elementary classification system of the collection. Even though it is not considered as such, a simple, widely used classification system is one based on date of publication, which divides an entire collection into classes and sub-classes based on the century, decade, year, month, and day of publication. The utility of such a classification system is unquestioned and it is in general use. Other classifications are more limited in scope. For instance, a 'physicist classifier' may divide a collection, first into generic subject areas, choosing physics as a generic subject and then further sub-divide it into the more specific subject areas, for example, mathematical physics. A worker in mathematics may reverse the ranking of these two subjects. The position taken here is that a classification system is a matter of convenience to the user rather than repre-

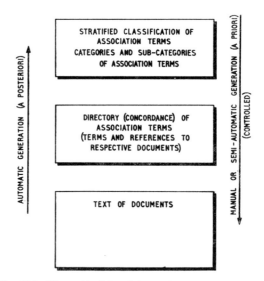

Fig. 15.2. Hierarchical breakdown of an information bank

senting any 'true' or 'natural' ordering of the collection. By establishing *convenience* criteria it is, therefore, possible to generate automatically the classification system that will divide the concordance and the document collection into progressively smaller groups which consist of more closely related terms.

Another approach to classification and indexing is that of applying human judgment *a priori*. An example of the latter approach is the establishment of the Dewey Decimal Classification System which has divided the library collection into progressively more specific classes. Thereafter, professional indexers in libraries assign subject headings (stated in terms of class numbers) from a controlled schedule to the documents as they enter libraries. In time, such a classification system must be expanded and revised by the library community to recognise new areas which were not included in previous schedules. However, re-examination and re-classifying of the documents already in the collection is necessary to assign to them the new subject headings. Alternatively, a rule must be stated to define how the documents in the old classes are to be divided into the new classes.

There has been considerable variance on whether classification and indexing should be performed *a posteriori*, based on the text of the documents, or *a priori*, based on pre-supposed judgment and experience. If we accept the utilitarian approach, empirical evidence to date does not support claims for more effective retrieval with human 'quality' indexing as compared with mechanical *a posteriori* indexing. Also, the manual selection of terms from thesauri has not become easier with *a priori* indexing in spite of the compatibility and standardisation of terms used in different collections.

In Fig. 15.2, the *a priori* and *a posteriori* approaches are illustrated as two opposites. But in practice, a variety of mixes of these two approaches is possible.

The information banks may contain great diversity of information and may serve multiple functions. The structure described above applies generally, even though some components in the breakdown may be missing in certain kinds of documents and different search and content analysis techniques would need to be applied. For instance, in a document retrieval system, the association terms of a document constitute information similar to that on the library catalogue card and usually a search may be restricted to this information. In a question-answering system relating to a file of messages, many association terms may be missing altogether and the search would be based largely on systematic content analysis of the text. Thus, the methodology of information storage and retrieval should be applicable to small or large collections, private or public, dealing with voluminous documents or short statements and messages. The choice is only with regard to order of application of methods selected from an entire spectrum.

CONTENT ANALYSIS

Content analysis, which was developed for magnetic tape serial scan systems, is applicable in the modern environment as well. Among the systems of this type in use are The General Inquirer,[7] SMART[8] and LITE[9] (Legal Information Thru Electronics).

The content analysis of text is illustrated below by the General Inquirer System which is the one most widely used, and has proved the most suitable for many applications. It is available on the IBM 1401–1460, IBM 7040–7090–7094, and the MAC Time-Shared System at the Massachusetts Institute of Technology. This system has been applied in numerous institutions, primarily in the social sciences in fields such as psychology, sociology, history and political science. Though the system has been developed for application as a research tool, it is directly useful for information storage and retrieval.

The SMART System has been developed for studies of the effectiveness of retrieval with initial emphasis on techniques of text content analysis. More recently, emphasis has been on experiments on the effectiveness of storage organisations in search strategies. However, only small collections have been involved in the experiments which have been conducted.

The LITE System has been applied in the specialised area of legal information. The language in the legal information area is claimed, by comparison, to be better standardised and not as vague as general text, so that the more thorough search techniques or highly organised directories are not required for a satisfactory search.

Stone defines content analysis as 'Techniques for making inferences by systematically and objectively identifying specified characteristics within text,' (Reference 7, p. 5).

The General Inquirer process is summarised in Fig. 15.3, where the two inputs are the text to be analysed and the directory which specifies the characteristics within the text which will be identified in the content analysis. The text constitutes the document collection and the directory in a stratified classification which represents the *a priori* human judgment to be applied. The tagging procedure in Fig. 15.3 corresponds then to automatic indexing of documents according to an *a priori*-determined classification schedule. This procedure establishes an indexed and classified repository. It can then be followed effectively by retrieval.

In the General Inquirer, the construction of the classification system is referred to as the application of *categories*. The introduction of categories in this system is motivated by the same considerations as the introduction of a stratified classi-

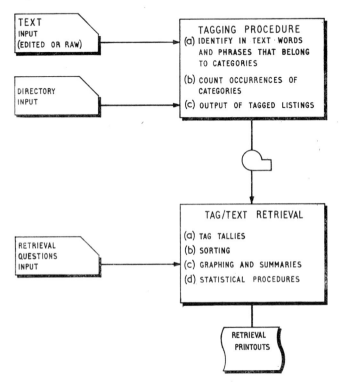

Fig. 15.3. Summary of the General Inquirer process

fication in information storage and retrieval. One reason is that the documents have been authored by many people at different times, and there are many occurrences of use of different words for similar things. Each category may contain various instances of word usage, each word being given in context. A query to the system can then be stated in terms of a category rather than in terms of the exhaustive list of words in context, which would be tedious and would result sometimes in omissions.

The construction of categories or a classification system is a crucial aspect in content analysis as well as in information storage and retrieval for another reason. Indiscriminate input of raw text has been referred to as GIGO—Garbage In Garbage Out, meaning that the raw status of input is retained in the voluminous and useless output of computer search. This, however, disregards the capability of the computer to process large quantities of information with great speed and sift through it, according to extensive algorithms and specified characteristics. Reference to a classification structure permits an easy specification of characteristics that the computer can search, and of the algorithms required for analysis of text. Therefore, whenever the cry of GIGO is heard, it is necessary to examine the situation to find if an adequate structuring has been applied.

The preceding discussion of the General Inquirer illustrates some of the functions of organisation in the information storage and retrieval process.

Content analysis processing, however, is extremely time consuming in terms of preparation of text input and computer use. This approach, therefore, has been applicable only to small volumes of information. How can documents in large libraries he handled? Co-ordinate indexing, discussed below, has been presented as the answer to both large and small volume applications.

CO-ORDINATE INDEXING

The methodology of content analysis described above is frequently impractical to apply, because of the large investment required to convert the text into machine-readable form so that the material can be used as an input to the computer. As long as optical character recognition devices have limited capabilities, the transcription of the document collection into machine-readable form must proceed manually, and this is wholly impractical because of the cost. Input of lengthy text in large public collections or even in small private collections may continue to be prohibitive in cost even when adequate character recognition equipment is developed. The solution then is to divide the document into two parts, store the text on library shelves and input into the computer only the accession number, abstract, and the associative terms shown in Fig. 15.1. Even this, however, may require considerable cost and effort which is frequently unavailable. It is then necessary to reduce further the input information to the basic essentials, such as accession number, title, author, date, publication and descriptive terms. This is essentially the information appearing on library catalogue cards. The assignment of the descriptive terms to documents has, however, posed a major problem to librarians.

Co-ordinate indexing may be illustrated by the 'Peek-A-Boo' technique that made it very easy for individuals and small organisations to maintain and use their own collections. There must be thousands of users applying it to their own private collections, using Peek-A-Boo cards to store the information and having the associated equipment for search of the information in the cards.[10] There is a card for each term, with a hole position on the card for each document in the collection. The respective hole is punched if the term applies. A typical 9 in×9 in card can accommodate 10,000 documents. A search for a conjunction of terms is performed by superimposing (co-ordinating) the term cards and using a light source to locate visually the coincidence of holes. However, as the number of terms and the number of documents increases, the indexing becomes uncontrollable, and the effectiveness of retrieval diminishes.

A controlled vocabulary approach to the problem is based on preparing manually an *a priori authority file* of descriptive terms and then examining manually each document as it enters the collection and assigning to it terms from the authority file. This approach has rejected the traditional classification schedules as being too restrictive in cross referencing, too difficult to modify or make additions to accommodate new terms, and as not being sufficiently expressive to allow indexing in depth in areas of specialisation.

The authority file, also called a *thesaurus*,[†] contains alphabetically ordered listings of terms and possibly listing of words by categories. Additional information is provided with each term. For instance, *scope* notes give meanings, context and areas in which the term is applicable. Other information contained for each term consists of lists of other terms considered to have *broader, narrower,* or *related* relationships, namely are more generic, specific, or synonymous to the listed term.[11]

This approach is based on a number of assumptions which, in the writer's opinion, have not been substantiated. These assumptions include; (1) that manual indexing has a 'quality' superior to algorithmic indexing based on selection of words from the abstract or even from the title; (2) that the vocabulary needs to be controlled and only highly competent persons in a specific area should exercise judgment with regard to adding terms, otherwise confusion will prevail (another example of GIGO); and (3) that standardisation among information storage and retrieval systems is desirable and can be enforced by commonality and control of terms.

To provide 'compatibility' between document collections in the same and related fields, some proponents of this school have claimed that an all-inclusive controlled authority list is required. To this end, committees of the Engineers Joint Council (EJC) were formed from twenty-seven participating member engineering societies, including documentalists and interested people from numerous organisations, for the purpose of merging existing indexing authority lists in the various fields.[12] Almost a hundred thousand terms were considered. This is equivalent to a fairly large English dictionary. The results, containing tens of thousands of terms, were published and even though copies are available in libraries, they have found little general use.

Information from the EJC states:

'It was recognised that the primary usefulness of a published thesaurus is simply as a model or guide for construction of specialised thesauri and as a means of recording sound intellectual decisions for resolving language ambiguities.'[13]

Once this example was set it was followed by many other organisations that prepared 'specialised' thesauri, equally bulky and equally having little general application. In 1966, the EJC joined with the United States Department of Defense under the auspices of Project LEX to provide a larger, even more all-inclusive thesaurus.

Another assumption made was that a prime obstacle to the utility of the thesaurus was the lack of training in its use. To this end some training courses have been instituted by EJC for authors and editors, documentalists and librarians, on the application of indexing using the thesaurus. However, the public authors and editors for whom the courses were intended showed lack of inclination to index the documents using the thesaurus.

In visiting numerous institutions, it became apparent that, although an all-inclusive thesaurus in the field of a specific institution was available, the indexing

---

[†] The word 'thesaurus' is here used incorrectly, as it has the much broader meaning of a repository of knowledge. For instance, it would also cover the concept of an encyclopedia.

staff had invariably chosen to include many additional terms, as many as 50% more than those included originally.[14] Therefore, even where the thesaurus is referenced, the vocabulary varies considerably from one institution to another, and even this aspect of 'compatibility' is not attained.

The complexity of the generic-specific, broader-narrower relationships among terms is such that they are very difficult to use. EURATOM has published a thesaurus showing the relationships in diagram form.[15] However, to obtain a meaningful diagram, the thesaurus had to be divided into a number of unrelated areas which were not cross referenced and the number of relationships had to be reduced greatly.

In the opinion of the writer one of the major shortcomings of the co-ordinate indexing thesaurus such as that of the EJC is the lack of a stratified classification system. This impairs the utility of the thesaurus in an interactive man-computer system where the value of back and forth referencing between levels in the stratified classification has been demonstrated.[16]

SOME CONCLUSIONS

In the foregoing sub-sections some of the conceptions or mis-conceptions have been reviewed with regard to where the line should be drawn between the manual and computer portions in an information storage and retrieval system. There is very little evidence in support of, or against, the hypothesis upon which the various approaches are founded. It is questionable, therefore, to reach any firm conclusions. The little evidence that is available, however, is significant and various implications may be derived from it.

The proof of an information storage and retrieval system is in the retrieval effectiveness. Tests of retrieval effectiveness have been seriously challenged on a variety of grounds, such as use of small collections and query samples, subjectivity of evaluations, and irreproducibility of results.[17] Most of the tests have not been relevant to the question of manual versus automatic indexing. However, there have been two series of tests of retrieval effectiveness of special interest here—the ASLIB Cranfield Project[18, 19] and the SMART System, (reference 8, section 5). The Cranfield Project data have been examined in detail.[20, 21] The SMART experiment has been designed very carefully. The conclusions of these experiments agree qualitatively on the major questions of interest here. Since this is the only evidence available, there is no alternative but to consider it.

Two measures of retrieval effectiveness have received wide acceptance:[20, 21] the *recall ratio*, which is the percent of relevant material retrieved out of the total material relevant to a query in a collection; and the *precision ratio* which is the percent of relevant material retrieved out of the total material retrieved in response to a query.

The Cranfield reports[18, 19] indicate that recall ratio is between 70% and 90% and precision ratio between 8% and 20%. There appears to be an inverse relationship between recall and precision.[8, 18] Cranfield Project reported, for instance, that 1% improvement in precision results in a 3% drop in recall. Thus, only the two measures jointly can reflect the quality of a system. For instance, measuring recall alone is meaningless, for, in an extreme example, if the entire collection was considered to be retrieved the recall would be 100% but the precision would be practically nil. Claims for systems based on recall measurements alone (as in the LITE system[9]) should not be acceptable.

Assigning a larger number of index terms of equal generic nature is reported to improve recall but degrade precision. On the other end, assigning a larger number of more specific index terms would improve precision, but degrade recall.[8, 18]

What are the possible conclusions from these recall and precision measurements?

First, the tests indicate that information storage and retrieval systems are operated at a low, almost unacceptable precision ratio. The human problem solver requiring specific information is overwhelmed with irrelevant information. The precision ratio can be improved as indicated in the tests[8, 18] through the use of a larger vocabulary of a more specific nature. It appears that indexing with a large vocabulary of *specific* index terms, (but not with generic terms) is a requisite for satisfactory retrieval effectiveness. The retrieval effectiveness tests also indicate that grouping the index words into a stratified classification system[8, 18] and using such a stratified vocabulary in an interactive man-machine mode[8] will offset the deterioration in recall due to the use of a larger number of more specific index terms.

One problem with systems having a large vocabulary of index terms is that the vocabulary is unwieldy and the user omits some of the index words which should be included in his query. The application of directories which include synonyms (in context) can overcome some of this difficulty. In a traditional classification system, however, the collection and the corresponding index term vocabulary are divided into groups of related documents and the corresponding index terms. Such groups are progressively broken down and further refined. This provides the user with better recall through a method of search for appropriate index words and documents by scanning those terms contained in groups which are related to an area of a query. In an interactive mode of search, relevant words found in response to one query may be included in subsequent queries, which also improves the total recall in a series of queries.

The major questions here relate to the advantages and disadvantages of the *a priori*, manual, controlled-vocabulary indexing versus that of an *a posteriori*, machine, uncontrolled-vocabulary indexing. The retrieval effectiveness tests do not indicate that *a priori* indexing is superior to *a posteriori* indexing; that, minimal indexer involvement is required with manual indexing, as shown by the tests that indicate no further improvement in retrieval when a trained indexer who is not a specialist in the area of the document spends more than four minutes per document; and that an *a posteriori* indexing system may perform well even where there is lack of term control.[18] There is no conclusive evidence to suggest that either of these two approaches or any combination of them has any advantage over the others.

Other evidence, such as cost, weighs heavily against the manual approach. Also, creative people—potential authors or editors—are reluctant to refer to large controlled vocabulary listings in indexing documents at the source.

Another outstanding question concerns the use of a non-stratified authority file of index terms versus a classification schedule. The latter represents a methodology on which an interactive system may be based.[16] A conventional classification system points to related documents which are grouped together, for instance, on a shelf in a library and easily examined. On the other hand, there has been some doubt about the facility of use of numerical notations as in a conventional classification. The evidence indicates that the difficulties in using numerical notations, as with the Universal Decimal Classification (UDC), do not represent an excessive demand on the effort of the user, and no adverse effect on retrieval effectiveness has been found.

Clearly, it is very important that much more empirical evidence is gathered to answer the above questions more conclusively. But until such information is forthcoming, it appears to this writer that the limited evidence at present available tends to support the following hypotheses. (Because of the many possible combinations of approaches, each of the following hypotheses can be considered separately and independently of the others.)

1. The indexing process should be performed entirely by the computer; it should be based on the *a posteriori* indexing approach with a vocabulary that need not be controlled. Provisions should be made for authorised staff (of libraries) or users (retaining their own copies of a catalogue or collection) to add or delete index terms assigned to the document representation in the file.

2. The vocabulary of index words should be organised in a stratified structure constituting a classification system. This is necessary for two reasons: to provide a methodology for systematic search in voluminous vocabulary lists so that they do not become unwieldy; and to provide the structure for interactive man-machine refinement of queries to pin-point the area of interest of the questioner.

3. The structuring of a classification system should be developed automatically by a computer *a posteriori*, based on the documents in the collection and the association term listings. Provision should be made for authorised staff or users to edit and modify the classification structure.

4. The interactive man-computer search offers the best potential for improving retrieval effectiveness to the point where information storage and retrieval systems become really useful as an extension of human memory and recall.

In view of these conclusions, the remainder of this paper is devoted to the methodology of organisation of information, including in memory the representation of associations and hierarchical relationships which are requisite to the man-machine interactive mode.

MEMORY AND RECALL WITH AN ASSOCIATIVE MEMORY

To extend human memory and recall effectively, the human user should be able to use the information storage and retrieval system in a manner that appears to him both convenient and natural. Use of the system would be facilitated, therefore, if the information in the computer memory was organised to simulate as closely as possible human memory and recall processes as a user understands them. The concept of an *associative memory* and the methods for its realisation in computer memory discussed in this section are intended to describe such a model. The associative memory as envisaged here may be very large and complex; it stores past 'experiences', that can be retrieved later by reference to interconnecting associations. In the context of this chapter, 'experience' is the input of documents only. (In the related field of problem solving, the term has a much broader connotation.) Input information is transferred to the associative memory through the establishment of associations with past experiences. Within the associative memory are chunks of information, lists, and trees in ascending order of complexity. 'Chunks of information' for the purposes of this chapter are *documents*. These documents are interconnected through associations and for each association there is a *list* linking all the documents thus associated. An illustration of the model is given in Fig. 15.4.

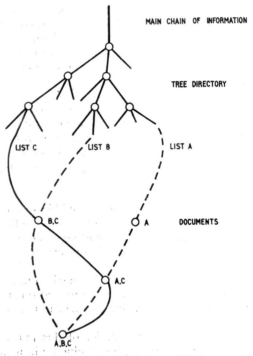

MAIN CHAIN OF INFORMATION

TREE DIRECTORY

LIST C   LIST B   LIST A

B,C   A   DOCUMENTS

A,C

A,B,C

Fig. 15.4. A diagrammatic illustration of the model of an associative memory

In the proposed model the documents in the associative memory are organised into *list* structures. A list can be visualised as a linear string of dots linked together, representing a chain of information; the dots on the lines represent cells storing documents linked in the chain. Information is stored in these cells, each of which has a number of lists branching out or intersecting. Each link represents an associative term and has a corresponding 'name.' The branching lists make up what is known as a *tree* (or network). The word 'tree' describes figuratively the branching out of lists from the main chain of information which make up the paths within the associative memory. Thus, the processes of memory and recall are regarded as establishing and following association links among information chunks.

The growth of information in the memory starts with usage, all kinds of input information being memorised (stored) in the associative memory for further use. The system as a whole thereby 'accumulates knowledge.' The incoming information must be edited automatically and indexed with association terms so that

296

it can be retrieved in response to future queries. The tree directory of association terms is open ended and new terms may be added to it by the input of new documents or by the user. New documents may be added or old documents expanded or contracted.

An integral part of this structure is a language, with a vocabulary which includes all the association terms. The recall or memory processes may be initiated by communicating to the associative memory a *description* of desired information. This is part of a language which communicates problem solving steps. To 'describe' a class of documents, it is necessary to supply the common association terms, as well as relationships between the terms. The procedure in a query is to give the association terms of the lists which link the desired documents, and specify requisite logical or arithmetic relationships among some of the information elements within the documents.

The sharing of the information in a mechanised associative memory is technically one of the most demanding, and intellectually one of the most intricate functions of such a system.[3] Continuous enhancement of this capability must be provided through re-indexing and re-classifying the changing organisation of the total information.[22] These are, however, major subjects that require separate discussion beyond the scope of this chapter.

ORGANISATION OF INFORMATION IN THE MULTILIST SIMULATED ASSOCIATIVE MEMORY

The MULTILIST methodology of simulating an associative memory in the storage of a computer has been developed as an integral part of the Problem Solving Facility, at the University of Pennsylvania.[23] This methodology is reviewed below, with examples of its use.

Part of Fig. 15.4 is shown in more detail in Fig. 15.5 The tree-like directory leads from the main chain of information to the lists that traverse documents. The tree directory consists of nodes, each with branches leading to lower level nodes. The upper parts of the tree are stored in the higher speed storage. The lower level nodes of the directory are in slower memory. The tree directory contains all kinds of association terms, called here *keys*, without reference in the structure itself to the type of associations that they convey. It may, for example, include author names and subject headings, intermixed and arranged in ascending alpha-numeric order. In storage, each node contains a number of keys and the respective associated memory addresses. For instance, at the top of Fig. 15.5, a portion of a node is shown with an author-name key HANSE with an associated memory address 10. Following this link to address 10, there is a node with other keys (FEDER, GAGNE, GREEN and HANSE). The addresses in the latter node in Fig. 15.5 lead to nodes in mass storage. For instance, the link from the key GREEN (address 13) leads to a node containing keys in the range GALAN to GREEN. One of the keys in this range, GORN, is shown to have a link associated with it that leads to a document by the author GORN. The document includes a number of keys, such as for date of publication, authors, and subject headings. For each of these keys, there will be a list traversing the documents. Each key in each document is provided with an address linking it to the next document with the same key, until the end of the list is reached. In the case of retrieval of all documents by GORN, for instance, reference to the top level of the tree in Fig. 15.5 indicates that GORN is alpha-numerically (adjusted to left) in the range

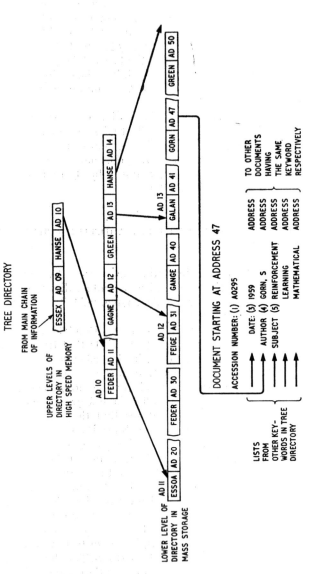

Fig. 15.5. A detailed diagram of part of the tree directory shown in Fig. 15.4, and of a document

of ESSEX to HANSE. Therefore the address 10 (associated with the upper limit HANSE), is accessed as that of the next lower level node to follow. A search of the keywords of this node indicates that GORN is in the range of GAGNE to GREEN, which would lead to address 13 where the keyword GORN is found with the address 47 associated with it. The address 47 then leads to the first record containing information on a document authored by GORN. Following this list, another document by GORN would be found. This retrieval example is further illustrated in Fig. 15.6, showing retrieval of all records with key GORN.

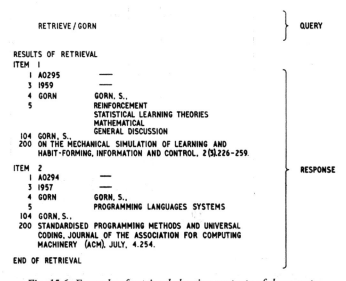

Fig. 15.6. Example of retrieval showing contents of documents

As new documents are introduced into the mass storage they are either added to the top of existing lists (in pushdown fashion) or new keys are added to the tree directory and corresponding new lists are established.[24]

AN EXAMPLE OF RETRIEVAL BASED ON HIERARCHICAL POSITION

There are numerous instances where a query may specify retrieval in terms of a position or a relationship in a hierarchical stratified breakdown of the information. This is an essential memory and recall process which is also facilitated by the MULTILIST method. This is illustrated below by an example of a collection of papers in physics, and retrieval from such a collection by position in a hierarchical structure of references or citations.[25]

The physics articles collection has been indexed automatically with title words. Each title word or subject heading has been entered as a key in the directory with a corresponding list, as described above. The references given in each publication are also included in the corresponding document entries. These references also serve as keys and there is a list corresponding to each one of the references. Each article is represented by a rectangle as in Fig. 15.7 with the corresponding Journal, Volume, and Page Code (JVP_k). The references in each document are identified by a similarly derived code preceded by the letter 'C' ($CJVP_j$). At the

KEYS IN DIRECTORY

CITATIONS   PUBLICATION

CJVP₀   CJVPᵢ   CJVP₄   CJVP₅   CJVP₆   JVPᵢ   JVP₂   JVP₃   JVP₄   JVP₅   JVP₆   JVP₇

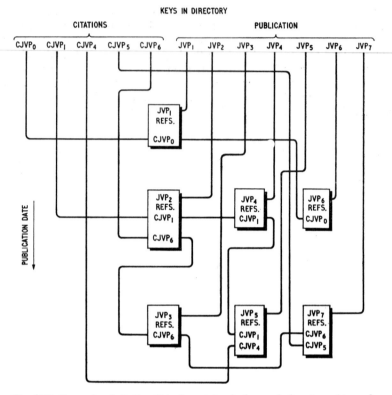

Fig. 15.7. Example of citation lists for retrieval of records forming a hierarchy

top of Fig. 15.7 are shown the article identification and reference keys in the terminal level of the tree directory. The connecting lines show the lists threaded through the documents. This organisation of the information is used to denote the hierarchy of documents which are 'predecessors' or 'successors.'

Two programs, RETHI and RETLO, provide retrieval based on a position of a document in an hierarchical structure. The function of RETHI and RETLO is to retrieve all the documents which are placed higher or lower, respectively, in the hierarchy than the records specified in the operand. For instance, in Fig. 15.7 the query:

RETHI/JVP₇/E (reference)

will retrieve all documents which are referenced in the JVP₇ document (considered higher in herarchy); namely: JVP₅ as well as those referenced by JVP₅, i.e. JVP₄, JVP₁ and JVP₀ which is referenced by JVP₁; JVP₆ as well as those referenced by JVP₆, i.e. JVP₀. The query:

[RETLO/JVP₁/E (reference)

can retrieve all the documents citing JVP₁ (through following the CJVP₁ list) and all their successors (lower in hierarchy) consisting of JVP₂, JVP₄, JVP₅ and JVP₇. This retrieval by hierarchy can be output on a graphic display console in diagram form as illustrated in Fig. 15.8.

300

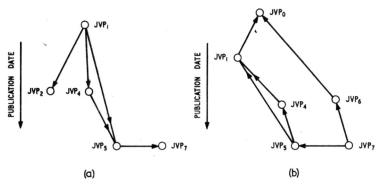

Fig. 15.8. Diagrams for retrieval by position in hierarchy (a) Retrieval of document lower in hierarchy than JVP_1 (citing directly and indirectly) (b) Retrieval of documents higher in hierarchy than JVP_7 (referenced directly or indirectly)

AUTOMATIC CLASSIFICATION SYSTEMS

Several references have been made in this chapter to the necessity for and importance of an automatically prepared classification system for improving recall and precision in an interactive man-computer environment. Below is a discussion of what a classification system is, how it works, and how it can be prepared automatically.

The basic definition of classification systems has survived the development of modern computers. Quoting Margaret Mann:

> 'Classification is, in simplest statement, the putting together of like things, or, more fully described, it is the arranging of things according to likeness or unlikeness.'[26]

A classification system has a dual purpose: it is a methodology for classifying a document entering a collection, namely placing it (on a shelf or in a memory cell) with 'like' documents; it is also a retrieval method, by which one may be guided to the group of 'like' documents that deal with one's area of interest. In conventional classifications the criterion of 'likeness' for grouping documents together is the common concept with which the respective documents deal. As a concept becomes broader it includes a number of narrower concepts. The broader-concept group can then be broken down into several narrower-concept groups. Thus, the idea of a classification system is also that of a tree as illustrated in Fig. 15.9. Each node in the tree corresponds to a concept, and a group of corresponding documents which are 'like' in the sense of the concept. The branches from each node show the breakdown of the group into sub-groups. Fig. 15.9 also shows how the nodes can be named systematically by attaching numerical notations to each node. A notational system using decimal numerals is called a *decimal* classification system. The terminal nodes in the classification tree, as shown in Fig. 15.9 are actually the cells in memory or shelves in a library where the documents are located.

Searchers for 'true' or 'natural' breakdown of information would not heed Melvil Dewey's warning of 1878:

301

'Long study of the subject makes it clear that a classification satisfactory in theory is in the nature of things an impossibility, and a scheme can be satisfactory in use only to those who realise those inherent difficulties and are satisfied because of their knowledge that a plan free from annoying difficulties is wholly unattainable.'[27]

In this respect an automatically generated classification system differs greatly from the conventional classification systems. It does not even have a theory of breakdown of information by concept; its only criteria is to be 'satisfactory in use.' Like conventional classifications, an automatic classification system may be used to put documents away, but *only after* it is made up from the documents.

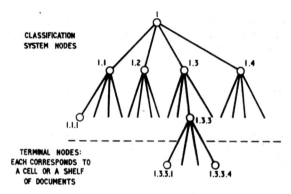

CLASSIFICATION
SYSTEM NODES

1.1 1.2 1.3 1.4

1.1.1 1.3.3

TERMINAL NODES:
EACH CORRESPONDS TO
A CELL OR A SHELF
OF DOCUMENTS

1.3.3.1 1.3.3.4

Fig. 15.9. The tree as an illustration of a classification

That is, it does not precede the documents, but follows them. However, like a conventional classification, an automatic classification also constitutes a retrieval and search methodology. As outlined earlier, there is a two-step process. In the first stage, the documents are automatically subject-indexed, resulting in a vocabulary of index terms. In the second step, the vocabulary of index terms is structured into a classification system. An automatic classification is represented by the same type of tree structure as shown in Fig. 15.9. The difference is that the nodes in the tree no longer correspond to concepts, but instead correspond to groups of index terms.

The methodology of search and retrieval using such an automatic classification, consists of selecting a path in the tree from the apex to a terminal node by selecting index terms from the nodes along the path. This is further illustrated below.

Since an automatic classification is derived from the documents themselves, accomodating changes due to new documents or new index terms can be performed automatically as well. This is an advantage over the *a priori* conceived conventional library classification where changes require considerable manual effort.

USE OF AN AUTOMATIC CLASSIFICATION SYSTEM

It is important to reiterate here that the primary object of the automatic classification is to overcome the reduction in recall ratio due to a large, uncontrolled vocabulary of highly specific index terms (as shown on pp. 289–91).

302

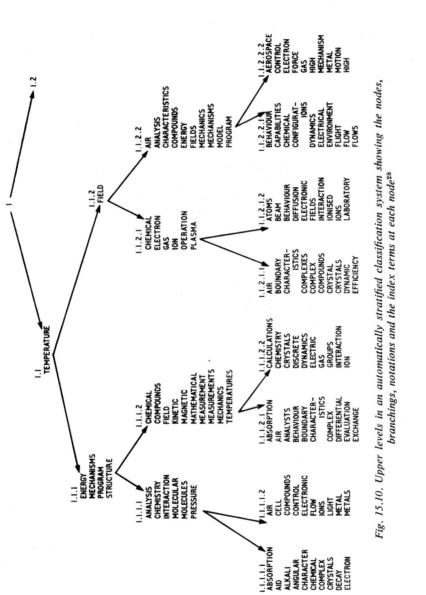

Fig. 15.10. Upper levels in an automatically stratified classification system showing the nodes, branchings, notations and the index terms at each node[28]

The automatic classification system provides a method of searching for index terms in the 'like' groups of terms associated with nodes in the classification tree or in the documents associated with terminal nodes of the tree. A user can, for instance, proceed from the apex of the tree, selecting a path consisting of nodes from which he selects some index terms; he rejects paths consisting of nodes in which the index terms are inappropriate. Eventually, a query consisting of the conjunction of index terms selected may be submitted. The user can then examine the retrieved documents as well as other related documents in the same or 'adjacent' cells. This may suggest some new index terms and the process repeats itself until the desired information is found.

An illustration of this process may be found in the work of Lefkovitz and Angell,[28] and Fig. 15.10 shows the upper levels of a classification system which Lefkovitz and Angell generated automatically from documents in a collection. The classification system stratifies a 6,000 index term vocabulary derived automatically from 4,000 documents. An 8 level classification tree was produced in which two branches emanated from each node. Only a portion of the top 4 levels is shown in Fig. 15.10. Next to each node is shown the notation of the node and the index terms associated with the node. This is one form of computer display that can be shown to a user upon demand.

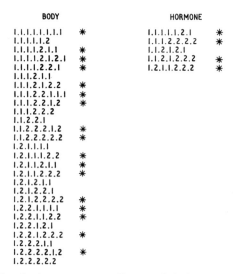

Fig. 15.11. *Listings of nodes in an automatically stratified classification system for the nodes BODY and HORMONE*[28]

It is of special interest to note that the index terms associated with the nodes close to the apex of the classification tree are those that appear *most frequently* in the collection. This is unlike the conventional classifications, where the nodes close to the apex are associated with broad concepts independent of frequency of occurrence. For instance, in Fig. 15.10 the terms temperature, field, energy, etc., are associated with the nodes close to the apex. This means that these terms, which have a very high frequency of occurrence in the documents would, if used, result in retrieval of a large number of documents. These terms may still be considered 'generic' or 'broad' but in a different sense. The 'breadth' refers to the number of documents rather than to a concept. The use of these index terms in a query retrieves a larger group of documents. This is another example of setting criteria for a classification based on being 'satisfactory in use' and not 'in theory.' A user is wise to continue to follow a path in the tree to the outer branches and select terms near the apex only in conjunction with other terms at lower nodes. The lesser frequency of the latter terms results in better precision without downgrading recall.

The user may refer to the information in the automatic classification system and this may be presented in varying formats. One possible format, shown in Fig. 15.11 consists of node listings for selected index terms. The listings in Fig. 15.11 give all the nodes in the classification tree in which the index terms BODY and HORMONES appear. Based on the notations of the nodes in the listing it is easy to find (by computer or manually) the paths in the classification tree in which both index terms, BODY and HORMONE, are included. Documents including the conjunction of these two index terms will be in the terminal cells *only*. There are two such paths from the apex node which terminate at nodes 1.1.1.1.1.2.1 and 1.1.1.2.2.2.2 respectively. A search in the corresponding cells reveals documents which have the index term BODY or the index term HORMONE as well as some documents which have the conjunction of these two terms. However, a search in the classification tree along the two paths or in the document cells indicates that more specific terms such as BRAIN, CEREBRAL, etc., which are less frequent and which identify specific parts or functions of the body may result in a more selective retrieval. A similar search procedure may follow, using index terms specifying the parts of BODY which are of interest to the user.

AUTOMATIC PREPARATION OF A CLASSIFICATION SYSTEM

The scope of this paper does not permit a description of the processes for creating automatically a classification system.[8, 22, 28-33] It should be noted, however, that in selecting a process the following factors should be considered. It is desirable that a human be able to modify a classification system. Therefore, he must be able to apprehend the changes required in the index terms assigned to documents resulting from the change in the classification. Should the reverse be true, if index terms are added or deleted from documents, the user must be able to understand the impact on the classification. Therefore, the processes which employ statistical techniques[29, 32, 33] or place weights on associations between documents[8, 30, 31] are at a disadvantage in this respect, as compared with those employing only co-occurrence[22, 28, 30] of index term considerations. The relationship between indexing of documents and a classification based on co-occurrence of index terms is far simpler and can also be displayed simply by the computer in the form of graphs. The following remarks are confined only to the latter approach, which is believed to be readily comprehensible to a user.

Graphs and graph theory have proved to be applicable to the study of automatic classification. Fig. 15.12 illustrates the automatic classification process by showing an example consisting of a vocabulary of 13 index terms. In Fig. 15.12, the 13 index terms are represented by nodes, each identified by a corresponding number (from 1 to 13, which may be considered abbreviations of English language index words). Whenever two index terms co-occur in any one of the documents in the collection, a 'branch' line is drawn between the nodes of the

corresponding index terms. Thus the graph of Fig. 15.12 shows all the co-occurrence relations between index terms in the small collection used for this illustration. (A coincidence matrix is another way of representing the co-occurrences.) In
this example, the entire vocabulary of index terms is partitioned into two groups,
thus creating a node (having notation 1) with two branches (leading to node
1.1 and 1.2). The classification tree will offer best selectivity between the two
nodes if the two groups are as distinct one from another as possible. This crite-

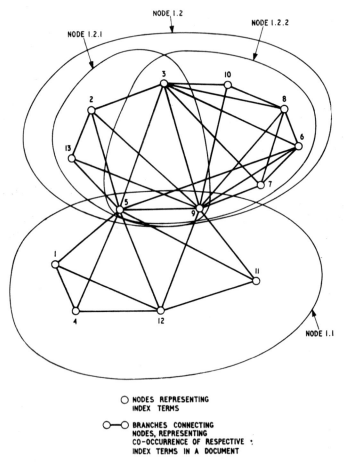

O NODES REPRESENTING
INDEX TERMS

O—O BRANCHES CONNECTING
NODES, REPRESENTING
CO-OCCURRENCE OF RESPECTIVE :
INDEX TERMS IN A DOCUMENT

Fig. 15.12. A graph showing partition of a vocabulary of thirteen index terms into groups to
stratify automatically a classification system

rion may also be stated by the rule that the two groups should have the smallest
number of index terms in common, i.e. have the least possible 'overlap.' The
partition of the group of index terms into two groups requires, of course, sever-
ing some of the branches. Terms assigned to any one document should all also
belong to at least one of the groups. In this way, the document is said to belong
to the group to which its terms belong. The index terms assigned to one document obviously co-occur with all the others. Thus in a diagram they form a *com-*
plete sub-graph where each node is connected to all the other nodes. Examples of

complete sub-graphs are a triangle, or a rectangle with all the diagonals, where the vertices are the nodes, and the sides and diagonals are the branches. In order to retain all the relationships in the collection, the partitioning should be done in such a manner that each complete sub-graph is retained unbroken in at least one of the groups. (The reader may want to verify this rule for himself.) This also means that groups in which each index term co-occurs with all other terms cannot be partitioned further. The largest of such groups are called *maximally complete*

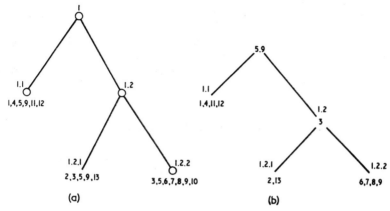

Fig. 15.13. *The tree resulting from applying a classification process to the data in Fig. 15.12 (a) Tree of Fig. 15.12 with node notations. (b) Tree of (a) showing high frequency terms common to both sub-groups at a higher level node*

graphs and a computer program has been written to find them.[34] It is also advantageous for the two groups to be approximately equal in number of index terms. The algorithm[22] divides the vocabulary of index terms into the two groups identified in Fig. 15.12 as nodes 1.1 and node 1.2. A further breakdown of node 1.2 into nodes 1.2.1 and 1.2.2 is also shown and further illustrated by a corresponding tree structure in Fig. 15.13.

CONCLUSION

The information storage and retrieval system emerges as consisting of a repository of information, which is rich in relationships and associations, and an extensive library of algorithms for memorising—through automatic processing of new information, and for recall—through search and retrieval.

The utilitarian approach which is based on computer processing of 'words' and symbols rather than concepts has been shown to be capable of retaining a wealth of relationships of many kinds for many uses. Equally important, however, there is also the community of users who enrich the repository directly, through adding associations influencing the classifications, and indirectly, by adding to the library of algorithms to create new organisations or search procedures.

The function of the human, however, is restricted to only influencing and guiding the work of the computer. He cannot possibly undertake the tremendous routine portions of the processing. Routine indexing and structuring of classifications are examples of tasks which should be in the exclusive territory of the computer. The human can effect them only through specifying the rules or the exceptions.

There is the other, altogether different, area of devices and communications which has been barely touched upon in this chapter. Engineers have applied great inventiveness to produce economically feasible approaches for automatically handling documents, storing and retrieving them, and to represent information—text, association terms and directories—by electrical phenomena, transmitting the information to distant places and communicating with the human sensors.

The extending of human memory will obviously have a major impact on our understanding of problem solving, on simulating human problem solving[35] and on our being able to have, eventually, very effective man-machine relationships in problem solving.[36]

ACKNOWLEDGEMENTS

This paper is based on research supported by Contract NOnr 551(40) from the Information Systems Branch, Office of Naval Research and from Rome Air Development Center.

REFERENCES

1. OVERHAGE, C. F. J., 'Plans for Project Intrex', *Science*, **152**, 1032, May 20 (1966).
2. FANO, R. M. and CORBATO, F. J., 'Time Sharing on Computers', *Scient. Am.*, **215**, 122, September (1966).
3. HSIAO, D. and PRYWES, N. S., 'A System to Manage an Information System', *Proc. FID/ IFIP Conf. 1967 on Mechanised Information Storage, Retrieval and Dissemination*, June (1967).
4. RUBINOFF, M. (Ed.), *Toward a National Information System*, Spartan and McMillan, Washington (1965).
5. SAYERS, W. C. B., *A Manual of Classification for Librarians and Bibliographers* (2nd ed.), Grafton, London (1944).
6. STEVENS, M. E., *Automatic Indexing: A State of the Art Report*, National Bureau of Standards Monograph 91 (1965).
7. STONE, P. S. *et al.*, *The General Inquirer: A Computer Approach to Content Analysis*, M.I.T. Press (1966).
8. SALTON, G., *Information Storage and Retrieval*, Scientific Report No. ISR-11, Dept. Computer Science, Cornell University, June (1966).
9. 'LITE Legal Information Thru Electronics', *United States Air Force Law Review, Special Issue JAG*, **8**, No. 6, Nov–Dec (1966).
10. *Nonconventional Scientific and Technical Information Systems in Current Use*, National Science Foundation, No. 4, Chapter 3, December (1966).
11. BOURNE, C. P., *Methods of Information Handling*, John Wiley, 27 (1963).
12. *Thesaurus of Engineering Terms: A List of Engineering Terms and their Relationships for Use in Vocabulary Control in Indexing and Retrieving Engineering Information*, Engineers Joint Council, New York, May (1964).
13. SPEIGHT, F. and COTTRELL, N. E., *The Engineering Information Program 1966–67*, Engineers Joint Council, 5, February (1967).
14. RUBINOFF, M., (Private communication), Moore School of Electrical Engineering, University of Pennsylvania.
15. *EURATOM Thesaurus EUR 500e, Volumes 1 and 2*, Press Académique Europeennes, (2nd ed.), Brussels, Part 1 (1966) and Part 2 (1967).

16. FREEMAN, R. R. and ATHERTON, P., 'File Organisation and Search Strategy Using UDC in Mechanised Reference Retrieval Systems', *Proc. FID/IFIP Conf. on Mechanised Information Storage, Retrieval and Dissemination*, Rome, June (1967).

17. BOURNE, C. P., 'Evaluation of Indexing Systems', in *Annual Review of Information Science and Technology*, Ed. Cuadra, C. A., John Wiley (1966).

18. CLEVERDON, C. *et al.*, *Factors Determining the Performance of Indexing Systems, Volume 1, Design, Part 1, Text*, ASLIB Cranfield Research Project (1966).

19. CLEVERDON, C. W., *Report on Testing and Analysis of an Investigation into the Comparative Efficiency of Indexing Systems*, ASLIB Cranfield Project, October (1962).

20. SWANSON, D. R., 'The Evidence Underlying the Cranfield Results', *Libr. Quart.*, **35**, 1 (1965).

21. SWANSON, D. R., 'On Indexing Depth and Retrieval Effectiveness', *Proc. 2nd Cong. on Information System Sciences*, Eds. Spiegel, J. and Walker, D., Spartan and McMillan, Washington (1965).

22. PRYWES, N. S., 'Browsing in an Automated Library Through Remote Access', in *Computer Augmentation of Human Reasoning*, Eds. Sass, M. A. and Wilkinson, W. D., Proceedings of a Seminar, June 1964, Spartan and McMillan, Washington (1965).

23. PRYWES, N. S., 'Man-computer Problem Solving with MULTILIST,' *Proc. Instn Elec. Electron. Engrs*, **54**, 1788, December (1966).

24. LANDAUER, W. I., 'The Balanced Tree and its Utilisation in Information Retrieval', *Trans. Instn Elec. Electron. Engrs*, (Electronic Computers), 863, December (1963).

25. A collection of physics articles prepared by a project at the Massachusetts Institute of Technology under the direction of Kessler, M. The experiments are described by GABRINI, P., *Automatic Introduction of Information into a Remote Access System: A Physics Library Catalog.*' Thesis, Moore School of Electrical Engineering; Report No. 67–09, University of Pennsylvania, December (1966).

26. MANN, M., *Introduction to Cataloguing and the Classification of Books*, American Library Association 1930, 41 (1943).

27. DEWEY, M., 'The Amherst Classification', *Libr. J.*, **3**, 231, August (1878).

28. LEFKOVITZ, D. and ANGELL, T., *Experiments in Automatic Classification*, Report No. 85–104–6, Computer Command and Control Company, December (1966).

29. BORKO, H., 'Research in Automatic Generation of Classification Systems', *Proc. Spring Joint Computer Conference*, 529 (1964).

30. NEEDHAM, R. M., *Automatic Classification in Linguistics*, Rand Corporation Report No. AD 644 961, December (1966).

31. NEEDHAM, R. M., 'A Method for Using Computer in Information Classification', *Proc. IFIPS Congress*, August (1962).

32. WILLIAMS, J. H. JR., 'A Discriminate Method for Automatically Classifying Documents', *Proc. Fall Joint Computer Conference* (1963).

33. BAKER, F. B., 'Information Retrieval Based upon Latent Class Analysis', *J. Ass. Comput. Mach.*, **9**, 512, October (1962).

34. WOLFBERG, M. S., *Determination of Maximally Complete Graphs*, Moore School Report No. 65–27, University of Pennsylvania, May (1965).

35. NEWELL, A. and ERNST, G., 'The Search for Generality', *Proc. IFIP Congress, May, 1965*, Spartan and McMillan, Washington (1965).

36. PRYWES, N. S., 'Associative Memory in Heuristic Problem Solving for Man-machine Decisions', in *The Psychology of Management Decision*, Ed. Fisk, G., CWK GLEERUP (1967).

PART 5

CYBERNETICS AND SOCIETY

'Why does this magnificent applied science which saves work and makes life easier bring us so little happiness? The simple answer runs: Because we have not yet learned to make sensible use of it.'

Albert Einstein, *Address*, California Institute of Technology, February (1931)

Chapter 16

Management Cybernetics

A. CRAWFORD, B.Sc., Ph.D.
Marketing Director, IPC Magazines Ltd. (U.K.)

SUMMARY

Management cybernetics is concerned with complex self-organising systems which are interconnected probabilistically both internally and with the external world. The subject has not progressed very far and its content is confined mainly to problem area description rather than knowledge accumulated from problem solutions. The present scope of the subject appears to be:

1. The analysis of structure
2. Assessment of system performance including its betterment
3. The study of goal selecting mechanisms.

In this chapter, these areas are described followed by a brief assessment of the probable future impact of modern digital computors on the organisation of business enterprises.

INTRODUCTION

Management is the profession of control. Cybernetics is the science of control. In each case the control is of exceedingly complex, highly probabilistic, self-regulatory systems. From these propositions the conclusion is inescapable. Backed up by a scientific discipline and its body of knowledge, the artisan could become a technologist—structures could be planned in advance and errors and mistakes minimised by the application of theory. But this does not, of course, happen unless the practitioner comes into contact with the scientist or his discoveries.

Very few managers have ever come into contact with cybernetics or cyberneticians. Yet one aspect at least has entered everyday management consciousness. *Feedback* is a term that is now used casually and naturally by many managers,

313

and one rarely finds it necessary to explain the term, even in management training seminars. Accountants write that part of their function is to provide the 'feedback' and indeed there are scarcely any writers on management topics in the the 1960's who do not use the term in some context. *Management by objectives,* born of the notion of a command input and goal seeking performance, receives the ready assent of the sophisticates in most large corporations and it is actually practised in many.

Yet one cannot say that management cybernetics has 'arrived'. Most managers or accountants, or even computer experts would be appalled at the thought that cybernetics is the science they are applying in their several spheres. Very few would realise the essential operating characteristics of the sub-system because of the feedback they refer to. Information flow and problems of communication are worried about everywhere, yet how infrequently is cybernetic knowledge applied in solving them. Thousands of firms use computers, very few firms (as distinct from computer departments) have learned how to.

One searches almost in vain for the industrial expert describing himself as a cybernetician. The foremost exception in the U.K. is Stafford Beer. So much of the development of the management cybernetics has occurred in and because of his work, that inevitably this chapter owes more to him than to any other person.[1]

THE SCOPE OF MANAGEMENT CYBERNETICS

Most of this chapter is concerned with business management. There is no *a priori* reason for limiting the scope of the subject to business firms, management cybernetics is relevant to everything from tax collection to gardening (both of which are concerned with signal-to-noise regulation) and the government of a nation to the one man retail business (both of which are concerned with pursuit and adaptation). The reason for restricting this chapter to business management is that the author is not familiar with work done in these areas, and the problems of management of a business enterprise appear to encompass all aspects.

The business, or any other complex human system, is an organism whose boundaries are rather ill defined at any particular moment. The supplier of raw materials cannot be described as outside the business; contrast this with a consumer who at the moment of viewing an advertisement is inside the system but can be regarded as outside the business. The connections to the parent system are in both cases probabilistic; the probabilities are usually both positive but otherwise of quite different size.

The unique feature of an organisation containing people as elements, such as a business, is that these elements are probably organisationally more complex than the parent system (the business). In principle, this means possibly that the reasons for having more than one individual in the system should be looked at very closely. The reasons which do appear to stand up to this scrutiny are:

1. One individual does not have the capacity to deal with the rate of change of the events in the environment.
2. He may not 'know' the system or the equations linking the principal variables in the business and the environment.
3. He may not be sufficiently reliable, particularly since other aspects of his life will intrude.

4. The members of a management group bring to it a wider experience of possibilities than one man, and it has been demonstrated that such a group can do very much better than one man, however well trained he may be, in solving a complex 'black box' problem.

The possibility exists that a computer-centred organisation may someday provide sufficient mechanical extension for a single person to do the job. As things are, the organisational memory is vested in separate individuals and the overlap between individual memories is at best haphazard. Even if they all have the same experience, humans will remember different aspects or weight them differently in the act of recalling. Personal sub-goals are manifest and in the majority, some of these accord with the departmental sub-goals which themselves converge to the organisational goal only for short periods of time. Conflict and organisational inefficiency are endemic to the orthodox structure of management organisations. Production, for instance, minimises its costs with a minimum product range and steady level of manufacture, whilst sales maximises its own performance when both of these are most variable. The optimum cost-revenue position for any of the functions taken separately is far from that required for the overall optimum.

To summarise, management cybernetics is concerned with a complex, self organising system which is interconnected probabilistically both internally and with the external world. The organism is required to adapt to changes in its environment and to maximise those changes which are to its advantage. It is composed of complex elements and supplied through them with a diffuse memory system, probably arranged so as to maximise the sub-goals rather than the overall goal. At the present time many of these types of organism are attempting to make use of (absorb) a mechanical extension (the digital computer) and this is tending to highlight the problems of structure and function both as a whole and with respect to each of the elements. As a result the present scope of management cybernetics appears to be:

1. The analysis of structure, including the identification of sub-systems.
2. The assessment of systems performance including its betterment.
3. The study of goal selecting mechanisms.

There is no taxonomy or detailed sub-structure of research within each of these areas and the following sections, which contain illustrations of the sort of thinking relevant to each area, are not meant to be exhaustive.

THE ANALYSIS OF STRUCTURE

There are two essential aspects to the analysis of structure:

1. The building bricks or elements of 'operation' of the business.
2. The interconnections between the elements.

It is extremely difficult to generalise about the elements except at low levels of the organisation. For instance, there is no point in attempting a complete model of the human who may be the element or form part of several elements, since only part of a human is ever involved in such an element. Technically we are dealing with a multi-stable system defined by the requirements of the subsystem function and by the human capacity to play the required role.[2] In manual tasks, the human may serve as a primary servomotor; he may play the part of a sorting mechanism as in some management tasks, or he may be merely part of a transformation element, as in copy typing or the transformation of a sales order into an invoice.

In the traditional analysis these elements appear as labelled boxes. The labelling may be by mathematical equation (transfer function) or by verbal description of the transformation. Such an element is often referred to as a *black box* which in this case means a collection of detail which we cannot or do not wish to evaluate separately. For preference, the black box should encompass detail for which the transfer function is single valued or statistically stable. If the element contains one or more humans this is not often possible.

The first level of structural complexity or organisation occurs when the element in some sense controls itself by monitoring its operation against an external goal. Feedback is, of course, necessary for this control to be exerted. If the simple transformation unit, defined as $X(s)$, has a negative feedback loop and a differencing device at its input the relation between response and input changes from:

$$R(s) = X(s) \cdot I(s)$$

to:

$$R(s) = \frac{X(s)}{1 + X(s)} \cdot I(s)$$

This simplest model of a goal directed organisation is probably the basic element of a business organisation and it serves to emphasise the arbitrariness of describing the elements of the organisation separately from the structure or the goals.

The sorting unit can also have feedback. In this case the various sorted outputs are compared with standards to ensure that the 'decisions' are consistent. To obtain a description of a more complex and versatile organisation, numbers of transformation units and storing units are interconnected but, almost by definition, one can expect that there will be conflict of goals. The creation of an ultrastable system involving internal adaptation of the previously separate systems is not predictable in its outcome except in certain over-simplified cases. But in the assembly of the units on the analysts' drawing boards, no hint of the homeostatic behaviour or the outcome is likely to be found.

For this and other reasons we have recently developed an alternative element, described as an operation. It is signified by a circle in which only a date and a time lag are entered. Three inputs are required to every operation: the operand, the operator and the operative. These can be illustrated as shown in Table 16.1.

Table 16.1. THE NOTATION OF AN 'OPERATION'

Operation	Making a box	Computing
Operand	Wood plus nails	Data
Operator	Instruction what and when	Program
Operative	Man plus hammer	Computer

There are two results: the effective outcome and the ineffective outcome or the waste.

Sussams[3] has used the notation as in Fig. 16.1. This unit is a ternary 'and-gate'. The inputs can be the outcome of a previous operation and both types of outcome can be inputs of any type to other operations. The notation is variable in scale and can refer to a whole business, which would be represented as in Table 16.2, or it can refer to the act of signalling that an event has occurred

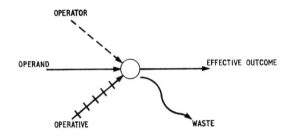

Fig. 16.1. Simplified diagram of an 'operation'

Table 16.2. THE NOTATION APPLIED TO A WHOLE BUSINESS

Operand	Working capital
Operator	Apply a conversion at a rate greater than the cost of capital
Operative	Assets
Effective Outcome	Profit

(e.g. the box is now made). Descriptions of what travels down the arrows are required. In the case of 'operator' it may be a mathematical equation or a logical statement or an instruction carrying time information (e.g. when). The particular value of this notation is that it emphasises the time cycles of the system and permits them to be examined. It emphasises the existence of the goal of the operation (via the operator) and implies the existence of a meta operation in which information about the effective outcome is compared with the operator according to meta rules. It also isolates the state of the 'machinery' (the operative) in this cycle from its states in previous cycles. Thus, it describes non-stationary, non-linear systems as easily as others. (It is beyond the scope of this chapter to extend this description further.) A description of part of a business is given by means of this notation in Fig. 16.2 for the production sales and marketing system. (Lack of space precludes inclusion of descriptions of the central control, the accounting system, the engineering and supplying control system, the personnel services control system and the management services control system which are also necessary for a complete business description.)

The terms used to describe what we know of the structure or pattern of inter-connections of a system are *flow, relationship, transaction* or simply *connection*.

The system definition (i.e. its boundaries) is itself completely arbitrary. This is because any system so defined will always fit into a larger one. It is not only desirable, but absolutely necessary to define the boundaries of the system to be

studied and to know the implications of that definition. The steps in the definition of an organisation have been described by Beer[4] as follows:

1. Identify an assemblage by its coherence and obtrusive relationships
2. Describe its pattern in the assemblage of the relationships
3. Define its goal or purpose.

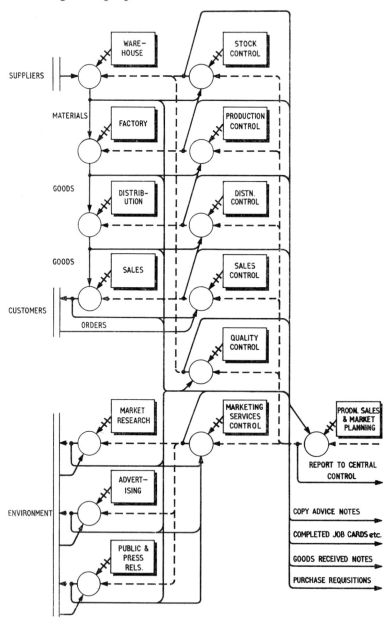

Fig. 16.2. Production, sales and marketing system as represented by the 'operation' notation

The last step is vital. It is not satisfactory simply to equate the organisation with its communication network. The network sets the limits to the organisation but there has to be a goal or purpose. We can talk conveniently of a system defined by the network of communication elements and an organisation within this as defined by its goal. The more goals, the more organisations—which may or may not overlap. In the extreme case of overlap, where the same elements within the same network of interconnections are behaving differently because of a reversible change of goal, this definition becomes a matter of convenience.

ASSESSING SYSTEM PERFORMANCE

Cybernetics meets the manager through the experts in industry who are concerned with the efficiency of the business operations, namely, computer experts (including O & M), operational research scientists and sometimes behavioural scientists. Operational research is perhaps the principal medium. This is not necessarily because the O.R. discipline is the most suitable, though it could be, but because within its ranks are able individuals who tend to be stimulated by the concepts of cybernetics. In principle the scope of their work is identical with that of management cybernetics and the willingness, training and ability to cope with the complexity and sensitivity of real life situations is essential to the operational research activity.

OPERATIONAL RESEARCH

The attempt to view an enterprise objectively and scientifically leads to an unwillingness by O.R. practitioners to accept the problems exposed by managers at face value, since: (1) the problems are most frequently in the wrong terms, having been described by an 'inside-man'; (2) quite often the problems are verbal reflections of self-justifying systems—in these cases, management think they are acting in response to outside influences when they are in fact reacting to the effect of their own or their colleagues responses to another situation; (3) the greatest tendency is for managers to try to isolate the area of their present decision from their past and future activities and indeed some training in decision making is to this end.

The O.R. scientist is likely to act in the same way as a cybernetician in that he refuses to be delineated by the particular section of the organisation which throws up a problem. At this point, however, the O.R. practitioners divide. On the one hand there are those who have met cybernetics (or have virtually re-invented it); these are most likely to look for their models amongst biological systems. On the other hand, are the larger number who expect to apply the models of mathematical statistics and make assumptions as to the stability of the uncontrolled variables and perhaps of the linearity of the system. These assumptions are frequently valid when applied to the logistic aspects of the enterprise, e.g. raw materials intake, productive processes, distribution and sales effort. They are almost certainly invalid when applied to the control, i.e. management processes.

Working on the logistic level of the enterprise (that of first line management) O.R. has been very successful. Not surprisingly, therefore, many O.R. practitioners have withdrawn from the full breadth of the problem area into the detailed development of that part of the technology which lies in the mathematical-statistical area. As a result, some of them have made major contributions. The area they have withdrawn from is the cybernetic component of O.R. This can be illustrated with reference to a formal statement of the performance of a system (after Ackoff and Rivett[5]) which can be phrased as follows.

A system's overall performance (P) is equated to some functional relationship (f) between a set of controllable aspects of the system (C_i) and a set of uncontrollable (by the system) aspects (U_j). That is:

$$P = f(C_i, U_j)$$

Mathematical statistics will produce a model of U_j and find values for C_i to maximise $f(C_i, U_j)$. Provided that U_j really is stationary and that the functional relationship of U_j and C_i remains constant, this is satisfactory. Yet it ignores the presence in the system of managers, at middle and senior level whose function is often to set C_i according to the difference between the performance P and their own targets. Once this 'meta system' is admitted into the model the assumptions become invalid. One is constantly surprised that the challenge to mathematics set by this change of model is so rarely taken up.

In many systems the situation is more complicated since the performance (P) is measured by the response of the environment (i.e. a subset of U_j). To get over these difficulties the model (computer program) is usually re-run at intervals taking into account new values of U_j and resetting C_j. Now the values of U_j are the result of the previous 'decisions' about C_i and this is not only likely to produce an unstable system but often invalidates most of the assumptions necessary in creating the statistical model of U_j. Sales and advertising activity aimed at targets based on forecasts derived from previous sales is a common example.

Cybernetic studies have indicated that there is a minimum complexity necessary for survival in a changing world. The danger of O.R. models and control systems is that they are deliberately low in complexity, yet management cybernetics presents no alternative methodology and it cannot predict the workings of systems controlled by adaptive meta systems. Together with mathematical statistics, cybernetics is one of the two principal bases of operational research but its application must await some further developments in management cybernetics.

INDUSTRIAL DYNAMICS

The O.R. scientist is concerned to specify the data and its desirable transformations during its passage through the management network so that action is indicated and taken. Because of its complexity, he tends to ignore the true 'shape' of the management network and its actual transformation of the data as a direct result of, for instance, the effects of time delays introduced by indecision. The manager with the decision problem is not usually aware of the precise effect of the period of his delay or of the force of his action on the total operating characteristics of the business. Industrial dynamics has provided a method of analysis of the enterprise based on the analogy of system components with the performance of component groups in an electrical or electronic circuit. The first and only representative of this class of analysis, which is in the mainstream of the early cybernetics based on the servo-analogy, has been given by J. W. Forrester.[6] The subject is still in its infancy, yet it is too complicated to do more in this chapter than give a general introduction.

Industrial dynamics is the study of the information feedback characteristics of industrial activity, to show how organisational structure, amplification (in policies) and time delays (in decisions and actions) interact to influence the success of the enterprise. It examines the interactions between flows of information, money, orders, materials, personnel and capital equipment in a company, an industry or a nation's economy. Essentially, it is concerned with the inefficiencies in the actions of the firm as information of change in the environment spreads through and effects the whole firm. The most usual case is change in the demand pattern (sales) and the following discussion will be limited to this aspect.

It is possible to identify non-linear elements in any machine or collection of machines and this is particularly true of the logistic part of a business—production upper limits, warehouse capacity and so on are pointed to by Forrester. There are a number of sources of time delay in information transmission in the form of decision lags, pipe lines, and the averaging or smoothing of data. These will create distortion and given the presence of amplifying elements (inventories and re-ordering) plus internal cyclical patterns of activity (annual holidays, monthly board meetings etc.), there is a strong tendency for businesses and even whole industries to be frequency resonant. The effect is that a small perturbation in sales, possible in the form of a step or ramp change, will last in the system in the form of oscillations for a very long time, possibly for tens of months, and do very great damage to the profitability.

The warehouse or inventory is a particularly interesting element since it acts as a low-pass amplifier. The effect becomes serious when there are several in cascade. This is not at all uncommon. For instance, we usually have the retailers (who collectively form a huge inventory), the wholesalers, the finished goods store, the work in progress inventory and the raw materials store.

As an example, take three stages of inventory, say, the retailers collectively, the wholesalers collectively and the finished goods warehouse. The demand comes from customers to the retailers, and let us imagine that it has been steady for all previous weeks at 100% and that in week 2 it rises to 110% and thereafter remains steady. Let us also imagine that the replenishment order takes one week to arrive and that each of the three stages orders sufficient to bring their stocks up to one week's usage at the rate of demand prevailing at the time of the order.

From Table 16.3 it will be seen that the step change is filtered and the fluctuations are amplified by each stage. To respond to the orders from the finished goods warehouse the factory would have had to run three shifts plus extra help in week 4 and lay off all staff in week 5. If the work in progress and the raw materials stores were also added to the cascade, it is easy to see that under almost any conditions of change in demand at retailers, and with the most carefully arranged re-ordering policies, the raw material supplier would find it very difficult indeed to service this manufacturer. The process is complicated by the quite reasonable re-ordering policy but worse effects can easily be envisaged. The use of a short term forecasting technique based on the trends in orders at each stage would do this by 'overshooting'.

All inventories are designed to accommodate small fluctuations in demand and to pass large ones which persist. In life, the consumer sales pattern contains fluctuations at most frequencies. The faster ones will be filtered by the retailer stocks. Wholesaler stocks will further attenuate the higher frequencies leaving the slower ones which can appear to be seasonal variations by the time they reach the manufacturer.

The recurring problem of matching the production rate to the rate of final

Table 16.3. AN EXAMPLE OF THREE INVENTORIES IN CASCADE

(The figures are percentages)

Week	Retailers				Wholesalers				Finished Goods Store			
	Out	*In*	*Bal.*	*On order from wholesalers*	*Out*	*In*	*Bal.*	*On order from finished goods store*	*Out*	*In*	*Bal.*	*On order from production*
1	100	100	100	100	100	100	100	100	100	100	100	100
2	110	100	90	130	100	100	100	100	100	100	100	100
3	110	130	110	110	130	100	70	190	100	100	100	100
4	110	110	110	110	110	190	150	70	190	100	10	370
5	110	110	110	110	110	70	110	110	70	370	310	Nil
6	110	110	110	110	110	110	110	110	110	Nil	200	20
7	110	110	110	110	110	110	110	110	110	20	110	110

consumer sales is the central core of many business anxieties, and this is partly because of the most striking characteristic of complex systems—they are very frequency selective. When the retail sales are basically random variations from a steady level, over-production is often a result of this frequency selectivity. To oscillate, such a system must amplify. So, the characteristics of the amplifying mechanisms amongst the elements of the system have to be determined.

Orders for goods or materials, etc., between successive stages in the process have three components, two of which can be amplifiers:

1. Orders to replace goods do not amplify.
2. Orders to adjust inventories up or down as the level of business activity changes do amplify. It is common practice for retailers and many others to build up and decrease inventories as the sales level rises and falls, as in the example given above. This is inherent in carrying inventory equal to a specified number of weeks of sales. Because current sales rate fluctuates from day to day, the data must be averaged in some way in order to have figures on which ordering and inventory plans can be based. The 'noisier' the data the longer must be the averaging time, and hence the bigger the delay and therefore the bigger the order when it is placed. In addition, retailers would not respond immediately to the full extent of any difference between the actual and any 'desirable' level of inventory.
3. Orders to fill the suppliers' pipeline. The level of orders in the pipeline is proportional to the average level of sales, and serves therefore as a variable delay. Amplification is caused when there is a 'proper' functional relationship to the cause of variation, e.g. if the firm advertises when sales are expected to rise.

Distributors exhibit the same behaviour as retailers on the orders from retailers already containing amplification, thus increasing the effect further. Upper limits of production rates add another non-linearity. If factory capacity is limited, delays to orders are increased and distributors will increase their order rate when this happens. Distributor inventories rise sharply when the factory becomes able to meet orders once again. This causes a further suppression of orders from the distributor to the factory as he tries to bring his inventory into line with the apparent slight sales slump.

It may be that factory inventory can be designed or made to avoid adding a further stage of amplification, but it seems very doubtful, largely because the production departments have to pay attention to the times when the storage space is nearly full or empty. The situation from this point of view is made worse by the techniques of forecasting (beloved of modern management) in two ways:

1. Many sales forecasting methods tend to accelerate the inventory reactions to changes in sales levels and hence make the operation of the system less stable. This is because inventory and pipeline corrections are concentrated at the peak or trough (i.e. they overshoot).
2. Forecasting procedures can introduce further amplification by being part of a sub-system. If the past pattern of sales is the basis of a forecast, and if this forecast leads to actions that can affect future sales, we have a closed-loop information feedback system and hence the potential for amplification of certain frequencies. If the effective past data entering into a forecast are shorter than one period of fluctuation of actual demand, then the forecast will amplify the actual fluctuations.

Truly annual influences of even minor magnitude can serve to synchronise these system fluctuations to the calender, e.g. reduced ordering on production during the vacation season, annual budgeting, management policies adopted in response to the seasonal pattern, etc. These synchronising influences, including the monthly board meeting, are supplemented by phase changers in the system. As well as being potentially a low-pass amplifier, an inventory is a time delay as are pipelines and management decisions.

The manager is in the position of trying to filter out and ignore fluctuations introduced by other decision makers (in the business or the environment) while at the same time trying to detect as soon as possible any enduring changes to which he wants to respond. This is smoothing. It occurs to some extent at all decision making points. In turn these same decisions contribute their source of noise to the rates being controlled. The most obvious method is averaging, the most frequent is wait and see!

Averaging can be formal and based on policy, but full and immediate action is rarely taken on a change of information; so smoothing is also based on judgement, indecisiveness and procrastination. One is caught in the dilemma between more smoothing to reduce meaningless noise, and less to reduce the time delay in extracting the meaningful information. It is necessary to filter out noise, but smoothing introduces delays and changes the sensitivity of the system to different periodicities.

One of the values of industrial dynamics is that it demonstrates that production volumes have a propensity to oscillate unnecessarily and that alarming results can occur. For example, the phase changers and frequency sensitive amplifiers have resulted in labour being laid off just when there are shortages of the product at the customer end of the chain. The brick industry has been mentioned in this connection and some have commented on the periodicity of the British economy in much the same terms. Identification of the system dynamics is important because the computer can be used either accidentally or otherwise to reduce these problems, or more easily, to aggravate them.

Forrester[6] provides a method for the identification of the probable pattern of response to change in the environment, e.g. of demand, etc. His high level language 'Dynamo' allows such systems to be simulated using a digital computer. This development, though incomplete in the sense that it does not define easily the ways of avoiding or mitigating the problem, is one of the most important lines of development in management cybernetics.

THE STUDY OF GOAL SELECTING MECHANISMS

When business organisations are set up or changed, managers are 'put in charge' of the several functions and usually told of the organisation's objectives. They are rarely told their own objectives in precise terms and each manager may be asked to suggest a job brief and budget for himself. It rarely follows that the actual set of objectives chosen are compatible. Given the goals selected: (1) some departments will be independent of one another for their success or failure; (2) one department may be most successful when another one succeeds, i.e. there will be an extra payoff by co-operating; and (3) other departments will have chosen mutually exclusive (conflicting) goals, one of which can only be achieved if the other is not.

There is usually some notion that the chief executive will rationalise the goals before agreeing them. No doubt attempts are made but success is elusive and most times illusiory. The reasons are three-fold. First, some departments will always be in conflict unless they work to a joint goal and are essentially merged into a single organisation. These are the adjacent departments in the logistic stream of the business, e.g. purchasing, production, distribution and sales. It is precisely because any one of these stages in the logistic sequence can benefit at the cost of those on either side, that the creation of an overall goal is necessary. Secondly, the chief executive is prevented, perhaps because of work load and certainly by being part of the system, from analysing the overall optimum performance of the enterprise which would enable him to identify the exact departmental sub-goals which converge to this optimum. Yet it is only on his behalf that such an analysis could be made. (This defines the organisational position of the management cybernetician as being a staff planner on behalf of the chief executive.) Thirdly, personal sub-goals of the individual managers become identified with the success of their own operations. It leads them to the attempt to maximise their departmental performance. This might be satisfactory if there were not several indices and measures of performance, most of which are oversimplified and many of which will not converge to the organisational optimum. It is also to be noted that the pyramidal heirarchy of most organisations leads to personal goals which include taking over the job of the immediate superior or his equivalent. Unless the enterprise is expanding at a high rate, people have to leave or abrogate personal ambition and this leads to the question of how to retain the most able. Perhaps the answer lies by including in the definition of 'able' the willingness and capacity to work to the organisational optimum rather than to personal sub-goals.

STRUCTURAL CONFLICT

The internecine warfare at top management level is found everywhere. It probably occupies as much time as any other feature of senior management activity and is testament to the prevalence of the conflict of goals. The arms, as it were, are perpetually trying to lop off one another and the head. It would be simple minded in the extreme to identify this activity entirely as the cross of personal ambition. The chief executive is unlikely for the reasons given above to be able or even willing to risk trying to optimise the enterprise's performance by rationalising the sub-goals before agreeing them. Also, because of the complexity of the elements and their interconnections, we would expect a homeostatic machine to develop in which the circuits and goals are changing constantly in an attempt to locate a point of equilibrium. Regrettably, time lags and latencies will be very different in different parts of the circuitry and as a result, sub-stable states will be formed in some faster moving areas against the present state of the slower changing elements, only to be upset by subsequent change in the latter. This is the nature of politics, and alignments and realignments of the contenders indicate stages in these adjustments. Structural conflict is thus endemic to large organisations and we define it as occurring when the objectives (expected outcomes or goals) are related to the extent that if one is obtained the other is not. Most departmental and other goals are only partially conflicting and are partly co-operative. Both must be achieved to some extent for either to succeed, but only one can be maximised and this at the expense of the other. There will also be elements of the goals which are independent and these usually permit the necessary partial successes on which the conflict depends.

Evidence is given in a recent review of research into small group behaviour. Raven and Euchus[7] conclude that for situations in which the group members' actions do not affect each others performance, competition is likely to produce better results than co-operation, but if the members actions are interdependent, co-operation is likely to be more effective. Thus where there is independence of outcome the existance of a meta criterion or meta goal is desirable, whilst on the other hand if each members' performance depends on what the others do and if they now complete for reward (a meta criterion), one member can and will try to gain advantage by obstructing the other. The structure of the organisation creates this behaviour. Only if it is clear that they cannot gain an advantage in the long run do they eventually resort to co-operative behaviour.[8]

The question of how to reward interacting members of an organisation rests on the question as to how their performances should be measured. Measures of performance are frequently set up which become meta goals and which then deprive the organisation as a whole of its effectiveness, even if the sub-units (members) do their best. In fact, it is very difficult to avoid designing inefficiency and conflict into the structure of an organisation. The humans become caught as the elements of a homeostatic machine in a perpetual state of search for equilibrium. Changes of personnel, their attitudes to each other or the communications between them cannot remove the conflict or its source. Because of the complexity of the human elements they can and do identify themselves with a position or sub-state in the organisational conflict and personal battles ensue often with the demise of one of the elements. He may leave the organisation or become ill due to the personal stress.

Ackoff[9] has provided a formal basis for the analysis of structural inefficiency but little has been done on its practical application, particularly amongst those actually concerned with these problems. This group includes the advisers special-ising in management development as well as the operational research scientists.

AUTOMATIC GOAL CHANGING

If an organisation has several alternative actions prepared, together with the rules for selecting amongst them when external conditions change, it can control its effectiveness better than by using the simple feedback system. Such a system requires a 'second order' feedback or meta system and implies that a reserve or 'memory' of possible alternatives exists within the organisation. The problems outlined above under the heading of Structural Conflict are related to the attempt to change goals. We cannot be satisfied with an organisation just because there is no conflict at any given period. A change in the environment can lead to the need for selecting new goals and the conflict will reappear if the sub-units have selected goals which are no longer in equilibrium. It is a feature of management organisations that the memory of planned alternatives (which is often only 'experience') or the rules for selecting them differ between sub-units. This is where an autocratic structure gains. It can provide a central control of the separ-ate goal changing units. By avoiding internal conflict it will obviously minimise the likelihood of an imaginative choice of goals. The ultimate in automatic goal changing is the automatic telephone exchange.[6] The immediate goal is to search for and find a specific number dialled by a subscriber. The exchange must be prepared to receive different numbers and take different courses of action for each one. This is a system which can be said to specialise in changing its goals quickly. Other mechanisms, often with fewer possible goals, engage in much more activity to achieve a goal before the environment (input) changes in such a way as to require the next change of goal. The human engaged in a manual skill is one of these.

If an organisation can control itself, particularly if it can change its goals, it is called autonomous. If it does not involve any biological elements its name be-comes automaton. The autonomy lies in its memory and ability to recall. The better the memory and faster the recall, the more autonomous the organisation is likely to be.

The process of information storage and retrieval which allows the organisa-tion to prepare various alternatives for action is, of course, the process of learn-ing. This may be thought of in the manner suggested by Campbell[10] as 'Blind Variation and Selective Survival of the Variants'. Starting from the time when the organisation was first switched on, set up or born, learning of this type will be initially trial and error, but later will become classificatory and so on. Increase of the memory reserves generally requires a greater complexity of interconnec-tions. Learning may result in a reconfiguration of the organisation's communica-tion network, i.e. of its structure. Thus the sort of questions which the manage-ment cybernetician should ask must include the following (after Have[11]):

1. How do the control processes change with time?
2. How do the inner channels of communication develop, maintain themselves and fall into disuse?
3. Where is the memory of the organisation located, what kind of information is put into it and in what manner is it stored?

4. What is the content of the memory, how does the content change and what kind of information is taken out?
5. How does the organisation forget?
6. Is it learning anything now?
7. What can it predict from its memory?

The existence of a system memory also means that certain messages have greater priority of transmission into and out of the memory. Similarly with courses of action, their priorities for application in different situations will vary. We need to know about these priorities (or values) to understand the action of the system. The memory systems of automatic telephone exchanges are wired in and there is no learning—though there is no good reason why not. When ten telephone calls are received at the exchange at the same instant it must decide which to answer first. If a business or a person has multiple goals and these have not been ranked for priority or are mutually contradictory, then we have the 'mentally ill' or erratic organisation. The cure is to re-structure the memory to eliminate inputs that produce conflicting cases or by a direct attack on the goal evaluation process of the system.

The process of evaluation of goals requires a second order meta system. (The issues of goal choice were outlined in the section on Structural Conflict). The facility for recombination from memory which provides the goals for evaluation gives greater versatility and autonomy to the organisation. If the recombinations from memory can be examined in the light of classifications from previous experience with similar or different combinations, then a small proportion can be selected from the many possible for later trial and further combination. This is the action of a reflective goal changing organisation. It will reflect on the contents of the memory for the purposes of formulating new courses of action. Under the control of this mechanism, information intake and learning can be selective to that which is relevant to survival or to other major goals. Courses of action can be initiated or terminated based on the incoming information. The mechanism can investigate network conditions in the organisation, search the memory and so on.

Thus, the organisation with a 'consciousness' can direct its own growth and practice innovation. In an industrial firm, the actions (or inactions) of the departmental heads are the second order meta system. Unfortunately the organisational memory is vested in separate individuals and the overlap between individual memories is at best haphazard. Personal sub-goals are manifest and in the majority, since there are several per individual. The structural conflict may very well be eliminated if the memory were made adequate and the accessories for recall, recombination and selection were made efficient. The digital computer may be able to satisfy this need and the final section of this chapter is a discussion of the manner in which this might be accomplished.

THE COMPUTER IN BUSINESSES

Wiener[12] wrote:

'...... any use of a human being in which less is demanded of him and less is attributed to him than his full stature is a degradation and waste. It is a degradation to a human being to chain him to an oar and use him as a source of power; but it is an almost equal degradation to assign him a purely repetitive task in a factory which demands less than a millionth of his brain capacity'.

In 1969, not only is the human degraded, but the computer is too. Firms have purchased these machines without much idea as to their uses. To be sure the question was asked 'How can I use the computer in my enterprise?' but as Beer[13] has pointed out, the question is silly. A better question, he says, would be 'what should my enterprise be like, now that computers exist?' The new question encompasses the power of the modern computer both for calculations and for changing the whole basis of the organisation. It is, for instance, obvious in this context that the organisational memory would be more efficiently held by the computer. With adequate recall facilities the arguments about what really happened 'last time' or last year, etc., disappear. The organisational model which will allow the correct choice and testing of sub-goals can also be held and tested in the computer. Thus, the computer becomes an integral part of the service supplied by top management to the business. Sad to say, the computer has been little used by those at this level.

There have been several attempts by Beer to answer his own question[1,4,14] and recently Crawford[15] has put forward a suggestion which encompasses Beer's descriptions and describes the sort of business organisation which would be built up around modern computer technology, rather than trying to hang the computer on the edge of an independently planned organisation.

The developments in computer technology which have created the possibility of using it as the nervous system of the business are:

1. The multi-access facilities and input-output terminals remote from the computer. The GPO system of data lines means that 'remote' can be hundreds of miles if necessary.
2. Development of CRT (television tube) terminals with which the computer can display graphs, numerical data in tabular form plus comments and instruction in 'clear' language, e.g. English.
3. Development of the light pen and the touch sensitive wire[16] for input from management registering choice, instruction and modification.
4. Development of the multi-programming mode of operation in which each terminal appears to the user to be connected to a computer entirely dedicated to his requirements.
5. The trickle-percolate memory system in which rarely used items are successively 'written' away in the less accessible, but more economic parts of the memory storage system. This is in the true meaning a forgetting system, and permits the continuous use of a system without filling up the available immediate access storage and perhaps over-writing valuable data.

The principal outcome of designing a business around the computing system is to divide the organisation into three types:

1. The sensing departments, which are there to know about and react to changes in the environment. It is possible to recognise five areas of the outside world which the business must react to and these are listed in Table 16.4, together with the respective departments concerned. These five departments are critical for, if the environment changes significantly in any

Table 16.4. AREAS OF THE OUTSIDE WORLD THAT AFFECT A BUSINESS AND THE DEPARTMENTS WHICH ARE CONCERNED WITH THEM

Environment	Departmental title
The money market: including competition for capital with other firms in the same group of companies	Finance
The labour market: including the state of training of the potential recruits	Personnel
The consumer market: including the relevant national economic matters	Marketing
The raw materials market: including alternatives	Purchasing
The technical know-how market: including equipment	R & D (including Engineering)

one area without the organisation detecting it, the firm can be left with a shortage or a surplus and lose profits and perhaps even get out of control. Each of these departments should act independently of the others, though there should be cross connections between them. As well as serving as a sensing department collecting data of its part of the environment, each would have the task of digesting the data, of working (with the aid of the computer) a many-one transformation into various forms of index, and finally, by this act of perception, of pointing out the size and relevance of any changes.

2. The operational (effector) division. This will encompass the traditional production, warehousing, sales, etc., activities, described previously as the logistic functions.

3. The planning and goal changing sections of the business. This collection of departments will tend to view the business as a whole and relate it to knowledge and information about the environment and policy decisions by the board. The main differences between the departments in this group is the time requirements for their conclusions. The management committee will deal with problems requiring immediate solution to keep the operation efficient. The planners will be concerned with how the enterprise should change to meet the overall goals set by the board. The board will decide new long term goals in the light of other information of environmental change and operational success.

In all the functions, the computer would act as the nerve network, which in itself will transform the information it carries to suit the needs of each particular part of the enterprise. The human will be left finally to choose the overall goal, control the systems operation and serve as the point of contact with the outside world. The greatest change to be expected is that as they get used to the system, managers will spend less and less of their effort in 'running the business', i.e. taking decisions and making sure they are implemented, and more and more time dealing with the question of why it runs the way it does and how it should change. Management cybernetics will in this case be required as the scientific basis to the profession of management.

REFERENCES

1. BEER, S., *Decision and Control*, John Wiley, London (1966).
2. ASHBY, W. R., *Design for a Brain*, Chapman and Hall, London, 2nd ed. (1960).
3. SUSSAMS, J. E., 'A New Approach to Business Systems Analysis,' paper given at the Operational Research Society Annual Conference, 1967, *Opl Res. Q.* (In press)
4. BEER, S., *Cybernetics and Management*, English Universities Press, London (1959).
5. ACKOFF, R. L. and RIVETT, P., *Managers Guide to Operational Research*, John Wiley, London (1963).
6. FORRESTER, J. W., *Industrial Dynamics*, M.I.T. Press, Cambridge, Mass. (1962).
7. RAVEN, B. H. and EUCHUS, H. T., 'Co-operations and Competition in Means Interdependent Trials,' *J. Abnorm. Psychol.*, **67**, 307 (1961).
8. RAPOPORT, A., 'Laboratory Studies of Conflict and Co-operation,' in *Operational Research in the Social Sciences*, Ed. Lawrence, J. R., Tavistock Publications, London (1966).
9. ACKOFF, R. L., in *Operational Research in the Social Sciences*, Ed. Lawrence, J. R., Tavistock Publications, London (1966).
10. CAMPBELL, D. T., 'Blind Variation and Selective Survival,' in *Self-Organising Systems*, Eds. Yovits, M. C. and Cameron, S., Pergamon Press, London (1960).
11. HARE, VAN C., in *Introduction to Operational Research*, Eds. Churchman, L. W., Ackoff, R. L., and Arnoff, E. L., John Wiley, New York (1957).
12. WIENER, N., *Human Use of Human Beings*, John Wiley, New York (1950).
13. BEER, S., 'The Computer as a Creative Tool of Management,' *Accountant*, April (1966).
14. BEER, S., 'Towards the Cybernetic Factory,' in *Principles of Self-Organisation*, Eds. Von Foerster, H. and Zopf, G. W., Pergamon Press, Oxford (1962).
15. CRAWFORD, A., 'Brave New Business,' *Mnmgt. Decision*, **1**, No. 1, April (1967).
16. JOHNSON, E. A., 'Touch Displays: a Programmed Man-machine Interface,' in *Human Operator in Complex Systems*, Eds. Singleton, W. T., Gasterby, R. S. and Whitfield, D., Taylor and Francis, London (1967).

Chapter 17

The Structure of Disorder

R. W. REVANS B.Sc., Ph.D.

Senior Research Fellow of the European Association of Management Training Centres, Brussels (Belgium)

SUMMARY

The story of Babel was, of course, retold by Norbert Wiener in the language of modern technology. For him the cracks in the elaborate edifices of contemporary life were caused, not by inconsistences in our use of science, but by simple failures of meaning, by confusions or ambiguities of purpose, by mistaken identities or by avoidable breakdowns in communication. Disasters occur, not because the necessary laws of nature are unknown nor because the means of safeguard are lacking, but because the danger signs are misread and the misreadings go unchecked. The thesis may not be new: 'Where there is no vision the people perish' was written nearly 3,000 years ago. But it is nevertheless instructive to dwell once more upon the function of information in cementing the modern institution, and upon the design of the messages by which this information is most effectively conveyed.

In this essay I have tried to describe both the main limitation of the open-ended system, namely, the impossibility of automatic access to all potentially useful information, and some of the grosser errors to which the reception, transmission and interpretation of messages are subject. I am sure that the writer of *The Human Use of Human Beings*[1] would have forgiven my extensive use of illustrations from political and social systems to explore a field more frequently held to be the preserve of engineers alone.

INTRODUCTION

When I was asked by the general editor of this volume to write about the faults of automatic systems my immediate response was to see what Norbert Wiener himself might have to suggest about the subject. It did not take long to find my first text. On p. 9 of *The Human Use of Human Beings*,[1] in Chapter One, 'What is Cybernetics?', Wiener wrote this:

> 'It is the thesis of this book that society can only be understood through a study of the messages and the communication facilities which belong to it; and that in the future development of these messages and communication facilities, messages between man and machines, between machines and man, and between machine and machine, are destined to play an ever-increasing part.'

This suggests that Wiener attaches the greatest possible importance to the study of messages, whether in our understanding of society as such or of the machines on which society increasingly relies; the failure of the system is the failure of the message. I have therefore tried to treat my subject in terms of messages of many kinds, often merely between man and man, without specific reference to mechanical or electrical machines. For one of the fruitful outcomes of Wiener's work on automatic control has been our better understanding of the nature of feedback in purely human situations, in social decisions and in individual learning. Thus, my essay also has something to say upon the pathology of managerial decision networks as well as upon the failure of such artificial contrivances as aircraft landing systems. I have shown elsewhere[2] that the scientific method, the rational decision and the learning process alike have the same logical structure, and that feedback, or inputs about outputs, is the element common to all three. It is generalisations of this kind that are revealed by a study of Wiener's writings; he also makes it possible to understand how the system fails through lack of feedback and it is the consequences of such a lack that I have tried to trace on the following pages.

THE NATURE OF SYSTEMS

A general theory of systems failure might be found anywhere between the transparently simple and the inscrutably profound; it might even be called upon to explain the Fall of Man. Failure, in this sense, is defined as an outcome not necessarily unintended (for many beneficial discoveries were sheer good luck), but harmful—or as behaviour henceforth to be avoided by deliberate precautions. And it is not sufficient to consider only the sophisticated systems of the electronics engineer; our general theory of contrivances in trouble must embrace Aberfan and the *Torrey Canyon* as well as the power supply to New York City and the Vanguard that crashed in the London fog. Insofar as things go wrong by, for example, some part of a system becoming overloaded (as the weakest link of a chain may part under excessive stress, or a gang of generating stations revolt at some freakish surge)—or by the relationships between two or more elements of the system varying outside permitted limits (as in the speed of the gramophone governor subject to wear, or the stability of a mountain tip upset by the erosion of a spring)— a general theory of failure might be reasonably simple, since we are working in the familiar areas of physics and geometry. We should need to use a judicious blend of existing mathematics, such as the second order differential equation with coefficients varying in time; the theory of extreme sampling values, suggesting the likelihood of excessive surges within specified intervals; the study of Markov processes, predicting how far one semi-critical state, from which the system might take time to recover (such as an aircraft in touchdown just clearing one patch of fog), is likely to be followed at once by another; even the theory of games might have applications, should the system be served (as was the oil company using the *Torrey Canyon*) by a human monitor disposed to guess incorrectly at the degree of adjustment called for.

It is possible to describe a wide range of system breakdowns in such quasi-analytical terms, but only as long as we are not called upon to forecast accurately the specific malfunctioning of the specific part of some specific system. For example, we may show that the laws found by mechanical engineers to govern the distribution of breakdowns of iron bars under stress have the same general form as the distribution of wars by their duration or severity. Industrial strikes, that is, collapses of managerial authority rather than of international relations, seem to follow similar general laws. It is also clear that the system failure known as an industrial accident is distributed both by frequency and by severity in accordance with other known mathematical expressions. It is, indeed, our insight into the statistical reliability of many relations such as these that permits the growth of a variable insurance industry; the very word *average* can be traced to the premium paid by the merchants in the consortium against the likelihood of their own cargo being lost at sea.

But individual misfortunes are contemptuous of general laws, and a theory that would enable us to predict with confidence the time and place of the next shipwreck would put a strain upon our powers of analysis too great for them to carry. Indeed, the philosophers might point out that any failure, any breakdown, any emergency is, by definition, quite unpredictable, since it is the outcome of events we do not understand save in relation to the *probability* of their occurence. If we demand that the future is, by some cerebral alchemy, to be revealed in the present, it is to Old Moore that we must turn, not to the experimental scientist. Nor must we forget the myth of Cassandra, endowed with the gift of foreseeing the future, but also under the curse of never being believed. The misfortune that can be foretold can also be anticipated; it can thus be forestalled, so that prophecy, by its very nature, is a self-defeating art.

CLASSES OF RESPONSE

Granted that one or more purposes may be built into the system, our next step is to enquire by what general means these purposes are fulfilled. The system receives some kind of stimulus or input from its environment and it is designed to make a response acceptable to the person whose wishes the system is to satisfy: the chain is input, treatment, output; reception, process, transmission. These responses can be of two general kinds: specific and non-specific. Specific single-choice systems are extremely common: inspection gauges that, from a wide range of possible inputs to a system, allow through only those within fixed limits; given keys that will turn only particular locks (or given locks that will be turned only by particular keys, for the total system is the lock and key taken together); penny in the slot devices, like gas meters, that give only one response to one input (although they accept pennies of different dates and give the same volume of gas, whatever its calorific value). Specific multiple choice systems may not be quite so common, but they are still very plentiful. Three colour traffic signals that give the driver the choice of 'slip across' or 'brake hard' on the yellow, but the instruction 'stop' on the red; vending machines that for the same sixpenny input allow the choice of a dozen different packages; the telephone exchange that allows ten million choices, but that nevertheless denies automatic access to the number that is not, in some way or another, connected to it through a trunk dialling system; the ideal library filing system, so classified that all its available references involving such and such a combination of topics are thrown up automatically for scrutiny: all these are illustrations of the multiple choice system. Provided that the potential response has already been built into the system, it crouches alert to make that response once the signal to do so is flashed before its consciousness. In this, it does not differ from the shepherd's collie, differently responsive to the dozen different whistles of his master, but silent and impassive to all others.

The truly automated system, however, is rather more than the multi-response specific system. It may appear to seek goals that need not be specifically built into it, although it must necessarily be endowed (in order to qualify as a system) with goal-seeking behaviour of some kind. A child on a railway station, for example, given sixpence to buy itself an apple, orange or banana from a vending machine, may find all the appropriate boxes empty and turn for satisfaction to a nearby stall offering an irresistible display of golden pears, new to its experience; it may put the sixpence in its pocket hoping to run across another vending machine opposite the next platform and able to provide for one of its first desires; these responses are not built into the empty machine. The child is now part of a system able to go beyond the first specific multiple-choice situation and to seek for alternatives (like pears) outside it. A telephone subscriber unable directly to dial the number that he believes himself to need will seek the enquiry desk, in the hope of being given a new range of alternatives. This might include relatives or business friends of the person he is seeking. He may learn that his first goal is outside the telephone system, and that he will need to reach for it in a different manner altogether; he may find, for example, that the man he seeks has moved to an unknown address, that his telephone has been cut off for non-payment of charges, that the name of his exchange has been altered, that the exchange cannot be reached because the lines are damaged, and so forth. It is true that responses appropriate to all of these contingencies could, at varying degrees of ingenuity and expense, be built into the existing specific multi-choice system, although within limits that soon force themselves upon the attention of practical men. If, for example, the number were unobtainable because the subscriber had moved, it might be possible for an automatic device to tell the caller what new number to dial; it might even then go on to dial it for him. But if the subscriber had moved into, say, hospital or prison, such automatic transfer might be embarrassing or even impossible; there must be some limit to the degree of particularity built into the system, and, even if the 'subscriber not available' response could be further broken down into such specific details as hospital or prison, it is unlikely that it could then give the visiting hours at which the subscriber could be reached. The enquirer might then need to decide whether he should try to find the wife of the man he seeks, or any other relative; these are shifts of objective forced upon him by the necessarily limited responses of the specific system to which he has addressed his questions. And there comes a point beyond which any specific multi-response system is no longer able to help the exceptional goal-seeking client; whether it is the large-eyed child with sixpence to spend on fruit, the Scotland Yard detective after a reluctant witness, or the professor seeking all the interesting references in the million volume library, there is a finite chance that the built-in or automatic possibilities of any existing system, however, expansive, will from time to time be exhausted. A fresh search, based upon criteria more general than those already in the specific multi-response system, will need to be launched. It is the nature of these more general criteria—that may themselves be varied by the difficult requirement of trying to observe them, thus demanding that the new system be open-ended—which now demands our attention.

CONCEPT OF OVERALL PURPOSE

The degree of open-endedness of any system has to be limited by some overall set of values; it must be constrained by some recognisable boundaries. Otherwise it is no system, in that there is no correspondence between output and input; any input could create any output. The degree examination that requires the candidates to answer any four questions out of the seven printed on the paper is partly a multi-choice specific system, but the particular answers that each candidate gives may draw widely upon knowledge or ideas not within the official syllabus, or indeed not within the published literature of the subject. Yet these responses may be perfectly admissible and show great originality on the part of both student and examiner. It is said that the old mathematical tripos at Cambridge was an open-ended system of this type; the examiners would put up questions admitting of many responses, some unforeseen by the examiners themselves. But even so there was some essential common ground between the opponents; any originality either in question or in answer would bear some relation to what was formally known; the outcome might be surprising but it would be intelligible inside the tradition. (The surrealism of Lewis Carroll is in this same tradition.) To prove Pythagoras' theorem in a totally new way would be admissible: to scrawl across the paper 'Sorry, weak on triangles, but here is a list of the battles of Napoleon' would not be. The first candidate demonstrates evidence of goal-seeking behaviour related to the goals of the system (to test mathematical ingenuity); the second does not, because although he recognises the goal he admits also a lack of resources enabling him to reach it. A third candidate might produce an answer to the question that was already known within the tradition, a response perfectly admissible (one of the multi-choice specifics) but unoriginal; a fourth might develop an argument that, accepting the tradition, appeared to be brilliantly original, but turned out on close inspection to be based on a logical error. Some very rare fifth candidate, a Bolyai or Lobatchevsky, might snatch the opportunity to point out that the foundations of geometry were misconceived; there could well be other responses. Which would the examiners reject? By what criteria do they judge the performances of the candidates? How specific can be any statement of what the system is intended to do, in the first place, and how accurately thereafter can its response to different inputs be measured? Even on these few illustrations one can argue many cases. Most professors would be uneasy about the Lobatchevsky: and some might even fail him; some might be deceived into giving first class honours to the speciously brilliant candidate; others might favour the man who faithfully reproduces their own standard proof; some would reward highly the original and valid demonstration; others might even mark it down; all would probably fail the student of Napoleon.

No less a variety of responses may be found in a purely mechanical system —or in a set of such systems supposed to be identical—once it is recognised that the total system, having been contrived to meet human desires and needing to be operated by human subjects, must suffer all the consequences of human error. For human desires can never be predicted definitively; we will always consider reasonable alternatives to what we ask for. All our observable activity attempts to reach goals that cannot be specified exactly by means of systems whose performances cannot be predicted accurately. The captain of the aircraft has to fly it to Montreal, but in giving instructions to the automatic pilot he is prepared to allow some range, e.g. arriving within X miles of Montreal at some instant between time T_1 and time T_2 and at an altitude not above H_1 nor below H_2. The many conditions under which this instruction is then to be obeyed will —or may—vary as much as the candidates taking the tripos examination. Unless the pilot is supplied with information about each particular set of conditions (and they may vary during one particular flight) his automatic system is of no use to him, although in limited circumstances the automatic system may be able to collect some information itself as it goes along. For example, once within range of an automatic landing system (but not before), the pilot may be able to resign control. But even then (as has happened) he may spot a herd of cows on the runway and his automatic landing system may not be designed to take stray cattle into account. He will then need to take over again, whereas stray chickens would not bother him unduly, unless the aircraft happened to be a jet and the chickens were capable of flying twenty feet or more into the air when taken by surprise. Quite evidently, the number of contingencies to be built into the completely automatic landing system would be so great that the very hardware for storing and getting access to them on receipt of the appropriate signal might prove too heavy for the aircraft to leave the ground. For this would strictly demand some automatic device for dispersing cattle; otherwise the system must fall back upon (that is, embrace) men or dogs on the ground capable of being alerted by whatever language the aircraft captain chooses to employ. And no less strictly, the system must correct for similar possibilities in the future; it must, in other words, not only disperse today's cattle but also contrive to mend the fences through which the cattle have recently strayed, or even to cancel the lease of the farmer so negligent as to allow them out of their proper meadow. The most advanced automatic landing systems have, it would appear, some way to go before they attain these levels of comprehensiveness; for many years to come we shall need to fall back upon the human judgment to settle many of the next moves that our open-ended or automatic systems are to make, even if we are confident about those for making single or multiple specific choices.

INFORMATION AND BEHAVIOUR

We may pursue the idea, implicit in Wiener's work, that intelligible human behaviour is the pursuit of goals that cannot be specified accurately by the employment of systems whose responses are not absolutely predictable. Insofar as we can, by improving our messages, increase both the accuracy of our goal specification and the predictability of response of our systems, so can we advance the use of automation. If we cannot define our goals or do not understand the response of our systems we must continue to rely largely upon the human monitor. Since goal definition and system understanding depend largely upon the information available to us, it follows that the key to automation is our success in understanding the use of information. The reason that the human monitor is so powerful an accessory of the total system is due to the many sources of information open to him and to his capacity for organising this information and bringing it to bear in the appropriate form at the appropriate time and place. Irrespective of the particular form of automation—whether automatic machining, automatic transfer or automatic assembly (of which landing an aircraft is merely an example)—the success of the process depends upon the treatment of information about either the goals to be achieved or the progress of the system in achieving them. We therefore turn our attention to the basic information process, for it must be in the failure of these that the basic faults of societies and of machines alike must be sought.

The reception, processing and transmission of information is collectively known as *communication*. This involves not only the transfer of content, but the interpretation of the original content into a message by the sender, and the interpretation back again from the message into a final content by the receiver. Any imperfections in either interpretation or in transmission will distort the information and, in general, lower the quality of the decisions that depend upon it; information of outstanding importance is thus normally returned to the sender by the receiver to check the accuracy of its transmission. It is convenient to deal with each of the three stages, reception, processing and transmission, in turn, although there may be no absolute distinction between them. When, for example, one man, A, is helping another, B, to clarify B's understanding of a situation, B's processes of reception (B's view, grasp or perception of the problem) may actually be clarified by his own processes of transmission (B's imperfect efforts to explain to A what he, B, thinks the problem to be). On reflection, one may see that this sharpening of the understanding is, in fact, an exercise in learning; inputs about one's own outputs, namely information about what one is doing, criticism of one's opinions or corrections of one's mistakes, form a pattern with the same logical structure as the decision cycle, namely, proposition, action, feedback: suggesting the goal, trying to reach it, enquiring how far off one remains.

THE RECEPTION OF INFORMATION

'The light of the body is the eye: if therefore thine eye be single, thy whole body shall be full of light. But if thine eye be evil thy whole body shall be full of darkness. If therefore the light that is in thee be darkness how great is that darkness! ... 'And why beholdest thou the mote that is in thy brother's eye, but considerest not the beam that is in thine own eye? Or how wilt thou say to thy brother, Let me pull out the mote out of thine eye; and behold, a beam is in thine own eye? Thou hypocrite, first cast out the beam out of thine own eye; and then shalt thou see clearly to cast out the mote out of thy brother's eye.'

St. Matthew, chapters 6 and 7

The most common form of reception of information is listening to what one is being told; after this comes reading reports of more remote events. In organisations under stress men become emotionally unable to listen; generally in industry today senior executives do not listen attentively enough to what they are being told. They are often so busy that they say that they have insufficient time; courses in rapid reading have no parallel in the field of listening. When control information bears unexpected or undesirable interpretations men may simply refuse to listen to it. This is convenient for those obliged to use hearing aids, who need merely to switch off the apparatus; the parallel is known in aeronautical navigation, where the mechanic investigating the failure of the automatic control begins by testing whether or not the apparatus was live at the time; busy doctors leave their telephone receivers disconnected.

The existence of an organised information input (daily, weekly or monthly reports; a good radar installation; frequent conferences with the salesmen; regular calculations of the operating parameters by the computer; spot inspection of the machine shop quality; checking of the satellite's position; and so forth) is in itself no guarantee of high standards. Any information system may, for its present purpose, suffer from serious faults of design or operation of which the following are examples:

1. Attention is focussed on the wrong subject, perhaps because the observer is incapable of perceiving anything else; wrong or useless questions are being asked; the wrong plans, the wrong accounts, the wrong specifications are being consulted; the radar system is measuring positions so as to launch the missiles at its own bombers; the top management has no clear idea of how it should be spending its time, nor of to what issues it should be devoting its agendas; the aircraft pilot is absorbed in landing at the wrong airport; the general manager is doing work more appropriate to the factory manager; the surgeon is reading the case notes preparatory to cutting off the wrong leg; all these are examples of misapplied attention.

2. Information is presented in the wrong form; a report that might be easy to read if it contained a simple sketch is practically unintelligible; a document has no logical order in its paragraphs; although factually true, it is not clear who wrote it, when it was written, who was expected to read it, who else has, or should have, seen it; its units of value or measurement are either not stated or confused; a report containing routine or control information includes data on new subjects that should be reported separately; priorities or categories of confidentiality are assigned wrongly; the language is not intelligible to the person supposed to act upon it. Into this class of reception failure falls the inability of experts to understand each other; the computer able to accept punch cards is baffled by paper tape, and although it can accept instructions in FORTRAN it can do nothing with other high level languages; the gramophone needle that reads monaural records soon destroys the message in stereo; the automatic landing system perfect under one ground control is useless when tried in a foreign country supporting another patent.

3. Information is fed to the input at an inappropriate speed; too many messages are arriving within the period; it is impossible to discriminate between high and low priorities; the ticker-tape cannot keep up with the torrent of falling share prices; telephone messages are lost because too many correspondents are trying to get their message through; the traffic policeman's radar is useless because the density of cars on the highway it too high for the individual offender to be identified; the automatic process control is taking readings at intervals so close together that there is insufficient time to check the efficacy of previous corrective action before new data arrive to engage the monitor's attention; the doctor is talking so fast that the nurse has lost the thread of her instructions. Or, reception may be too slow; matters cannot be decided because some information is still lacking; the horse race is over before knowledge of form has come to help the backers; impatience leads to guess work and the substitution of wish for fact and managers with predisposing ways of judging events act upon half the story. The

development of on-line computer systems is to obviate this fault, but mixed systems with human operators as well as electronic devices (such as distribution systems using fleets of trucks from fixed centres) may fail unless information about goods and their destinations is brought quickly to the computer; it is of little use to speed up the arithmetic for suggesting improvements on the dispatch clerk's routings if time is lost in getting details of what is to be sent where from the order department; much critical path analysis, used as an operational control, suffers from such lack of balance.

4. The reception of data is distorted; the reading of a report is biassed, lays emphasis upon irrelevant detail, offers interpretation, opinion or prejudice in place of clearly set out and ascertainable facts, the person reading it mistakenly introduces recollections of past experiences into the present narrative; a motorist, reporting on oath an accident in which he was engaged, honestly misinterprets the reading of his speedometer; the doctor unconsciously ignores important information about a critically ill patient because it is offered by an unqualified nurse or by a sister whom he dislikes; the television set, by receiving one station more easily than another, keeps its owner better informed on cat food than on Vietnam.

5. The sensitivity or response of the reception is not suitable to the information being submitted to it; too much time is spent upon recording the detail being sent in; top management calls for reports that are too long to read, or the secretary to the manager shows no discrimination in what letters to answer without consulting him; the stewardess checks the number of passengers in the crowded aircraft by counting them separately rather than by glancing at any empty seats and subtracting from the total accommodation; the light on the zebra crossing responds to the pedestrian's signal so quickly that even a careful driver has difficulty in stopping; the microphone picks up so much of the background chatter that the conversation between the ambassador and the foreign moneylender is virtually lost; the governor of the steam engine over-corrects, so that its functioning becomes highly unstable; a young manager hoping for promotion may take too seriously the fact that his boss passes him in the corridor without speaking, by reading too much into his preoccupation with immediate tasks. On the other hand, reception may be too insensitive; the secretary to the board of directors is an empire builder and keeps matters of importance off the agenda, and the town clerk regards the council as merely his private rubber stamp; the impartial judge hangs every prisoner; the traffic light turns red against the fire engine and thea mbulance as readily as against the picnic party and the hearse; a manager may fail to understand how serious is a complat being madein to him by the men in his factory, and be astonished next dyn to find them on strike; the thermostat may be so sluggish that it responds to yesterday's weather; the television screen is so lacking in contrast that only the sound enables one to discriminate between the dog food advertisement and the Middle East campaign; the ship's radar is so insensitive that the sailing vessel is run down.

THE PROCESSING OF INFORMATION

'For which of you, intending to build a tower, sitteth not down first, and counteth the cost, whether he have sufficient to finish it? Lest haply, after he hath laid the foundation, and is not able to finish it, all that behold it begin to mock him, Saying. This man began to build, and was not able to finish. Or what king, going to make war against another king, sitteth not down, first, and consulteth whether he be able with ten thousand to meet him that cometh against him with twenty thousand? Or else, while the other is yet a great way off, he sendeth an ambassage, and desireth conditions of peace.'

St. Luke, Chapter 14, v. 28–32

After information has been received and before instructions can be issued or decisions taken, the information will need to be treated in some way. This may be a spontaneous reaction, like selecting some programme of action already stored in the memory, or going to the right file for further information; it may involve estimating a cost in one's head, or pursuing a most elaborate analysis of many alternative courses of action, using computers and operational research exercises, followed by a board meeting to take a multi-million pound decision, such as how to re-route the world's oil traffic after the possible closure of the Suez Canal. The first steps of such processing are normally sorting, or deciding which pieces of information received are related to each other; listing, or setting into some agreed order those items that are related; assembling, or bringing fresh information into the proper relation with known facts about the same subject; and correlating, or determining whether matters that at first sight appear to have no relation with each other are, in fact, interdependent, and vice versa. These early steps, that read so simply when put in this way, become immensely complicated in large organisations where several centres may be working, unknown to each other, and at different speeds, upon the same or similar information. These steps may also be looked upon as the activities of the librarian: to receive, classify and lend books, and to show readers what is related to what in the catalogue without passing judgment upon the content of the books or advising the reader as to the use he should make of his information. In an industrial organisation a multi-level filing system corresponds to a set of branch libraries. The information services of this kind in large organisations are often in charge of inadequately qualified persons, because it is not sufficiently understood how technically difficult and economically important the ready provision of this service may be. The obvious fact that much trouble solves itself as soon as the truth is known about it still does not elevate information storage and treatment to the social level of laboratory research, and librarians remain an underpaid profession; the majority of research workers, too, seem to prefer to spend time in rediscovering for themselves what is already known and published rather than seeking it in the literature.

After sorting, listing, assembling and correlating, the next stage in data processing is analysis. This often demands technical skill; calculations or measurements may be needed to interpret the facts reported. Such analysis may be called technical interpretation—given the task that the machine was being called upon to do, and the information about its performance, was its capacity likely to have been sufficient? Technical interpretation demands not only persons able to ask the right questions about the information reported, but also access to other facts that should be available in the filing system, catalogue, memory or other storage associated with the information network. Clear technical interpretation, made against the standards set in the first place, should lead directly to the central function of control, namely, corrective action; this is, in effect, the taking of secondary decisions, based upon the further information now made available by the trial experience.

340

The faults of data processing systems are many, apart from the electronic and mechanical errors of computers or office machinery. Among the more common are the following:

1. Information, having been received, is wrongly classified or catalogued; there may be faulty recognition, letters may be put in the wrong file, or bills entered against an account of the wrong customer; a wrong telephone number may be noted down to be sent an urgent reply, the identity of a patient whose case is to be dealt with may be confused, the wrong drawings may be attached to some manufacturing specification; there is no royal road to the avoidance of such errors and only constant vigilance (or control) can help to minimise them.

2. There is inadequate storage for information, including imperfect access to the storage; the filing system may just as well be too elaborate as too skimpy; essential information may not be kept at the place where it is needed most frequently, the catalogue of files may be incomplete so that information cannot be found when it is wanted, the storage may be unreliable or worse than useless because information is out of date, or it may be inefficient because its files are open only at inconvenient hours. In some fields the accumulation of information is growing so fast that it is a major task merely to classify what is newly published. Information retrieval is now a sophisticated science in its own right; now that a thousand new papers a day appear in the field of atomic energy, it becomes a problem in itself to discover and record which of them contains what.

3. The speed at which the information is dealt with may be inappropriate; decision-takers are blamed for being too slow, but decisions are also often taken too hastily, because all reasonably essential facts are not available, as through anxiety to clear up one's desk before going on leave, or in condemning accused persons without giving them a fair trial. Processing, on the other hand, may be too slow; there may be vacillation over unpleasant issues, the distribution of papers or messages may be too leisurely, a committee may be given insufficient guidance by its chairman or secretary to understand what it is supposed to be deciding, the intervals between board meetings may be too long, office methods may be out of date and there may be a need for electronic computers, powerful or under-employed auditors may demand the unnecessary checking of information, and so forth.

4. The communication channels of the system are either overloaded or conflicting, or even both. For example, the telephone exchange may be too busy, or under-staffed because the operator has other work; the post-boy may have too many letters to open or stamp or enter into the letter-book; the manager may have too many matters in his in-basket or the board may be trying to deal with too many items at each meeting. On the other hand, different functional channels may give different reports of the same incident; at enquiries into accidents the evidence of material witnesses may conflict; managers may consult, at different times and with different levels of frankness, the subordinates who should more properly be brought together in order to arrive at a collective decision.

5. The information processing system may lack consciousness. Although it receives clearly (and can verify that it does so) the information offered to it, the system may fail to recognise its significance; what is intended as an imperative

instruction to act forthwith is perceived as a piece of advice to be borne in mind against the future; the burglar alarm sounds when a pigeon settles on the window-sill, but the Japanese aircraft reach Pearl Harbour. A system can lack consciousness when one party to a take-over bid under-estimates the resourcefulness of its opponent or competitor, and publishes an offer that is afterwards made to look foolish; the punch card sorter may not perceive that some holes have been made by mice; the television programme advertising the satisfaction of cigarette smoking may continue uninterrupted at the bedside of the man who has just died of lung cancer; the automatic lift, once signalled, will climb twenty floors and needlessly wait for the passenger who has returned to her apartment; the computer fails to stop when it is evidently using the wrong program.

6. An information processing system may be short circuited, and decisions taken without due consideration of necessary facts or consultations; the linear programming expert, in his concern to build an econometric model, leaves out the parameters he cannot measure; subordinate managers who could interpret incoming information more clearly than top management are not consulted because the need to ask subordinates for facts is read as incompetence; wage proposals are made without the views of shop stewards being determined, or changes in design advocated with insufficient reference to the workshops; the mariner ignores the broadcast weather forecast; the surgeon decides to operate without waiting to see the X-ray films; the board choose their new line even though market research suggests otherwise.

7. The objectives of the system (and hence the criteria stored within the information processing system) are unrealistic or ill defined; a local authority continues to believe that it can force a particular parking policy upon motorists when all other local authorities have been obliged to relax their regulations; the management of a firm exhorts its sales managers always to work for the best interests of the firm without saying what these are, or even encourages them to sell products not known to be marketed at a loss; an officer persists in throwing troops against a strong point even although he sees every fresh wave of them mown down before his eyes; a football-pools enthusiast knows that none of his personal friend win anything, and that his own hopes are kept alive by the immense publicity given to rare cases of destitute widows winning fortunes; the automatic fire quenching devices adequate when the shop was built forty years ago could now, even if they still work, deal with fires only at the places where they are least likely to break out; the electronic scanning system for controlling the flow of bus traffic on particular routes, although technically ingenious, is not based upon any proper cost benefit analysis of turning buses short of their destinations.

8. The objectives of a system may be changed in the light of past experience, but no effort may be made to check that the new goals are more appropriate; this is the essential problem of the political party and so many examples can be quoted that it is unnecessary to give even one; in the electronic field it is reported that on-line information about the flow of cars may evoke a total change in their circulation, brought about by computer control of the system of traffic lights; it is also said that from time to time the contents of juke boxes need to be changed; it may be felt that to do something else is necessarily to do something better.

THE TRANSMISSION OF INFORMATION

'For if the trumpet gives an uncertain sound, who shall prepare himself to the battle? So likewise ye, except ye utter by the tongue words easy to be understood, how shall it be known what is spoken? For ye shall speak into the air . . . Therefore if I know not the meaning of the voice, I shall be unto him that speaketh a barbarian, and he that speaketh shall be a barbarian unto me.'

I, Corinthians, Chapter 14

If a problem has been clearly perceived and the steps to reach a solution to it logically prepared, then the declaration of what is to be done is normally not difficult, although the physical work required to implement the solution may still be extremely difficult. This is not to suggest that it will be easy to get agreement from all concerned that this is the course of action to be followed. It is merely to say that the manager who knows what he wants to do and why he is trying to do it has, in general, the advantage over the manager whose information system does not reach a high standard of perception or of logic.

The principal activities of transmission are the issue of instructions, the printing of plans or specifications, of minutes of meetings, etc. Output of this type can be verbal, it can be from the print-out mechanism of a computer, or of an automatic posting machine; it can be as punched cards or as an announcement of the official receiver; it can be an exhortation at a pit-head meeting, the sentence of a judge, the benediction of a bishop or the Christmas message of the Chairman of the board; it can be an instruction to an individual or the majority vote of a group of men round a table; the starter of a race transmits his decision by firing a pistol, the warm-hearted girl by an insinuating wriggle of her miniskirt, the rebellious parliament by cutting off the sovereign's head. It is essential to realise that, since the output has first to be accepted from the processing stage, all the common faults of receptors can be repeated at transmission. Men can, in other words, misconstrue their own arguments no less readily than they can misperceive the original evidence on which these arguments have been conducted; the several members of a public committee who feel in honest and complete agreement when they sign their report one week may have very different interpretations of it to give when they speak as individuals from different platforms during the next. Some output, or transmission, is of a form more concrete than the verbal promulgation of decisions; the computer may be instructed not only to write music tub also to perform it; the wanted motorcar may not only be identified when crossing the bridge after having had its number read at one end and its record processed in transit, but it may be physically stopped at the other.

It is not always easy to isolate the common faults of transmission or output from those of reception or processing, but they include the following:

1. The person or machine called upon to take the action demanded for the proper working of the system may be directed wrongly; men may be sent to carry out wrong work, or given the wrong tools or plans; machines may be allocated to the wrong jobs or jobs to the wrong machines; a main committee may refer a perfectly sound report to the wrong sub-committee to implement; the wrong man may be arrested by an over-energetic constable; in a large factory a good decision causes a distressing strike because the manager overlooks a restrictive demarcation practice, and sets a carpenter upon a job demanding the use of a hack saw.

2. The person or machine correctly assigned a particular task gives the wrong response because, for example, the workman is trained wrongly, injured or ill, or because the machine is adjusted wrongly; in the absence of proper feedback such wrong responses may go on indefinitely, as, for example, when runs of faulty products are turned out by a machine process, or when some mistaken overpayment of wages persists for so long that men claim its continuation as a prescriptive right; (it is important to discriminate between a failure to give the right response, and a failure to understand the instruction; one is a fault of output or transmission, the other of input or perception).

3. The output, whether by a person or a machine, may be out of balance with the stimulus or instruction that motivates it. The loud speaker may suffer from distortion, the projector may be out of focus, there may be too much play in the rudder of the aircraft, the landing gear may be frozen, the cutting tool may wander from the expected position, the tuning of one radio set is so sharp that a given programme is fading continually, while that of another is so slow that every station has another in its background; the uncertainty of the manager's mood makes life too exciting, for none can say how mild or how violent will be his reaction to a particular piece of news; the penalties inflicted by the magistrate will vary with his temper, and the equalising influences of the law are set aside; in factory systems, the maintenance crew may be too slow in responding to an appeal about a machine that has broken down; or help may well arrive too quickly, if it cannot be used before some local tidying-up of the work place has been done.

4. The output may be subject to interference from outside; a country at war attempts to influence its enemies by radio broadcasts of persuasive propaganda; the shop stewards influence workmen not only against the general policies of the firm, but also against the specific instructions of their foremen; telephoned instructions become confused with crossed lines, or minsuderstood because of the clatter of teacups near the transmitter; a computer goes out of service because of sudden fluctuations in its power supply, a punch card system prints out the wrong figures because of dirt in some delicate but vital part, a strike of electricity workers in Paris puts out all the traffic lights, or a passenger's radio set distorts the pilot's landing signals. In the world of labour, a local sporting event may deflect men from their industrial purpose, or a sharp fall in the temperature may keep them all at home. These are a few examples of the influences of external forces upon the working of complex systems, and it may be helpful in analysing certain problems to see them in this light.

CONCLUSION

An examination of the breakdown of systems, whether machines are involved or not, and made (as Norbert Wiener would probably have made it) by concentrating upon the messages intended to hold the system together, shows not only the fundamental similarity between all forms of human contrivance, but also their common pathology. All teleology demands the vision of a goal, the knowledge of an organisation and the possession of the physical means to be organised. Whether these means are machines or men, whether the organisation is a national constitution or the blueprints of a jet aircraft, or whether the goal is to effect a revolution or to fly the Atlantic, the essence of the system is the information that it uses—whatever success it achieves it owes to that information. Perhaps one of the fruits of Wiener's work will be the wider recognition of the place of information in all that we do, and of the need to spread his ideas far outside the laboratory of the information expert. What he would have thought of my three quotations from the *New Testament* I do not know, but he would have been quick to recognise that anything as fundamental as his own work would certainly have been thought of by others.

REFERENCES

1. WIENER, N., *The Human Use of Human Beings*, Houghton Mifflin Co., Boston, Mass. (1950).
2. REVANS, R. W., *De Accountant*, Amsterdam, May (1967).

Chapter 18

Cybernetics, Technological Barriers and Education

J. ROSE, M.Sc., Ph.D. F.R.I.C., F.I.L., M.B.I.M., M. Inst. C.Sc.
Principal, College of Technology and Design, Blackburn (U.K.)

SUMMARY

Cybernetics is a powerful unifying concept. It can break down the barriers existing within technology itself, as well as those dividing science from technology. But these barriers are ultimately symbols of general cultural attitudes and consequently a general change of attitude will also be needed. This general change must be achieved through education and the development of the interdisciplinary science of cybernetics.

INTRODUCTION

Science and technology are separate but inter-related. The essential purpose of science is the broadening of knowledge and the deepening of understanding, while technology bends the knowledge won by science to real social use. Technology, unlike science, produces conspicuous and useful products by the aid of knowledge that science provides, though popular opinion attributes these products to science itself.

In the past two decades, science has made spectacular progress. The expenditure of enormous sums of money on scientific and technological research throughout the world, particularly in the U.S.A., Western Europe and Russia, is creating a vast amount of knowledge, so that the volume of books, journals, reports and papers is 'exploding'. For instance, nearly two million scientific articles of all types were published in 1963, while 23% of all chemical research ever done throughout history has been carried out between 1957–61. It has been estimated by the National Scientific Foundation of the U.S.A. that the doubling of the scientific and technological (the latter includes engineering) manpower in the next decade would involve a total expenditure of 65,000 million dollars.

346

This vast increase of scientific activity, accompanied by an upsurge in the realm of technology poses many difficult problems. One of the main tasks is the study of the way in which this gigantic activity proceeds. For instance, it is important to know whether there exists a scholarly training *about* technology by means of which man could gain consistently a greater understanding of the relations between society and the activities of those engaged in furthering technological progress. Sociology, planning and economics of technology, psychology of technologists and technological work, analysis of the flow of information, operational research, the role of technology in various societies, technological obsolescence and injury, the symbiotic relation between science and technology, the fragmentation of technology, the relations to humanities—all these are pertinent matters. While similar problems in science are already being studied by the science of science, a brainchild of J. D. Bernal, there is no corresponding discipline applicable to technology.

In all these considerations the problem of barriers looms threateningly. I do not think that the grouping of technological subjects or the introduction of new conceptual techniques such as operational research, would solve the barrier problem completely for the difficulties go very much deeper. There is the barrier separating science and technology from the humanities; there is that between science and technology, one aspect of which is the time lag between scientific discoveries and their application in technological fields. In addition, there is the fragmentation of technologies with the accompanying narrow specialisation. In some way, all these barriers have a great deal in common, at least in the historical sense. According to Dr. C. P. Haskins in his presidential report to the Carnegie Institution for 1964–65, the intricate social millieu for our day is for both science and technology a world society, though it is already apparent that in the future the environment created by humanity itself—that of human social forms, of individual human needs—must rank high in our reckoning. He emphasises that mankind is in the midst of an era of change in total outlook fully comparable with that of the classic scientific revolutions, though our society shows little awareness of the real implications in its efforts to develop institutions or habits of thought to suit our changing needs. Dr. Haskin's ideas about the social peril of the fragmentation of science, when the distinction between method and goal is not understood and the picture of fragmentation is extended to the modes of the search for knowledge, also apply to technology.

As we shall see, the problems concerning technology and society are essentially similar, but before these can be faced properly, science and technology must themselves be developed so that they can become merged in a new cultural entity; and for this the barriers within technology must first be broken down. There is no doubt that fundamental advances in technology are more likely to occur from searching for basic principles in related technologies and for the relations between them, than from pursuing the usual practice of studying them by industries. In other words, a more analytical approach to technology is required and technologists should be encouraged to look beyond their individual specialities. For, indeed, these barriers have been partly the result of specialisation, which brings about a narrowness of concepts and a reduction of inventiveness and creativity. These barriers are responsible in some measure for the lack of interactions between technologies observed in many instances.

In the United Kingdom and some other countries obvious practical remedial steps would be a radical re-organisation of industrial research associations, now based on individual technologies, into large units serving whole industries but working in conjunction with each other. The reduction of the numbers of technological societies, journals and institutions, a radical modification of the structure of university and college departments of technology, close liaison between universities and research associations, exchange of professors between industry and universities, the implementation of the principle of the sabbatical year, the establishment of independent sponsored research associations—all these and others would also contribute to the removal of bar riers between technologies. But what is really needed to unify the technologies is a common cybernetic basis. The spectrum stretches from purely engineering topics to management and economics, involving in all its aspects computer sciences, operational research and techniques aiming at optimising yields and increasing productivity.

THE CYBERNETIC REVOLUTION

The first industrial revolution produced mechanically powered tools, operated by man, while the cybernetic revolution (or the second industrial revolution) created implements which are able to perform an incredible variety of complicated tasks without any human intervention at all, by means of automatic feedback control. Thus, automation entered the industrial field; this must not be confused with automacity or ultra-mechanisation. A better term for automation is cybernation. These cybernated systems have become most sophisticated, since they can make judgements on the basis of instructions programmed into them and learn from past experience; they are even beginning to perceive and recognise, e.g. the perceptrons and various learning machines. There is every reason to believe that, during this century, machines will become available that will be able to think in a rational manner and be capable of performing tasks in ways that would be impossible for humans to duplicate. The cybernetic systems are already being used to design road networks, and houses, to print books, to translate tolerably well from some languages into others, and even to produce mediocre television plays! In general, the science of cybernetics concerns itself with the general principles of control and communication in machines and animals.

The means already exist which will enable the worker of tomorrow to be equipped with machines that will multiply his mental powers by a ratio similar to the one by which the mechanically driven tools multiplied his physical powers. Large data processing systems now exist which can transmit, store and process information, and which will enable leaders of large enterprises to make rational decisions about complex matters, instead of ruling by inspired guess work as at present. Already scientists and engineers are being aided by computer processed information in various spheres of scientific and industrial activity. The electronic digital computer, which can perform long chains of logical tasks at prodigious speeds, using enormous amounts of stored data, enables scientists and engineers to embark upon investigations which previously had been barred to them by the sheer bulk of necessary calculations. Computers became part of automated systems by including feedback loops of various complexity. They now assist in decision-making tasks. Moreover, the use of suitable computers for data processing in business is becoming more widespread, since they can execute a long chain of successive data processing steps, make the choice of alternative ways of proceedings, employ an enormous amount of stored data and can do all this at speeds equivalent to one million calculations per second. The lines of demarcation between 'scientific' and 'business' computers is becoming rather blurred, since both types now require large memory storage and rapid input and output facilities. Thus, 'business' computers with these attributes are now being used to solve mathematical problems arising from operational research techniques applied to business. Effective use of these powerful extensions to the human mind and power depends to a large extent on the computer content of technological education.

The use of computers in business is already reducing one of the basic problems of technology, that of time lag between scientific discovery and technological application. This has its roots in the lack of understanding of the rules, if any, governing the relaticnship between expenditure on development and research on one hand, and the resulting industrial innovation on the other. Thus, in the period 1959–62, only 5% of the 5,600 inventions put up to the National Research Development Corporation in Great Britain earned royalties by being exploited commercially. Various solutions have been advocated to reduce this waste, such as Government intervention, contract research laboratories, industrial research associations, and a study in depth of the relation between discovery and application. Though notable successes have been achieved in this field in Japan and the U.S.A., in other countries the situation still leaves a great deal to be desired. In the author's view, a radically different attitude is necessary which takes into account the spirit and substance of the second industrial (or cybernetic) revolution—a concept, which would, for instance, enable managers to use science to handle the increasingly large, complex and risky situations that arise in industry, business and government;[1] this concept would also eliminate the fragmentation of scientific thought and activity.

The arrival of powerful computers on the scene in the last two decades has produced, apart from other tremendous effects, a revolution of mathematics, particularly as regards its applications. It is only since the advent of computers that mathematics has become able to cope with industrial problems. Mathematics is becoming more and more acceptable to industry, and there is an increasing demand for mathematicians. In the period between 1956 and 1959 in the U.K., the number of mathematicians employed in industry rose by 40%; the actual figure is rather higher, since an appreciable number of men trained initially as mathematicians are classified, after a short training or employment period, as theoretical physicists, aeronautical scientists or engineers. In fact, one large firm of brewers in England has a mathematician as a Brewer-in-Charge of research and development, while former mathematicians such as Sir William Penney, Sir Alan Wilson or Sir Graham Sutton are at the top of the industrial management tree. Thus, mathematics based on analogue and digital computing acts as a unifying concept in technology, particularly since the major demand in technological education is for the mathematics to be taught to engineers, physicists, chemists and others. Some of the technologists and scientists will wish to use mathematics; others may wish to be made aware of what technologies and equipment are available and in what situations they are likely to be useful. In this scheme one must also note that computers and ancillary equipment may serve not only as tools for solving industrial problems, but also as teaching aids to illuminate mathematical concepts, ideas and operations; these aids can also stimulate interest in algebra, since the usual formal treatment is regarded by students as a trick to be learned merely to satisfy the examiners, and which cannot anyway be used in practice, for real problems are too difficult for such methods. This is illustrated by the well known, though possibly apocryphal statement by a research manager of a large industrial firm, that all engineers learn a lot of mathematics at university or college, but the first time they meet a differential equation in industry it is almost certain that none of the methods they had been taught would be of any use. In fact, the perusal of mathematics textbooks shows that they contain soluble equations for students to practice on, while an indiscrete silence is maintained about the vast insoluble remainder.

On the other hand, the use of analogue or digital methods brings an understanding of the nature of a solution for differential equations, which cannot be obtained from looking at an algebraic formula. Furthermore, the mathematics syllabus should include mathematics problems of industry, most of which involve one or more of the following; evaluation of formulae, ordinary non-linear differential eqations, differential equations, etc. The aim is to tackle real problems by numerical methods and computing, since the student is aware that the formal proofs so beloved of examiners are essentially a device of limited application, while numerical and computing methods have the generality and true ring of practical use. Also, scientists, technologists and mathematicians ought to be able to express practical problems in mathematical terms, i.e. they have to be able to construct a 'mathematical model of the situation', to solve equations and evaluate their practical use. Thus, it is essential to fuse together into a unit, the formulation of the problem, and the numerical and formal methods of dealing with it. Books such as *Engineering Analysis* by Crandall,[2] are attempts to present mathematics in this way. A task common to the solution of any problem with a computer is the preparation of a complete description of the problem and an algorithm to solve it, a description without a simple loose and untied end. In other words, the task of mathematics teachers in various technological subjects is to transform the statement of a mathematical problem into a representation of its solution. At the present time, computers are the main tool with which algorithms are actually carried out. It is also uneconomic in this age of fast computers to perform algorithms by hand or with a desk calculator. Pure mathematical theory and computer practice must produce a synthesis, which would have as its object the construction of universal mechanisms to solve large classes of problems, rather than the creation of tricks for solving particular cases. For many problems it is not nearly as important to create an efficient algorithm as to form one quickly and make it sufficiently general to avoid having to recreate one next time.

It is clear that the use of high speed computing methods and numerical analysis is of fundamental importance to pure and applied scientists alike. Indeed, those entering industry, research, business or the professions, must know how to use computers as a time saving device on standard problems, as a tool for solving problems numerically that could not otherwise be solved, as an instrument for analysis and design that is revolutionising industry, as an integral link in the rapidly changing field of instrumentation and control, and as an indispensable aid in the processing of economics and business information. In the words[3] of Dr. F. J. Weyl:

'the advent of the high speed computer has opened the way for an unprecedented mathematisation, not only of fundamental scientific research in the physical and biological sciences but also in the management of our industrial and social systems. This is about to assign to mathematics an entirely new part in our civilization with far reaching implications on what should be taught, how it should be taught, and to whom'.

350

The mass extension of man's intellect by cybernation and the partnership of man and machine in dealing with the information explosion may well be the technological advance dominating this century. The engineering field has already been revolutionised by the computer. The space programme could not have existed in the absence of computers, which eliminated most of the trial and error procedures by simulating designs and flights of space vehicles. Traffic control, weather forecasting, designing of computers, control of machine tools, automatic operations of whole factories, management decision-making are among the numerous tasks performed by the computers. Relevant methodologies such as systems analysis, operational research, critical path analysis, etc., bring together the knowledge of several disciplines involving sciences and economics, and so enable one to construct qualitative and quantitative models of a variety of possible systems; computers then facilitate the making of choices. Still in the future are the uses of these aids for translation of foreign books, retrieval of vital information from libraries, and simulation of the national economy. Indeed, cybernation, within the cybernetic concept, covers the whole spectrum of technologies and it is truly a unifying concept, not just as a practical aid for the cohesion of technologies but also as a basis for the technological ethos. On the other hand, cybernation is only one of the wide array of computer sciences which themselves are united and covered by the umbrella of the inter-disciplinary science of cybernetics. The term 'computer sciences', or so called synnoetics, includes such subjects as automation, information storage and retrieval, systems analysis and design, electronic data processing, artificial intelligence, applications of computers in the field of pure and applied sciences, computer design, algorithmic and heuristic solutions, cybernetics, operational research, recursive function theory, study of adaptive systems, theory of automata, theory of programming, etc., all based on the use of computers as the fundamental tool; in the above context, 'computers' refer to digital, analogue, hybrid and learning machines.

The interaction of all sciences and technologies in this way is the keystone of our modern edifice of economic life. No valuable work could be done today in any academic subject or in industry without some basic knowledge of science, and technology demands at least an understanding of social development in pure science and some appreciation of its historical background. Science is also needed to teach non-scientists as well as to train its own practitioners with the added responsibility of providing for a rapidly changing environment. In general, the concept of integration of technological disciplines must be achieved against the background of the scientific tradition and thought in the context of our total intellectual environment and social system. Though universities and colleges have set up departments for various branches in science and technology, nature knows no barriers, and a natural phenomenon may require the knowledge of many disciplines for its understanding. Many exciting fields of research are on the borderlines, e.g. biophysics, biochemistry, geophysics, molecular biology, ergonomics, materials science, technological economics or bio-engineering. The point is whether man is a *Homo faber* (a tool maker) or *Homo sapiens*, a creature whose intellectual prowess extends beyond the narrow confines of instrumentation to an all embracing vision of every branch of human activity. In all these activities —it is submitted—cybernetics could act as an essential link and scientific umbrella.

351

EDUCATION AND THE ENVIRONMENTAL BARRIER

As science becomes more specialised, two kinds of scientific communication are required; (1) that needed to tell the public about scientific advances; (2) that giving the relationship between researches in various branches of science. The importance of these topics is related to the need for bridging the gap between those who see the world in terms of a rapidly changing environment, which science has created, and those who see it in terms of a fixed emotional attitude of the past, i.e. a static environment. The latter category of people includes, unfortunately, some of our rulers. A. N. Whitehead pointed this out in his work[4] *Science in the Modern World*:

'the increased plasticity of the environment for mankind, resulting from the advances in scientific technology, is being construed in terms of habits of thought which find their justification in the theory of a fixed environment'.

In other words, though man has modified his environment profoundly, he is quite unable to predict, in general, the consequences of the changes brought about, and to foresee and prepare. Hence, though the potentiality of science and technology is great, the preparations made for their use are slight. A case in point is the inadequacy of our plans of dealing with the population explosion or the phenomenal growth of what Professor de Solla Price terms 'Big Science'. While technological progress has increased our power to satisfy our wants, it has also brought about immense social changes such as mechanisation, automation, urbanisation, a complex class system and a different intellectual climate based on new forms of thought. As pointed out by Clerk Maxwell:

'Experimental science is continually revealing to us new features of natural processes and we are thus compelled to search for new forms of thought appropriate for their description'.

The price to be paid for frozen modes of thought is exorbitant as regards the industrial and intellectual well-being of the community. When the Jesuit missionaries pointed out to the Chinese some two hundred years ago that 'the behaviour of things is ordered by the laws of nature', this was received with courteous scepticism. The Chinese paid, of course, heavily for this stagnation of scientific and technological idea since the advent of the Ming dynasty. In fact, the Chinese invented gunpowder but only used it in a limited way. Similarly the Byzantines invented clockwork but only used it to levitate the emperor! In this connection the problem of technological obsolescence and its solution in our times is of some interest.

This malaise is part of a wider issue involving an innate conservatism of the human mind. It has been pointed out by Hansons[5] in his *Patterns of Discovery* that human beings tend to enquire about causes only when they are confronted by some breach of routine. Thus, we ask why a person is ill, and not why they are well. In these and other difficulties a proper understanding of learning and its motivation would be of considerable help.

It is clear that education at all levels and for all is essential in order to remove the barrier corresponding to a contemplation of a static environment and frozen habits of thought. It is odd to relate that the scientific revolution has not touched the techniques of education—a technology in its own right—at institutions of higher learning. 'Efficiency' techniques, operational research and the study of knowledge about themselves are unknown to them. A study of efficiency undertaken by the U.S. Foundation for the Advancement of Education in 1961, led to some startling conclusions and also improvements. In all these fields, cybernetics has a vital part to play; in the last analysis, it all boils down to the problem of communication and interaction with environment.

THE PURPOSE OF EDUCATION

Education in its widest sense is a vital element of scientific policy, not only because it creates a psychological climate favourable to innovation, but mainly because it provides human resources without which technological progress is unthinkable. According to E. Denison,[6] education may be credited with 42% of the increase in real national income per person employed, while advances in knowledge contribute 36% and organised research and development accounts for a small part only. Education is not only a technology but also a semi-autonomous factor promoting an improvement of the quality of the labour input and greater adaptation of employees to new technological methods. To do this, Governments must have a clear educational and scientific policy with emphasis on proper priorities in research and management. The barriers erected in and around technology because of the 'information explosion', which lead to technology being regarded as a collection of mere techniques, must be abolished by invoking ideas of deeper understanding, rational priority and a humanistic approach. This is—in my view—a much more important task than combining a few sciences or technologies under one umbrella; it is also a task which only education can tackle with success. The greatest barrier of all resides in the prejudices and inertia of the human mind buttressed by an inadequate educational system.

The time has now come to think in terms of one discipline, though various approaches are possible, since the different branches are not separate entities but are part of a large unit which is based, like science, on the intellectual traditions of Europe. Dr. S. Toulmin examined this matter at length in his address to the 1962 meeting of the British Association for the Advancement of Science and pointed out that there is at present a transition from the Alexandrian intellectual technology with its pre-occupation with techniques, skill and gadgets, to the Athenian natural philosophy with its emphasis on general ideas, habits of mind and the importance of education. He asserts that scientific enquiry revived in the 16th century not because of the introduction of experimental methods but because the Athenian school of natural philosophy prevailed. There is danger that our obsession with technique may stifle the natural philosophy from which it sprang. Although these views are open to serious objections, there is no doubt that fundamental advances in technology are more likely to accrue from searching for basic principles in individual technologies and for the relations between them, than from pursuing the usual practice of studying them by industries. In other words, a more analytical approach to technology is required, and technologists should be encouraged to look beyond their individual specialities.

As regards education at lower levels, a more rational approach would consist of teaching at school the history of ideas, the understanding of factors which control innovation and discovery, and the development of a wider perception of

353

historical precedents of possible future advances. A curriculum incorporating the history of scientific discovery and evolution of scientific thought, the interaction of various cultures, the development of logic and mathematics—the precursors of computer science and automation—as well as the study of foreign languages, would tend to reduce the barriers in and around technology, while the introduction of psychology, physiology and fine arts would enable young people to understand our society in this so-called 'accidental century', when blind forces have been unleashed with their undertones of potential destruction and technological injury. There are many examples of the tremendous harm done by our ignoring the potentialities of technological advances, as cited in the 1965 Granada Lecture by Vice-Admiral H. G. Rickover. A professional and liberal approach is needed by technologists and those using the fruits of their endeavours. If an engineer were a liberally educated man with an ethical code, (like a doctor) then greater concern would be shown for human welfare; no-one dictates to a doctor the course of his actions, but at present laymen impose upon the engineer the course of action to be taken. Thus a 'humanistic' technology is of great import in our society, and this can only be achieved by rational education and informed public opinion, the former based on philosophical treatment, so that the student is able to assimilate concepts of the development of civilisation throughout the centuries. The important thing is for a man not to become the slave of knowledge but its master, a situation already described by Plato in antiquity when discussing his famous academy and describing the work of the students:

> 'They will be offered all at one time the sciences which they have studied at random in their adolescence, so that they can get a broader view of the relationships between the sciences and by this means become acquainted with the true nature of reality'.

Thus it is desirable to use the methods and techniques of the second industrial revolution, with its conscious application of its interdisciplinary science of cybernetics, to create a whole and unitary framework of knowledge of nature permeated by a humanistic philosophy for the greater good of mankind.

It would be appropriate to quote at this stage the prophetic words of the 'father' of cybernetics, Dr. N. Wiener, as given in his introduction to the original (1948) edition of *Cybernetics or Control and Communication in the Animal and the Machine*:[7]

> 'Those of us who have contributed to the new science of cybernetics thus stand in a moral position which is, to say the least, not very comfortable. We have contributed to the initiation of a new science which, as I have said, embraces technical developments with great possibilities for good and for evil. We can only hand it over into the world that exists about us, and this is the world of Belsen and Hiroshima. We do not even have the choice of suppressing these new technical developments. They belong to the age, and the most any of us can do by suppression is to put the development of the subject into the hands of the most irresponsible and most venal of our engineers. The best we can do is to see that a large public understands the trend and the bearing of the present work, and to confine our personal efforts to those fields, such as physiology and psychology, most remote from war and exploitation. As we have seen, there are those who hope that the good of a better understanding of man and society which if offered by this new field of work may anticipate and outweigh

the incidental contribution we are making to the concentration of power (which is always concentrated, by its very conditions of existence, in the hands of the most unscrupulous). I write in 1947, and I am compelled to say that it is a very slight hope.'

This panorama of confusion has been presented by Wiener in the language of modern technology. In his view the unsatisfactory developments in our contemporary life are mainly due to a breakdown in communications and failures of meaning. Mankind is at the crossroads because it ignores the signs of danger, though it has the scientific and technological capacity to seek effective remedies. Information appears to be dividing instead of cementing modern institutions.

It would be apt to close this chapter with another citation from Wiener:[8]
'The hour is very late, and the choice of good and evil knocks at our door'.

This is not a figure of speech but a stark reality; Wiener's Golem is at work. A possible cure is the new concept of cybernetics in the broad context of a 'humanistic' and an Athenian mode of education and philosophy, which could forge various disciplines into a unit that is part of the human search for truth and for understanding of man's place in society.

REFERENCES

1. BEER, S., *Decision and Control*, John Wiley, New York (1967).
2. CRANDALL, S. H., *Engineering Analysis*, McGraw-Hill, New York (1956).
3. WEYL, F. J., in *Computers in Education*, ed. J.A.P. Hall, Pergamon Press, Oxford (1962).
4. WHITEHEAD, A. N., *Science in the Modern World*, Cambridge University Press, Cambridge (1932).
5. HANSONS, N. R., *Patterns of Discovery*, Cambridge University Press (1958).
6. DENISON, E. *Why Growth Rates Differ*, Allen and Unwin, London (1962).
7. WIENER, N., *Cybernetics or Control and Communication in the Animal and the Machine*, M.I.T. Press, Cambridge, Mass. (1948).
8. WIENER, N., *God and Golem Inc.*, Chapman and Hall, London (1964).

Chapter 19

Epilogue:
Prospects of the Cybernetic Age

STAFFORD BEER
Development Director,
International Publishing Corporation (U.K.)

SUMMARY

Although we know how to automate anything that we can specify fully, our use of automative technology (and especially computers) is mainly trivial. This is because the technology is not properly related to the underlying science which could inform it—cybernetics. Control systems are unexpectedly constrained by a finite limit to computing power, which can never be large enough to undertake some of the activities of which people glibly assume computers capable. The answer lies in building brain-like controllers, for the brain faces (and overcomes) these problems of organisation and computing limitation.

   In the control of large scale systems, such as the firm, or the economy, or society itself, a hierarchical arrangement of computing sub-systems appears to be essential. The filters which govern the flow of information need to be learning devices, so that the whole controller is capable of adaptation. The influence which cybernetic developments of this kind are likely to exert on both management and society at large is examined.

A TECHNOLOGY IN SEARCH OF A SCIENCE

It does not take us long to make a technological inventory of our times where automation is concerned. Because we have much to consider, I shall take a great many details for granted. Let me distinguish merely between two major aspects of automation. All automation is really about control, and we may consider control as operating (1) at the micro level, on the shop floor for instance; and (2) at the macro level, in the conduct of affairs.

   We know first of all how to move, position, and manipulate materials; how to cut, shape and prepare them as components; how to gauge, inspect and

356

assemble these components; how, in short, to manufacture automatically. Using ingeniously contrived or tape controlled machine tools, using transfer lines, using electronic measuring gear, using process controllers that are themselves controlled by negative feedback, we know how to build factories that are themselves machines for making machines or highly refined products. We find it technologically less difficult every year to envisage an industrial society in which there are almost no industrial workers.

If we move rather slowly in erecting the automatic factory, it seems to be for two main reasons. The cost of automation rises steeply the further one goes in aggregating the parts of a firm, and we are not organised to collect the pay-off from very advanced large scale automation. Consider this example: we make a process automatic, and the output typically rises by an order of magnitude; the product is improved, and the labour force goes down to meet the cost. But if we turn the whole factory into an automatic machine, we do not typically want a tenfold (still less, by aggregation, a hundredfold) increase in total output, even if the product is improved, because we cannot sell it; and we have lost the erstwhile flexibility to reduce the labour force, because there is nowhere else to absorb it. Therefore, we cannot afford the high costs which would be involved.

And so we are stuck with an automation technology applied as if the task were simply to mechanise. There is more and more elaboration of machinery, and less and less chance to exploit its general capability. *How* we do things improves, but *what* things we do barely changes. And although I have spoken of industrial automation in these remarks, exactly the same points apply to automation in banking, in insurance and commerce, to automation in transport and other services, and to automation in or of the Government machine.

The second part of the automation inventory concerns our overall capability for control in the conduct of affairs. Except in a completely stereotyped production or administrative context, the planning, scheduling, programming and in general *managing* activity is paramount. To get the best out of any plant assets, these functions must be well done; to get the best out of more highly automated plant, which becomes by definition capital-intensive, these functions must be done superlatively well. The tool for this job is the electronic computer, and we have begun to use it. Scientists at least find it technologically less difficult every year to envisage an industrial society in which there are almost no managers.

But we move slowly in this direction, too, thereby exacerbating the difficulties in introducing more automation of the first kind. The reason for this seems to be very simple, but entirely intractable. It is that however much people may talk about rethinking their problems before they introduce computers, they almost never manage to do it. Surely it is a fact that almost all the world's computing capacity, which is by now very considerable, is devoted to doing things quickly and accurately that we used to do before slowly and inaccurately: the payroll, the stock-holding system, the costing, the data reduction. What happens when we acquire a computer? We buy ourselves a universal logical engine, but we install a souped-up adding machine. When we say 'but we rethought the job', we turn out to mean that a different coloured form goes to a different set of people more often than before.

What really is going wrong here? I think that the trouble is this. The automative engineer, the systems analyst, the computer expert, are all doing what management tells them, as they are bound to do. It really is of little consequence to a particular young specialist whether he applies his skills to this or that situation, so long as the job appears to be serious, so long as there is a professional challenge, and so long as he is allowed to maintain his integrity within that frame-work. It is not his job to select the framework, for this responsibility belongs to senior management: to directors of firms, to the heads of services, to Government itself. If these top people do not really understand the scope of the technology that is available, or if they are unwilling or unable to reconsider the question of what they are trying to achieve within the limitation of modern rather than antiquated technology, then nothing happens.

We are becalmed in these doldrums. We have not yet recognised managerially the science of which all this visible automation is the technology. That science is cybernetics, the science of control and effective organisation. Without its in-sights, we are committed to a slow and costly process of gradual self-improve-ment, to an evolution that is painful because its social and economic conse-quences are thrust upon us from below. But we know enough today, if we will stop to reflect and to put our various pieces of knowledge together, to aim at regenera-tion rather than improvement. We could make a plan for a new society in which we speak of new sources of wealth and a new kind of life for the citizen. Then the expense of automation becomes the calculated price of liberation from drudg-ery. It is no longer to be viewed negatively through that lugubrious phrase 'the rising costs of manufacture'. And the consequence of automation is the liberation itself in a more elevated life. It is no longer to be approached negatively in fear of large scale redundancy and the dole.

THE CYBERNETIC ORIENTATION

If the cybernetician is asked how management ought to think about these matters, his first piece of advice must be this. Stop thinking about all the pieces of the situation under your control: how to improve each one of them, how to join them together so that they mesh, how to obtain optimal performance from the total collection. Instead, contemplate your situation freshly, regarding it as an organic whole. Think of your situation as if it were itself a machine or an organism. What goes into it, what comes out of it, what is its overall *purpose?* Then ask what kind of control system will operate this whole thing. In short, work downwards and not upwards through the problem.

The first thing you are likely to notice is that you are now engineering with uncertainty. Real life is not fully predictable; but this does not mean that it is wholly arbitrary. We are not dealing with a shambles, but with a highly patterned system which seems to have its own motive power, its own major tendencies, and its own inherent constraints. What influences this system has a largely random component: we literally do not know what will happen next. But even that randomness turns out to have a pattern of its own—scientifically, we should call it stochastic. In the long run the procession of arbitrary events assumes a statisti-cal form. This does not make it any more possible to forecast what will happen next, but it does permit the design of a control system competent to handle varia-tion of known form, within known limits, and with measurable probabilities. That overall control system, based on cybernetic theory, is the key to our prob-lem.

The second thing we note is that control depends on information. In fact, the degree of control we can exert on our situation is proportional to the logarithm of the amount of information freely circulating within it.[1] So this is how we should first think about electronics and computers. Suddenly, over the last fifteen years that is, we have developed an almost unlimited capacity to collect, process and use information, to fling it about in the system. This, to be precise, is the technological capability that really matters. Our capacity to do this is our new capacity to control.

But surely it immediately follows that if we insert our own heads in the information circuit, insisting all the while on 'looking at the facts', we constrain the informational capacity of the system—and therefore its capacity to be in control—by the miserable inadequacy of our own brains to handle all these data. The informational capacity of our new machinery is far, far beyond that of the machinery in the cranium, but we refuse to let it move and work for us. We keep on intervening ourselves at the lowest levels. We print out the data and try to assimilate them. What we should be doing is closing the servoloop between the world and the automatic control system, allowing the computers to affect the situation directly. Shall we, then, as men, lose control of affairs? Not at all. For we monitor the effect of all that happens in the higher-order language of which our brains are splendidly capable. Please note, I do not lose control of my respiratory system just because I hand over its day to day running to a computer called the autonomic nervous system. I can intervene at the conscious level whenever I like with a general instruction such as 'take a deep breath' or 'hold your breath'. The physiological computer instantly obeys that instruction, and works out the consequences for its own lower-level control system.

We are talking, then, about the use of automation to introduce some kind of brain-like artefact into the control of a situation—whether that be industrial, or educational, or governmental, or whatever. The artefact should have a level of autonomic control, and a level of central control, and will obey the over-riding policy instructions of its human directors. We have, in my opinion, very nearly all the technology necessary to achieve this design, as I shall try to show. Strangely enough, the most serious weakness lies in what is perhaps the easiest research area of all: that of data capture. We need transducers of input and output, and these need much more attention. If we are to close the loop in bringing about effects automatically, then their monitoring by men requires a better understanding of human perception and comprehension than is evidenced by providing tabulated print-out. There should be a surge of research devoted to (what I can only call) automated epistemology. Electronic displays and projections, run by computers, and a dialogue mode of communication between man and machine, are essential aspects of this problem. To talk with the computer through a light pen working on a sensitised display panel is a start, but it is not yet good enough.

Now, all of this begins to sound very fine, and we are leading our minds towards a new and cybernetic orientation to automation. But soon, if we do not confront them now, we shall run into some serious mental blocks. Our whole training, whether as scientists or managers, has led us to think about problems according to a logic of analysis and synthesis which turns out to be rather inappropriate to the discussion of natural, organic, or—let us call it—physiological control. We are not really allowed, by our disciplines, to propose an attack on a situation which we have not yet analysed in detail. We are expected to understand precisely and in fine detail the way it all works. Then we are allowed to synthesise these many detailed descriptions into a whole, the behaviour of which is then supposed to be *optimised* under some equally well understood criterion. Indeed, it is in trying to follow through this methodology that we have come to a grinding halt. It cannot be done.

Everything I know about cybernetics is modified by the study of living systems. None of these, as far as I know, has any mechanism which can determine a goal, analyse the detail of operations, specify its own transfer functions, synthesise a global strategy, or optimise an outcome. And yet they work. We now know, or begin fairly well to know, how they work. At the least, we understand enough to tackle the problem of the brain-like artefact—provided that we look on it as a viable control system, and not as a means of emulating our own traditions for problem solving. For make no mistake about this, the methods in which we are trained work for small scale problems, but cannot work for large scale problems, as I shall now set out to show. That is the exact reason why we must think again.

THE SCALE OF THE PROBLEM

The first thing to realise is the scale of the problem with which we are faced. The brain-like task is to handle the afferent part of the system, its input, in such a way as to fix the efferent part of the system, its output, so that some criterion of success is met. The brain-like artefact will thus consider the pattern of n inputs, and match to it a pattern of m outputs. If we arrange for binary codes of information, there will be 2^n possible input states and 2^m possible output states. Since any output set may in principle be associated with any input set, the total variety of the brain-like artefact will be $2^m \cdot 2^n$. Even when n and m are small, this number is enormous. With only eight inputs and only one output we get $2^{2^8} = 2^{256}$, which is roughly equivalent to (Eddington's measure of) the number of fundamental particles in the whole universe.[2]

True, we may curtail the scope of the output set in any system we design; but the variety measure just proposed grows much more importantly with n than with m, and we have no real control of the number of inputs which the outside world proposes that we *ought* to take into account. Secondly, it is likely to be true that the input states will not after all range arbitrarily across all the possibilities, but will show preferences for particular configurations. This at first sight appears to simplify the problem—until one considers that the artefact will have to learn about these configurations themselves. Now such a configuration is a subset of the set of input states; and while 2^n input states is bad enough, the set of *sub-sets* of the total will number 2^{2^n}. Thus, even though the input system is in practice constrained rather than free-ranging, the variety that has to be handled is very large.[3]

Just how large it is turns out to be critically important, and not just daunting. A little reflection and a little trial computation on the back of an envelope will convince you that a brain-like artefact for controlling any real life situation, with hundreds if not thousands of input and output channels, generates a seeming need to process many millions of binary digits, or bits. For example, if we take a situation involving 300 variables, and permute the input/output possibilities in the way described already, we find ourselves trying to cope with the processing of some 3×10^{92} bits. We are accustomed to huge data reduction facilities nowadays, and it is tempting to hope that accepted optimisation techniques using enormous computers will eventually handle systems of the kind described. They will not. We owe to H. J. Bremermann[4] the first attempt to specify a limit to our ultimate computing capacity, and his argument runs like this.

Thanks to Heisenberg's uncertainty principle, a given chunk of matter cannot

360

be made to process more than a limited number of bits without collapsing into ambiguity. That is, at some stage the distinction between a 0 and a 1 will become obscured by uncertainty. What this limiting number of bits is depends on the value of Planck's constant. Since we know that this is very very small, most of us would have thought that it would not matter in any practical situation. But Bremermann worked it out, and arrived at the limiting figure of 2×10^{47} bits per second for one gram of matter having a density taken as average for terrestrial material. Thus, the lower limit for accurate measurement according to quantum mechanics places an upper limit on the information processing capacity of matter.

Even so, we might have said, we do not have to compress our computers into matchboxes, and we have longer than a second to use: it will be all right. But Bremermann doggedly went on with his calculations. Very well, he said, let us assume that the whole earth is really a gigantic computer, and let us suppose that it has been computing for the whole of its existence. In that case the *total* information that it can ever have processed is about 10^{92} bits. So much for the nice little problem with 300 inputs and outputs, which all on its own generated a variety three times as great.

Unless this argument is hopelessly—rather than marginally—erroneous, we have to face up to the fact that our classical methods of analysis and computation will *never* work in the case of brain-like artefacts. There is not enough computing capacity, however the technology develops. There is not enough time, however long we take. Therefore we must look to new methods. And there is no need to be too despondent about this, because we already know that the living brain—all three pounds of it—*can* handle such a situation. We each own an electrochemical, slightly alkaline, computer with some 10^{10} decision elements, or neurons, and it works. You now understand why I have talked, not just of computers, but of brain-like artefacts, all the way through.

BRAIN-LIKE SYSTEMS

Cybernetics has been struggling for the last twenty years or so with the brain's techniques of data reduction, and begins to know what to say about the problem. Much of the past research writing, such as my own already quoted,[3] has been very obscure. As is usual on the frontiers of science, we do not ourselves understand fully what we are doing or trying to say. By today, however, we begin to understand, and I hope I can tell you what I mean clearly and simply. First, we need artefacts of neurons which are partly analogue rather than purely digital, and which work with conditional probabilities rather than the differential equations usual in describing other transfer functions. Secondly, we need computational strategies that are heuristic rather than algorithmic. Thirdly, we must use hierarchies of control systems, expressed in orders of meta languages, rather than single-stage servomechanisms expressed in a single language. I think I can explain all these three points by discussing a very simple electromechanical system.

Consider a strip of wood on which are mounted two strips of brass, one following the other, with an insulation between. One strip is connected to a terminal of a lamp meaning 0 and the other to a terminal of a lamp meaning 1. The strips of brass are each swept by five contacts, all ten of which are connected to a roulette wheel bearing ten numbers, which is in turn connected to both lamps via a battery. When the wheel is spun, one number out of ten will be selected, and one of the ten contacts will become live. Therefore one of the lamps will light. There is a 50% chance that it will be the 0 lamp, and a 50% chance that it will be the 1 lamp. The roulette wheel represents the input which real-life arbitrarily proposes to the system. The system responds to the input by 'choosing' between the two lights, one of which represents a profit and the other a loss. It is clear that this machine will make a profit half of the time. Note that the language in which the machine is specified is not the same language as that which declares 0 = profit and 1 = loss. The latter is an environmental language specifying what the world outside the machine makes of its answers.

How is the machine to know about profitability, given that it does not itself speak the environmental language? The machine and the world, each speaking its own language, must be connected by a third—and common—language. We have learnt from living systems that this is a reward-and-punishment language: I call it *algedonic*, from the Greek words for pain and pleasure. Thus if in language (2) the machine has made a profit, the algedonic language (3) is something which must reinforce the machine's existing behaviour, language (1). If it has made a loss, the existing behaviour must be extinguished. It is, however, no good simply to say that the random number 7 has lit the 'wrong' bulb, and that therefore we must switch its contact to the other strip of brass. For in saying that, we are drawing on our knowledge of the inner workings of the machine, whereas in a large system we shall not necessarily be able to trace what is happening. Moreover, we have no means of knowing in a real system either that the input 7 will at all times be equated with the output 1, or that output 1 will at all times be unprofitable.

The algedonic feedback in my machine consists in sliding the strip of wood forwards or backwards. By doing this we expose more of one strip of brass, and less of the other, to the ten contacts. In fact, punishing 1 for being unprofitable, and rewarding 0 for being profitable, as we would say in language (3), turn out to mean the same thing in language 1. That is, that the brass strip connected to 0 is exposed increasingly to the contacts, and the other strip decreasingly so. If we go on punishing and rewarding long enough, moving the strip of wood a little at a time, the machine will 'learn' how to make a profit all the while.

Considered as an element of decision which adapts to its environment, the device so far works. But what happens when the environment changes? If the profitability of 0 and 1 are reversed in language (2), it seems that the machine's capacity to adapt is impaired. It can now be punished for doing what used to be rewarded, but it does not for a time produce a profitable response which could be reinforced. In other words, as we find in all viable systems, a capability for mutation must be preserved. This can be achieved by allocating a contact to each of 0 and 1 regardless of the probability transfer function. Thus we get a 10% chance of being wrong, even when the device has adapted fully; but this error-making capability is exactly what guarantees the learning, adapting and evolving capability.

I said that this device is partly analogue in character. If we replace the carefully positioned ten contacts with a random scatter of hundreds of contacts, the point becomes clearer. If we were to use magnetic fields with triggering thresholds instead of binary-state electrical connections, it would become clearer still. I said that conditional probabilities, rather than differential equations, described the transfer function, and so they do. As to the hierarchical systems and their appropriate meta languages, we find three of them already in this trivial device.

If we begin to arrange these neuronal artefacts into interacting networks, as I have actually done, we need more meta languages still. With four hierarchical ranks of these neurons we can control $2^4 = 16$ bulbs—that is, make eight patterned responses to a world offering four lots of modulo-ten inputs. Finally, we do this heuristically rather than algorithmically, because the profitability criterion is held in a meta language which cannot be made specific in the system's own language. The trick is done through the translation language of reward and punishment, using an algedonic feedback loop.

Given an apparatus of this kind, or more readily a computer compiler effecting this kind of system, it is possible to conceive of a brainlike artefact as controller of very large systems. It is in reality simple, although I fear I have made it sound more simple than it really is. But to work with these tools we have to clear our minds of several traditional notions.

Control networks are not necessarily designed structures made up of selected elements; they may be fully connected nets of all elements which adaptively structure themselves. Feedback loops are not necessarily to be controlled by comparators working from the feedforward function, but may be algedonic loops working from criteria expressable only in a higher order language. Transfer functions need not be immutable ⎸operators described by differential equations, but can be continuously modified conditional probabilities described by a transfer matrix.

THE FUTURE OF MANAGEMENT

The processes of control hereby advocated are heuristic rather than algorithmic because they search out satisfactory answers rather than nominate perfect ones in advance. We can specify heuristically how to learn, to adapt and to evolve without knowing what lesson is to be learned, to what circumstances adaptation is required, or the blueprint of the ultimately evolved organism we shall become. This is the biological trick for survival, and we ought to adopt it quickly in our managerial practice.

Although the individual firm offers the most obvious field for these developments, this is in many ways the most difficult application. Consider: we really do meet a huge number of input and output variables, and the situation that must be controlled is a manifestation of a most complex organism—intermingling men, materials, machinery and money. The job can be done, even so, if we adhere to the physiological model. Within the department, the manager represents conscious control. He owns a command structure, analogous to a central nervous system. At some level below him, the works' processes become (in his eyes) autonomic. To the manager of the division of which this department is a small section, the first manager himself may well be part of an autonomic system. *His* command structure is of higher hierarchical order, and his own thought processes represent a higher degree of consciousness. It is he, too, who operates the translation language which defines the first manager's algedonic loop. And so on up.

When we reach the board of directors, we have reached the upper bound on this expansion of hierarchical systems. It matters very much indeed that what is conscious, what is central, and what is autonomic with respect to this group is defined correctly. Typically in contemporary industry, the senior management is occupied for more than half its time with the detailed control of operations which ought to be autonomic in respect to itself. Thus the central model of the firm, which ought to be derived for the board by a learning process from the mere monitoring of autonomic outcomes, is never constructed. And if that is the case, there is no hope at all that the top management will ever succeed in making experiments on this non-existent model.

In fact, this is their most important function. For animals and firms have also this in common: they use their model of the world, acquired from experience, not only as a central control instrument in real time, but as a tool for exploring the possible future when the real time constraint has been removed. The human being calls this facility 'foresight'. The firm's own operational research scientists will call it simulation. The manoeuvre is fairly simple. We take our model of reality, and submit to it sets of bogus inputs. These are the ranges of possible conditions which one day may turn out to apply. Instead of responding to these inputs, which we must not do because they are bogus, we allow time to run on ahead and we *imagine* their outcomes. Thus we test our managerial strategies for robustness against the unpredictable future. We do not pretend to be able to foretell the future; we say only that a given strategy is more or less vulnerable than another to some possible set of alarming conditions.

In brief, this is the model for the automation of the firm. We have autonomic systems in control of day to day operations. The technique for doing this is well known: there are already almost automatic oil refineries, chemical plants, and mass production engineering works. We could extend that level if we wished (bearing in mind what was said earlier about transducers). Secondly, we have an heuristic model of the firm's total activity, fed by inputs from the autonomic level, which searches continuously in real time for better results than before. This it does by varying the parameters it has been using successfully to produce adaptive mutations, which are in turn monitored and reinforced by algedonic loops. We know how to do this, and have indeed done it many times in the past. Most worthwhile industrial operational research groups can demonstrate particular ad hoc examples. What is now required is the incorporation of this tool into the basic organisation of management, as a continuing instrument of routine control. Thirdly, we use simulation techniques to test our strategies for susceptibility to threats implicit in the future. And this is the best known operational research investigation of them all. There is no reason why this tool should not be incorporated as a routine as well.

What has not, I think, been done is to cohere all three of these hierarchical levels (each with its own sub-hierarchy) in a simple viable control system. It is a well nigh incredible omission, given that all the parts can be pointed out as working somewhere or other. Presumably the trouble lies in a narrowness of vision which fails to take the integral problem into simultaneous account; in the vested interests of those many people who jockey for position within one traditional area of the total activity, and do not wish their framework of power to be disrupted; and in the inadequate but traditional methodology of analysis, synthesis and optimisation. Certainly, the regenerative design of the firm cannot be undertaken from below: it is a task for the topmost people. When this cybernetic amalgam is effected, at any rate, the industrial scene will rapidly become unrecognisably different, and the accepted economic framework within which it has always struggled will be disrupted forthwith. There will then be the chance to adopt completely new industrial policies, and better technical practices which appear at present to be uneconomic.

If all this applies to the firm, and it could within the next five to ten years, I ask whether it cannot also apply to the State. Here are much the same problems, and much the same barriers to progress. We have too rigid an organisational framework, too little information and no heuristic approach. There can be as little objection to using computers for running a national pension scheme, or to back up a telephone system, as there is to using computers within the firm for payroll or stock control. But in both cases we run the risk of resting on these laurels, of throwing away the new opportunities. To persist in the physiological model: if every industry within the State is regarded as autonomous, then the Government machine is a central nervous system. This should be equipped with real time heuristic models rather than budgets and statistical year books. The third level of the model with its foresight capability now relates to cabinet policy, and uses the model to test its proposals before loosing them on the unsuspecting populace as items of political dogma.

The point here is particularly interesting. The whole history of human progress reveals a progression in the capability of science to tackle new problems. At any given time, a matter that was still beyond the scientific horizon had to be settled as an item of faith. Before we knew whether or not the world was flat, before we knew whether the solar system revolved round the sun or the earth, people did not on the whole say 'we do not know'. They said that they *did* know; it became impious, very often, to assert the contrary. Today science is on the verge of being able to produce an automated firm, of which the directors will still be in complete charge, and an automated State, of which the duly elected Government will have total command. Such brainlike artefacts will, for the very first time, contain and handle heuristically enough information to make adaptive control possible.

Then we shall begin to find out how large firms can best centralise and de-centralise (for those things are not mutually exclusive). Then we shall begin to find out how the State can both control industry and leave enterprise free (for these are not mutually exclusive either). We are not quite there, and what do we say? Certainly not that we do not know. Most people will back their fancy; they will talk of value judgments and political convictions. Typically, they will also deny that these matters can ever be resolved by science. In so doing they put such a brake on evolution that there is real danger that our institutions, whether industrial or political, cannot survive.

THE FUTURE OF SOCIETY

May I now remind you of the barrier to these developments caused by the use of an inappropriate methodology. It is true that we shall not be able to use automation in the higher control of the firm or the management of the state if we adhere to outdated analytic models that are actually beyond the capabilities of terrestrial computation. But we are not really training our youngsters to do anything else. It is a strange kind of education which fits people ever more sophisticatedly to attempt something that cannot be done. Let us think for a minute, then, about education.

Education itself can no longer be viewed as something essentially propaedeu-tic—fit and designed to train children. Education is an informational process which enlarges and fulfils every person, of whatever age. Every person, I said; and each person is unique. It follows that the educational need of every one of us is different. Why then, do we sit ourselves in classrooms for year after year, all learning the *same* thing? Why do we read books written by the author to himself, which cannot of their nature be fitted to each and every reader? The answer is simple: we have no choice. Or, rather, we have had no choice until now.

Today it is possible to bring automation to education, very much on the basis of a private service to the individual. We may publish to one man what he wishes to know, about anything at all, as a unique package. This is possible by the use of real time multi-access computers with remote terminals. The pupil has only to switch himself into the central computer, to select the file of magnetic tape which interests him, and to interrogate that file. This is really just like consulting an encyclopaedia, and presents no particular problem. But consider the matter the other way round. From the computer's point of view, *it* is interrogating the pupil. Every question the pupil asks, every supplementary question, every consequential calculation he requires to be done, all make information about the pupil available to the machine. Then let the machine begin to construct an heuristic model of the pupil.

We have at once a learning system, working reflexively. For the computer may soon assume an active rather than a passive role in this dialogue. Any piece of information in the file has, let us say, a half chance (to begin with) of being offered to the pupil. But as the pupil's interests, capabilities and difficulties reveal themselves, this probability will change. Here is the brain-like artefact again, working with a probability transfer matrix of the input-output connectivity which defines the situation. It must be at least ten years since the British cybernetician Gordon Pask invented machinery[5] working on this basis (although it was not connected in those days to information retrieval files in computers). I well recall experiments we made at that time with his pioneering machines, when we first realised that there was no formal difference between the teacher and the pupil. Each was making an heuristic model of the other, and using it to try and modify the other's probable response to any stimulus. It turns out to be impossible to say, by studying an electrical monitor of the man-machine interaction, which is the pupil and which is the teacher, which the man and which the machine.

This is a far more important type of learning system than the programmed branched teaching algorithm that is fashionable today. It is also the touchstone of a genuine understanding of the man-machine interface, which will dominate our society increasingly. We may begin by envisaging the provision of machines like this in schools, the experimental development of which has already begun in the United States. A central computer, using standard files for school use, feeds remote terminals that are used by every pupil—not continuously, but on a rota system throughout the day. And the pupil and the machine interrogate each other, heuristically, so that wise and patient individual tuition becomes possible. The few real human teachers we have, the inspirational few, will one day be released from the drudgery of transplanting the examination syllabus to their pupils' minds and be allowed to *teach* once more. Now once the individual is trained in this way, not only in being educated but in the sensible use of his slave the machine, he will certainly not wish to abandon the technique when he leaves school.

At this point, publishers must take over. In the long run, there will inevitably be computer terminals in every home—just as we have television today. In the shorter run, specialist real time services will operate for universities, technical and professional colleges, and many public and institutional services in this way. In London, we already have what may well be the first commercial service of this kind, which is publishing stock market prices and analyses straight into stock-brokers' offices on a bespoke, real time basis. This is why I said just now that education will be a continuing and personal activity; eventually, I suppose that we shall automate our acquisition of news, of data and of cultural information too. Moreover, because we shall become on intimate terms with the computer, just as today we are on intimate terms with our books and our slide-rules, we shall use its service all the time for purposes of accounting, shopping, banking and so forth. It will be interesting to see how long it takes for advertising to move into that.

If we build our vision of a new society on this revolution in public communication, we soon find that the fashionable fears attending the development of automation are chimerical. People will, I think, be leading lives that are a mixture of learning, communicating, and entertaining. Whatever happened to working? Work will be an integral part of the whole enjoyable business of living, just as it is for me (and I hope very much for you) today. In fact many of us are, within certain constraints, already doing exactly what we like all the time. We no longer think, as we used to think, of a working day spent miserably earning our living, so that we can afford to relax in the evening. I am suggesting that the long standing, puritanical dichotomy between work and leisure need no longer exist, and that the famous automation problem of 'too much leisure' is bogus. Emancipation from the tyranny of work versus play has always been enjoyed by an oligarchy of successful (or perhaps just courageous) people in every society. As with all forms of emancipation, this one will spread downwards through a more and more automated society. It would be silly to suggest that the mass of the people will never be able to rise to this elevated level of living, given a new education and a new means of communication. It would be as silly as to have said 200 years ago that the mass of the people would never be able to read, to understand public affairs, or to vote for their Government. This will not stop commentators from being silly, now as then.

In this bracket of thought let us not forget the special role of women who do not earn—the housewives. They could already—just about—claim to be living this integral life, since they do not go out to work. Some, with a very tough cast of mind, manage to see things this way. But for most of the housewives in our society, life is seen as nearly all work. They do not command the servants that their grandmothers commanded, nor alternatively live in the collaborative society of service that their grandmothers' servants shared. They have been half-emancipated by a feeble attempt at automation in the home. As to the rich cultural environment here predicted for society by the use of computerised publishing, their present day cultural environment is arid in the extreme. They are tied to the house by their children, and the communicating world outside barely penetrates into that isolated box. Here are all the elements of cultural and social deprivation, which can be expected to lead to a kind of simulated schizophrenia. In Britain, we sometimes call it the 'housewive's neurosis'. There is an urgent need to move in this matter. The difficulty is that individual households cannot afford to make automation and cybernetic studies, nor to apply their results. To get action here requires a combination of effort between government, the educational institutions, the building industry, the publishing industry, local authorities, broadcasting, churches and social workers, and so on. What a fantastic task—and yet it could be done. Poor housewives: perhaps they need a militant trade union. What they deserve is a truly automated home.

But we must not be too impatient. At any rate there is a realisable vision here, to which we could all agree to work. It is based on the cybernetic breakthrough in communication and control which has already happened, and on the very open possibility that there could be a totally new sort of national (and why not international?) system of heuristic intercourse, using computers.

I suppose there are dangers, too, but we must have the courage to face those. The one that concerns me most arises from the likelihood that we the citizens, shall not—as a total society—move in this business very fast. Meanwhile we, the scientists—as a society within society—are forging ahead. Some scientists already have remote computer terminals in their homes, and are therefore able to converse via the computer with other scientists. The potentiality for a new order of communication between two human minds which this opens up is rather devastating. Hitherto, face to face discussion between scientists has been our most profound means of sharing ideas. I say to you: 'well, if we invert this matrix then it ought to be possible to . . . . .'. You then wonder if that would be so or not, and remain unconvinced. Under the new mode of communication via the computer I shall say: 'when we invert this matrix, we get . . . . .'. And what you will hear from your remote terminal is the answer. This mode offers a much deeper insight into our own and each other's minds than ever before, makes the process of scientific discovery likely to accelerate rapidly, and above all—dangerously—places a great deal of power in our hands. The danger lies, as with all scientific advances, in the risk of abuse. Presumably a group of leading intellects, communicating in this way, could either make a huge advance in our understanding of the universe, or plot quite unbeatably to overthrow the Government.

CONCLUSION

I have tried in this address to open some new vistas, to issue an invitation to enter the cybernetic age. Let us think about it constructively; let us not be put down by pessimists, by troglodytes, by cynics or by bureaucrats. Beware, I should beg, of the argument that it cannot be done. Here is our motto: we can do anything that we know how to specify. Given advanced technology, that statement is almost tautologous. And yet we shall quite certainly be assaulted by those who would cling fearfully to the list of those attributes they acclaim as human prerogatives.

Learning, adapting and evolving, seeking and discovering, creating, and being intelligent—these have always been regarded as attributes unique to living things. But cybernetics has learned how to specify them as heuristics. What we can specify we can automate. The automated systems of the future will themselves be viable systems, and I do not think we shall be able to refute the claim that they will be intelligent. Besides, this development lies on the route of progress. Our first machines automated man's muscles and joints, and gave him lifting and motive power which amplified his own. Our next machines automated man's accuracy and finesse in craftsmanship, and gave him manipulative skills of a precision which amplified his own. Thirdly, came the machines which automated man's power of decision, and gave him a capacity to investigate problems on computers to reach conclusions of a subtlety and complexity which amplified his own. Now we reach the machines which automate man's power of intelligence, and they will assuredly amplify that too.

Although we are supposed to control our machines, they have always had a tendency to run away with us. The first lot knocked us down, the second lot blew us the pieces, the third lot took our jobs. The new lot will run our lives for us if we let them. Let us run them instead. Let us put our slave machines to work to solve the world's problems of economic stability, so that—for a start—a thousand million people will get something to eat. It would perhaps be more sensible than landing on the moon. But let people consider why science moves spacewards in the way it moves today, rather than moving to the direct benefit of humanity. The answer is not just military. It is because when scientists face up to the distant and lovely and challenging galaxies of outer space there are no frightened men between them and the stars.

REFERENCES

1. BEER, S., *Decision and Control*, John Wiley, London (1966).
2. BEER, S., *Cybernetics and Management*, English Universities Press, London (1959).
3. BEER, S., 'Towards the Cybernetic Factory', in *Principles of Self-Organisation*, von Foerster, H. and Zopf, G. W., Eds, Pergamon, Oxford (1962)
4. BREMERMANN, H. J., 'Optimisation through Evolution and Recombination', in *Self-Organising Systems 1962*, Yovits, M. C., Jacobi, ö., and Goldstein, ö., Eds, Spartan Books, Washington (1962).
5. PASK, G., 'The Cybernetics of Evolutionary Processes and of Self-Organising Systems', paper given at the *Proceedings of Third International Congress on Cybernetics, 1961*, Namur (1965).

BIOGRAPHIES OF CONTRIBUTORS

G. R. Boulanger*

Professor Boulanger obtained his diploma in civil engineering (mines) in 1933 at the University of Brussels and received the doctorate in mathematical sciences at the University of Paris in 1949. He made his career in university teaching and research and now holds a Chair at the Mons Polytechnic Faculty of the University of Brussels. His main field of activity is concerned with applied mechanics, machine building and modern techniques of teaching, particularly the use of teaching machines.

Professor Boulanger is a member of many scientific societies and he has published various papers in the realms of mathematics, engineering and education. He has participated in several international congresses, in some of them as president. He has been President of the International Association of Cybernetics since its foundation in 1957.

S. Demczynski

Mr. Demczynski graduated with first class honours in electronics in 1951 (Dipl. Ing.); his degree thesis was subsequently published as a monograph by the Institution of Electrical Engineers, of which he is a member (C. Eng., M.I.E.E.). His postgraduate work was concerned with research in electronics, servomechanisms and applications of digital computers in industry.

Since 1960, Mr. Demczynski has devoted his attention to operational research and he is now Manager of Cord Consultancy Limited, a firm of Operational Research Consultants in the Comino-Dexion Group. He is a member of the Operational Research Society (U.K.) and is the author of several papers and of a book concerned with the sociological and philosophical consequences of electronic data processing and information.

J. F. Schuh

Dr. Schuh has studied at the Universities of Leyden, Delft and Paris. He has spent many years at the Dutch Aircraft Company as chief of the Flutter and Vibration Department. In 1951 he joined Philips of Eindhoven, where—as he states—he 'found his vocation in the field of electronic computers and theoretical physics'. Dr. Schuh is the author of books on analytical dynamics, computer theory and modern physics.

V. M. Glushkov

Professor Glushkov graduated at the University of Rostov-on-Don in 1948 (Faculty of Physics and Mathematics). He was subsequently awarded a doctorate in physical and mathematical sciences. In 1956 he was invited to head the Computer and Mathematics Laboratory of the Kiev Institute of Mathematics and a year

---

* The biographical details are based on information supplied by the contributors. The size of the description has no bearing on the eminence of the individual authors.

later he was appointed to the directorship of the Ukr. S.S.R. Computer Centre. He became the director of the Ukr. S.S.R. Institute of Cybernetics in 1962.

Professor Glushkov was elected Academician and was awarded the Lenin Prize for work on digital computers. He has published a book on algorithms, and over 300 papers.

F. H. George

Professor George was educated at Taunton School and Sidney Sussex College, Cambridge, where he took the Moral Science Tripos and the Mathematics Tripos. For 19 years he was on the staff of the University of Bristol, where his research and teaching was devoted primarily to cybernetics and programmed instruction. He also became extremely interested in theories of learning and perception.

Professor George has been a visiting professor at Princeton University and the University of California, and he has also been a visitor at McGill and Stanford Universities. He is Computer Consultant to NATO. He has had six books published, including *The Brain as a Computer*, and has also written eight programmed books, form of which deal with computer applications.

Recently, Professor George was appointed Director of the Institute of Cybernetics, Brunel University. He still holds the post of Chairman of The Bureau of Information Science. He is also Chairman of the Council of the Institution of Computer Sciences.

W. Grey Walter

Dr. Grey Walter is the Director of the Physiological Department of the Burden Neurological Institute, Bristol (U.K.) He obtained his M.A. and Sc.D. degrees at Cambridge.

Dr. Grey Walter founded the Electroencephalographic Society and was co-founder of the International Federation of Societies for Electroencephalography and Clinical Neurophysiology, and co-founder and co-editor of a journal of the same title. He was also a co-founder and a member of the Council of the International Association of Cybernetics.

The author of several books and papers on neurophysiology and cybernetics, Dr. Grey Walter was the Maudsley Lecturer of the Royal Medico-Psychological Association and the Adolf Meyer Lecturer of the American Psychiatric Association. He spent one year as Professor at the Aix-Marseille University.

J. H. Clark

Dr. Clark read natural sciences and philosophy at Gonville and Caius College, Cambridge, and medicine at the Westminster Hospital, London. He then spent some time in the Department of Psychological Medicine at Guy's Hospital, London, and at the Fountain Hospital in Carshalton, where he gained the Diploma in Psychological Medicine.

During his stay at Cambridge, Dr. Clark was introduced to cybernetics by Dr. Gordon Pask and he became interested in the application of cybernetics to psychiatry. A Medical Research Council Fellowship enabled him to work at Bristol with Dr. Grey Walter at the Burden Neurological Institute and with Dr. F. H. George at the University, where he studied the problem of hypnosis and did work on psycholinguistics. Dr. Clark continued this work at the M.R.C. Psycholinguistics Research Unit at Oxford.

Dr. Clark is now a Senior Lecturer in the Psychology Department of the University of Manchester. He is a member of several scientific societies and a

Fellow of the Royal Society of Medicine and a Member of the Institution of Computer Sciences.

A. M. Rosie

Dr. Rosie graduated from the University of Glasgow with a degree in electrical engineering and obtained his M.Sc. and Ph.D. from the University of Birmingham. After spending several years in the communication industry, he became lecturer in the Department of Electrical Engineering at Queen's University, Belfast (U.K.). He is the author of a recent book on information and communication theory.

G. Pask

Dr. Pask obtained his M.A. from Cambridge, and his Ph.D. from London University. He founded Systems Research Limited, now a non-profit making cybernetics research organisation, in 1953, and he originated adaptive teaching systems. Most of this work has been on brain analogues, self-organising systems and the interaction between men and other men or machines. He is Director of Research, and System Research, and Professor in the Institute of Cybernetics, Brunel University.

In 1959 Dr. Pask visited Illinois University as associate research professor in von Foerster's department, and has subsequently been in the U.S.A. as consultant and visiting professor. From 1961 to 1963 he served as Chairman of Cybernetic Developments Limited. In addition to travelling and lecturing, he writes scientific papers and revue lyrics, paints pictures and has had two books published.

M. J. Apter

Dr. Apter is Lecturer in the Department of Psychology at University College, Cardiff (U.K.). He obtained his B.Sc. and Ph.D. from Bristol University. He has carried out research on social psychology (while at Princeton University in the United States), programmed instruction (while working for Educational and Scientific Developments Limited—now E.S.L. Bristol) and biocybernetics (at Bristol University and King's College London). Dr. Apter is the author of three books, including one on cybernetics.

C. T. Leondes

Professor Leondes obtained his Ph.D. at the University of Pennsylvania. He is at present Professor of Engineering at the University of California and is a member of several U.S.A. advisory and scientific committees, particularly in the realm of aeronautics and astronautics. He also serves as consultant to Government bodies.

Professor Leondes was the holder of the Guggenheim Fellowship and the Fullbright Research Scholarship. He is the co-author of several book on computer control systems, guidance control and astronautics, and he is the editor of an international annual series concerned with control systems, and of another series of applied system sciences.

J. M. Mendel

Dr. Mendel is a Senior Engineer/Scientist at Guidance and the Advanced Flight Mechanics Department of the McDonnell Douglas, Astronantics Co. Santa Monica, California. He received his Ph.D. (E. E.) at the Polytechnic Institute of Brooklyn. He has studied problems of process identification, time-optimal control, the application of pattern recognition techniques to the synthesis of sub-optimal controllers, and the application of learning theory to the design of control systems. He was a principal investigator of a study in which artificial intelligence techniques were applied to the design of a spacecraft control system, under an NASA contract. Currently, he is investigating problems in parameter identification and adaptive control. His publications are numerous and some of these have been translated into other languages.

Dr. Mendel organised and taught a one- and two-week national course on artificial intelligence, entitled 'Applications of Artificial Intelligence to Control System Design', at the University of California, Los Angeles, in 1966 and 1967. He is co-editor of the book *Adaptive Learning and Pattern Recognition Systems* (Academic Press).

V. Strejc

Professor Strejc, Dr. Sc., received his degree at the Technical University, Prague (Mech. Eng.) and afterwards worked for 10 years as project designer and chief designer of automatic control systems, mostly for the power-generating and chemical industries. Since 1956 he has been Head of the Department of Automatic Control in the Institute of Information Theory and Automation of the Czechoslovak Academy of Sciences. In 1958 he successfully presented his dissertation for the degree of Candidate of Sciences (Ph.D.) and in 1963 became doctor of sciences (D.Sc.).

Dr. Strejc was appointed assistant lecturer at the Technical University of Prague in 1953 and Professor of Technical Cybernetics in 1964. His professional activities are concerned mainly with problems of the analysis and synthesis of continuous and discrete control systems. He has published papers in the field of the identification of controlled systems, multi-parameter control loops and digital control. Dr. Strejc has also published a number of books concerned with control systems in industry and computer applications.

D. Foster

Dr. Foster obtained his M.Sc. and Ph.D. at London University. He has had several years practical experience in engineering and has held the posts of Technical Director, Powell Duffryn Carbon Products Limited and Production Director, Mullard Equipment Limited. Since 1957 he has been a consultant in automation, working for many leading companies in the United Kingdom, the United States and on the Continent. His technical speciality is now automated handling systems, whether these be oil pipelines, conveying systems or piece-part feeding systems.

Dr. Foster is a member of the Institution of Chemical Engineers and of the Institution of Mechanical Engineers. He is Chairman of the Computer Studies for Automatic Warehouses Committee of the National Joint Council for Materials Handling, and a past member of the Research Committee for the United Kingdom Automation Council. He has written two books on automation.

D. A. Bell

Professor Bell graduated from the Universities of Oxford (M.A., B.Sc.) and Birmingham (Ph.D.); he is a Fellow of the Institution of Electrical Engineers, of the Institution of Electronic and Radio Engineers and of the Institute of Physics. After a long period spent in the radio and telecommunication industry, he was appointed Reader in Electromagnetism in the University of Birmingham and has since been appointed to the Chair of Electronic Engineering at the

University of Hull (U.K.). He has also been Director of the A.M.F. British Research Laboratory and a visiting Professor of Telecommunication at McGill University.

Professor Bell's main research activities are related to noise and signals in noise, which led naturally to the communication aspect of cybernetics. He takes a great interest in automation, including its human aspects, and in ergonomics. Professor Bell is the author of four books concerned with communication and he has contributed an article on 'Cybernetics' to Reinhold's *Encyclopedia of Physics*.

N. S. Prywes

Professor Prywes was awarded a Bachelor degree from the Technion, Israel, an M.S. degree from the Carnegie Institute of Technology and a Ph.D. degree in Applied Physics from Harvard University. He has held teaching and research appointments at Harvard, and he has been concerned for four years with computer design at Remington Rand. Since 1958 he has been associate professor at the Moore School of Electrical Engineering, University of Pennsylvania, where he is now a professor.

Professor Prywes has published many papers in the realm of computer design, computers and information retrieval. He has developed a Multilist file system, which he has used in several large scale applications.

A. Crawford

Dr. Crawford is the Marketing Director of IPC Magazines Limited, part of the International Publishing Corporation, which is one of the largest companies in the U.K. He graduated with a B.Sc. (Psychology) from the University of Manchester and obtained his Ph.D. (Physiological Psychology) at the University of Edinburgh. Dr. Crawford has spent most of his working life in industry, mainly in operational research.

R. W. Revans

Professor Revans obtained his B.Sc. degree at the University of London, and his Ph.D. at Cambridge. He was a Commonwealth Fund Fellow at the University of Michigan and a Research Fellow at Cambridge and London. After some work on management of mines and a Directorship of Education with the National Coal Board (U.K.) he became Professor of Industrial Administration at the University of Manchester. His present post is that of Senior Research Fellow of the European Association of Management Training Centres in Brussels.

Professor Revans has published a number of books and articles on industrial management.

J. Rose

Dr. Rose is Principal of the College of Technology and Design, Blackburn, U.K. He was awarded the B.Sc., M.Sc. and Ph.D. degrees of the University of London. He is a Fellow of the Royal Institute of Chemistry and the Institute of Linguists, and is also a member of the British Institute of Management.

After spending several years in the chemical and metallurgical industries, Dr. Rose turned to teaching and research at Colleges of Technology. He is the founder of the Institution of Computer Sciences (U.K.). Dr. Rose has written several books, including two on automation, as well as several papers for a number of journals. His main interest lies in the field of computer usage and education. Dr. Rose was the Founder of an Institution of Computer Sciences (U.K.) and he was elected Hon. Secretary of the International Cybernetics Congress

Committee. He is also the **General-Organiser** of the International Congress of Cybernetics in London (1969).

Mr. Stafford Beer

Mr. Stafford Beer—philosopher, scientist, manager—was one of those who took operational research from the army into industry after World War 2.

At United Steel, he founded and directed what was to become the world's largest civil O.R. Group. In 1961 he started again, launching SIGMA (Science in General Management) for Metra International, of which he was a director. When he completed his term as managing director of SIGMA in 1966, it was the major British O.R. consultancy working for industry and government in the United Kingdom and abroad. Mr. Beer is now Development Director of the vast International Publishing Corporation. In February 1970 he will join Manchester University as the first Professor of Cybernetics and will then act as a consultant to I PC.

One of the European leaders in the interdisciplinary science of control, cybernetics, Stafford Beer has pioneered its management applications, for which he has received honours in both Sweden and America. He is a member of many scientific, educational and governmental organisations and committees. Current offices include membership of the Executive of the United Kingdom Automation Council, the O.R. Advisory Panel to O.E.C.D. and the General Advisory Council of the BBC. He is a prolific lecturer and broadcaster.

Stafford Beer is the author of over a hundred publications, including the standard book *Cybernetics and Management*, which is available in nine languages. His newest book, *Decision and Control*, published in 1966, won the Lanchester Prize. *Management Science* came out in 1967, and the *Brain of the Firm* is pending.

Index

Index

Index

384

Index